Dark Matter, Missing Planets and New Comets

(Paradoxes Resolved, Origins Illuminated)

Tom Van Flandern

North Atlantic Books
Berkeley, California

Dark Matter, Missing Planets and New Comets
(Paradoxes Resolved, Origins Illuminated)

Published by
North Atlantic Books
P.O. Box 12327
Berkeley, California 94701

Author's Address:
Meta Research
6327 Western Ave, NW
Washington, DC 20015
Author's E-Mail Address:metares@well.sf.ca.us
alternate:tvf@kelvin.umd.edu

Cover art copyright © Sally Bensusen 1991
Cover and book design by Paula Morrison
Typeset by Catherine Campaigne

ISBN 1–55643–155–4

Dark Matter, Missing Planets and New Comets (Paradoxes Resolved, Origins Illuminated) is sponsored by the Society for the Study of Native Arts and Sciences, a nonprofit educational corporation whose goals are to develop an educational and crosscultural perspective linking various scientific, social, and artistic fields; to nurture a holistic view of arts, sciences, humanities, and healing; and to publish and distribute literature on the relationship of mind, body, and nature.

Library of Congress Cataloging-in-Publication Data
Van Flandern, Tom, 1940–
    Dark Matter, missing planets and new comets : paradoxes resolved, origins illuminated / Tom van Flandern.
        p. cm.
    ISBN 1–55643–155–4 (pbk.)
    1. Astronomy. 2. Astrophysics. I. Title
QB43.2.V35 1993
520— dc20   93–12986
                                                                CIP

1 2 3 4 5 6 7 8 9 / 97 96 95 94 93

Dark Matter, Missing Planets and New Comets

To my wife,
Barbara,
and to my sons and daughter,
Michael,
Connie,
Brian,
Kevin.

The First Cosmology

. . . .

"The world is not flat, as it appears, but round, like a ball."
"Then what holds the world up?"
"The great god Atlas holds the world on his shoulders."
"But what does Atlas stand on?"
"He stands on a huge island."
"But on what does the island rest?"
"It rests on the back of a giant turtle."
"But what . . ."
"No need to ask further. It's turtles all the way down!"

Modern cosmology has discovered several new turtles in the chain, for which achievement it is very proud of itself. But what if the world is not held on the shoulders of the great god Atlas?

Contents

• •

Preface

• •

Something is wrong with science—fundamentally wrong. Theories just keep getting stranger and stranger.

Take, for example, my own professional field: astronomy. To the extent that you are already familiar with the three theories that follow, try to think about how they would impress you if you were just now hearing about them for the first time, without knowing any of the supporting background.

The Big Bang theory is the accepted model for the origin of the universe. This theory requires us to accept the following: time and space have not always existed; both began a finite time ago; and both the age and size of the present universe are finite; also that all matter and energy in the entire universe were contained in an infinitesimal point at the "beginning"; that for some unknown reason it all exploded; that space and time themselves expanded out of that explosion; that at first space expanded faster than the speed of light; that the explosion was so uniform it emitted an almost perfectly uniform radiation everywhere; and the same explosion was nonuniform enough to create the observed, quite irregular matter distribution in the universe; that the chaos from the explosion eventually organized itself into the structures presently seen in the universe, contrary to the principle of entropy (which basically states that you shouldn't get order out of chaos); that all matter in the universe expands away from all other matter as space itself continues to expand, although there is no center; that the expansion of space itself occurs between all galactic clusters and larger structures, but does not occur at all on scales as small as individual galaxies or the solar system; that vast assemblies of galaxies stream through space together relative to other assemblies; and that immense voids separate immense walls of galaxies, all condensed from the same explosion.

Gravity is accepted as the principal force operating on the scale of the observable universe. This force is always attractive, never repulsive; it causes every particle of matter in the universe to attract every other particle over an unlimited range; it is capable of warping space and time near masses; it appears to act instantly and without lighttime delay, while somehow its wave form propagates only at the speed of light; gravity does not lose strength as the universe expands; it is weaker than the other fundamental forces of nature by 20-40 orders of magnitude, yet has unlimited (infinite) strength when matter collapses far enough; and gravity has resisted all efforts to link it with the other fundamental forces.

The Oort Cloud is the accepted model for the origin of comets. According to the interpretation of comet observations, this cloud of comets is located at about 1000 times the distance of Pluto from the Sun within a volume large enough to hold all stars in all visible galaxies in the universe without touching; passing galactic stars plunge through this "cloud" from time to time; it requires about 10,000,000 years for an average comet within the cloud to orbit the Sun; the cloud gets wiped out occasionally by passing giant molecular clouds and must then be replenished; yet it currently contains about 1,000,000,000,000 (one trillion) comets a kilometer or larger in diameter, each with an average separation of about 1,000,000,000 (one billion) kilometers from its nearest neighbor comet; and has an average space density for the whole cloud of about 0.001 hydrogen atom per cubic meter.

Now astronomers have excellent reasons for accepting these intrinsically amazing theories with all these seemingly improbable properties. As a professional astronomer myself, I am familiar with those reasons. Looking at the observational data upon which these theories are based, it is difficult to see much room for argument. In many cases, the reasoning seems compelling, however strange the conclusions which result. At the time I was taught these theories, I, too, accepted them, with few reservations.

But events in my life caused me to start questioning my goals and the correctness of everything I had learned. In matters of religion, medicine, biology, physics, and other fields, I came to discover that reality differed seriously from what I had been taught. As a result of this questioning process, I was startled to realize how much of my "knowledge" was indeed questionable. I was even more startled to discover a few "extraordinary hypotheses" to be undeniably true, even while almost every reputable expert in those fields continued to deny that possibility. To take just a single example which can be verified with minimal effort: Fresh vitamin E applied directly to cuts and burns, even of great severity, relieves pain immediately and promotes healing without scar tissue at an accelerated rate. Although the healing action of vitamin E is apparently superior to that of any known drug, few physicians recommend it, or even know about this simple home remedy.

As this period of internal challenge continued, I began to form some hypotheses about what was wrong with these other bodies of knowledge, and why. I particularly noted a regular practice of not re-examining the fundamental assumptions underlying a theory once it gained "accepted" status, almost no matter how incompatible some new observation or experiment might be. And I saw powerful vested interests in a "status quo" develop around certain accepted theories.

It gradually became clear that a lot of people had a lot to lose if an accepted theory or practice were challenged: the authors of the original theory, whose names had become well-known; all those who published papers which reference or depend on the theory; journal editors and referees who have made decisions or criticized other works based on a theory; funding agencies which have paid for research which pre-supposes a theory; instrument builders and experiment designers who spend career time testing ideas which spring from a theory; journalists and writers whose publications have featured or promoted a theory; teachers and interested members of the public who have learned a theory, been impressed by the wonder of it, and who have no wish to have to teach or learn a new theory; and students, who need to find a job in their field of training.

It has been my sad observation that by mid-career there are very few professionals left truly working for the advancement of science, as opposed to the advancement of self. And given enough people with strong enough interests, professional peer pressure takes over from there. Peer pressure in science, as elsewhere in society, consists of alternately attacking and ignoring the people who advocate a contrary idea, and discrediting their motives and/or competence, in order to achieve conformity. Even when it is not effective directly, it is usually successful at ensuring that the contrary person or idea gains few allies, and remains isolated. In short, those who may suspect the need for a radical change in an accepted theory have no interests or motivations as strong as those supporting the status quo. And these people usually lack the background and confidence to challenge the "recognized experts" in the field who defend their own theories.

As if there weren't already enough inertia to major changes of models, I see yet another phenomenon—new to our era of rapid progress in science—which mitigates against change even in the face of overwhelming need for it. Few scientists consider themselves qualified very far outside their own areas of expertise. Since each expert can account for only a small portion of the data dealing with a model, he defers to the other experts to support the model in other areas. Few, if any, scientists have the breadth of knowledge to see the full picture for a given model. So the model remains supported because many individual authorities support it, none of whom have the expertise to criticize the model overall, and all of whom have the utmost confidence in the others collectively. Authorities can continue to multiply indefinitely, with no one taking responsibility for integrating all their combined knowledge. As a result, the existing models get perpetuated regardless of merit or the extent of counter-evidence, because "so many experts can't all be wrong." Thus each expert is persuaded to force-fit his own data into the accepted model.

After seeing these factors at work in other fields, and seeing their generality as social phenomena, I turned my attention to my own field of astronomy and sought to learn why it was apparently an exception to the situation present elsewhere. It seemed clear enough to me that my colleagues were all learned men who understood the Scientific Method; who were truly advancing the frontiers of knowledge; whose publications were carefully peer-reviewed for quality and accuracy; whose professional meetings were places where knowledge was advanced and problems given fair treatment;

and who were making responsible use of the salaries and facilities granted to them by sponsoring institutions. I could see individual astronomers and individual theories with problems, but I had to classify the field as a whole as a virtual model of what a scientific body should be like.

However, I had learned by then to start being more open-minded toward new ideas, no longer dismissing them out of hand without strong enough reason that even the idea's proposer could understand. Whereas before it was rarely "worth my time" to deal with proposed new ideas, I now felt quite the opposite. This was chiefly because even in the process of proving that a new idea was false, I learned a great deal about the fundamentals underlying the challenged theory. I came to see the soft underbelly of many theories with a tough outer shell. I found a lot of unsuspected weaknesses.

The first challenging new idea which I entertained as seriously viable was P.A.M. Dirac's proposal of the variability of the universal gravitational "constant." I performed a test of the idea using observations of the Moon's orbital motion around the Earth, and obtained results which supported Dirac's theory and seemed to be statistically significant.[a,1,2] This experience led me to realize how fragile were the assumptions underlying the Big Bang and other theories of cosmology, when even the constancy of gravitation, the most important force in shaping the large-scale structure of the universe, had been called into question. And I saw that very few of my colleagues were taking seriously the idea that anything could be

---

[a]See the next two references, one technical and one non-technical. Later, systematic errors turned up in the observations which called the statistical significance of this result into question. Unfortunately, the investigation was interrupted by my separation from the U.S. Naval Observatory in 1983 before it could be determined if a new analysis would continue to support, or would contradict, Dirac's theory. An analysis of Mars orbiter data at the Jet Propulsion Laboratory seemed to show no variation in the mean distance of Mars from the Sun compatible with a changing gravitational constant at the rate required by Dirac's theory. However, those observations were not as sensitive to variations in the atomic time scale relative to time kept by dynamical systems such as the Moon's orbit around the Earth, so it remains unknown at this writing whether or not the latter sort of variations do exist at the rate proposed by Dirac.

wrong at such a fundamental level. Their attitude was understandable, but unscientific.

From my disturbing experiences with the insubstantiality of fundamentals in other fields, I learned how I could sometimes spot the bad accepted theories from a combination of their

> "The first and primary obligation of any philosopher or scientist is to do nothing that would block inquiry."
> —Charles Sanders Peirce

strangeness, a certain lack of providing true insight into the underlying phenomena, and a continuing need to do "maintenance theorizing" to patch the theory in ever stranger ways as new data became available. I later added "derivation from inductive reasoning" as additional grounds for holding a theory suspect. All the accepted astronomical theories mentioned at the beginning of this preface are "suspect" by all these criteria. I also learned how to proceed when one encounters such a theory. This is discussed in the chapter "The Scientific Method," which describes the principal investigative tools of science and scientists, by means of which we try to separate good theories from bad ones. In that chapter I propose that a modification is needed to the theory of the Scientific Method itself.

One procedure I have learned to favor is to adopt a starting point and reason deductively; that is, from cause to effect. The advantages of this are easy to understand: inductive reasoning (from the effect—usually an observation or experimental data—back to its cause) does not, in general, lead to unique answers, while deductive reasoning, if valid, generally does. Obviously a model which allows us to deduce experimental results which were not used in formulating the model is intrinsically more reliable than one which merely explains the results after the fact. And deductions made from an incorrect starting point do not usually resemble the experimental data or reality. So only deductions made from a correct starting point might be expected to lead to models which add true insight into phenomena, agree with observations, and make successful predictions. This book is filled with examples to support this contention.

The products of applying this deductive methodology to the three accepted theories mentioned at the beginning of this preface are three completely new models: the Meta Model to replace the

Big Bang; the C-graviton model to replace the Newtonian and relativistic notions of gravitation; and the Exploded Planet model to replace the Oort Cloud. Numerous other examples of consistent applications of this methodology will be seen throughout the chapters. For example, the satellite model will be proposed to replace the dirty-snowball model for the nature of comets, through deductive reasoning. And we will see that only one of the several theories astronomers have proposed for the origin of the Moon can arrive at the observed situation deductively.

Even though this book deals with technical material, I have done my best to make the text readable even to those with little or no background in the field of astronomy. The book deals almost entirely with concepts, with little attention to ways to utilize those concepts in calculations. My college major was mathematics, and my field of specialization in astronomy is Celestial Mechanics, which is itself a field accustomed to descriptions utilizing the language of mathematics. But for this book I have invoked a working principle I wish others would use more often: "Mathematics should be used to describe the operation of models, not to build them."

In my opinion, equations cannot be made to substitute for the concepts which underlie them. And equations are generally blind to limitations of range and physical constraints. They are too general, and simply lack the sort of specificity that true, intuitive understanding demands. Every equation has a domain of applicability—usually the range of the observations and little, if anything, more. I use the following as a rule of thumb: If an equation can be extrapolated outside its domain and gives a singularity (basically, a zero divisor), that singularity does not exist in nature; instead, the model needs modification. Up to now this rule has always proved true. But advocates of "black holes" in the universe would have us believe that the equations which predict them can be relied upon far outside the domain of the observations used to derive those equations. However, we will see that when we derive the equivalent concepts deductively in our new "Meta Model," the possibility of a "black hole," or a singularity in gravity, never existed in the first place.

Each of the chapters is written to be reasonably independent of the others, although there is some cross-referencing; and the first five chapters all relate to the basis of the Meta Model. Those who wish to follow the scientific material closely are invited to make use of the glossary of terms at the end. I have added two indices, one for names and one for terms, to facilitate finding subject matter of any particular interest. References to footnotes at the bottom of the page appear in the text as superscript letters, while references to the Bibliography at the end appear in the text as superscript numbers.

It gives me great pleasure to acknowledge the artistic contributions of Sally Bensusen, Fred DeVita, William Hartmann, and Boris Starosta. It is primarily their figures and paintings which illustrate this book, along with some NASA spacecraft photographs. One of the latter has been reprocessed to bring out new details of Valles Marineris on Mars, courtesy of E. Hauber, DLR Institut fur Optoelektronik, Germany. Bensusen and Hartmann are both astronomers. Bensusen is the cover artist as well. DeVita and Starosta have also contributed to various improvements in the text for which I am likewise grateful. Starosta did all the computer graphics which comprise the figures not otherwise acknowledged in chapters I to XII, with the exception of those in the chapter "Do Planets Explode?"

I also acknowledge and very much appreciate the invaluable assistance of Brenda Corbin, librarian at the U.S. Naval Observatory, and her assistant Greg Shelton, in locating numerous references and securing a number of inter-library loans needed to complete this research.

For your part, you, the reader, will be presented with a number of interesting ideas which represent somewhat radical departures from conventional current thinking in the field of astronomy. You may, if the author is successful, find these ideas understandable, and perhaps even somewhat more appealing than conventional ones. But you may be inclined to wait and see what other experts think about these ideas, in preference to trusting your or my own judgment.

Unfortunately, nearly everyone feels that way, expert and novice alike. Indeed, do listen to what criticisms are leveled at the ideas herein, and listen to the defenses offered. For example, discussions are ongoing in the Science Forum on the CompuServe computer network, and in the sci.astro newsgroup on USENET. Consider whether the criticisms are scientific and meritorious, or serve mainly to try to preserve the status quo in the field. Watch for the outcomes of the many predictions made herein. As new data become available, ask which model assimilates them most easily. Determine which model explains best and provides the greatest understanding of the phenomena.

Then you must make the judgment of which model serves best. Please do not, dear reader, either here or for anything important in your life, defer your judgment to experts. Never assume that your powers of judgment are inferior to those of an "expert." Experts may have more facts and experience; but when they have brought both to bear, and you have seen the arguments on both sides of an issue and the recommendations and conclusions of the experts, you will often be in a better position to impartially judge the relative merits of competing ideas than are persons with a vested interest in the outcome. Experts who cannot easily make themselves understood are often concealing weaknesses in ideas they are defending. Experts have only the advantages of facts and experience. They do not thereby have better judgment than others. And they frequently do misjudge.

If you agree with these premises, and you look favorably upon one or more of the fundamental departures from conventional thinking in astronomy proposed herein, then you may wish to judge the validity of my final conclusion: that astronomy is not an exception to the rule that many fields of knowledge contain widely accepted theories which are incorrect, not merely at the frontiers of knowledge, but in the fundamentals and from first principles.

Lastly you may wish to judge if this phenomenon of adhering to certain theories which are fundamentally wrong does indeed apply to most human institutions, not just to the field of astronomy. In making such a generalization you will perhaps be at a relative disadvantage. I already had extensive evidence for the generalization, and in studying why astronomy seemed to be an exception discovered that it was not. You may initially have only the particular example, astronomy, from which you will be considering the generalization. This is precisely the sort of inductive reasoning which I suggest is hazardous. You should take a close look at the fundamentals in other fields (perhaps including your own field of specialization), to see for yourself if the phenomenon is general.[b]

For if you accept this conclusion too, it follows that your own life, your goals, and your own way of thinking may be altered, as mine were. But then you may be faced with your most important decision: how to cope with that "professional peer pressure" which is designed to isolate and repress those who choose to criticize an accepted theory. For me, this led to forming an independent astronomy research group where such pressures would not be an overriding factor.[c]

But if you find any of these steps unacceptable, and you prefer to put your trust in the accepted theories of the world's authorities in each field of knowledge, then perhaps you will find special comfort in a dominant and widely accepted conclusion of quantum physics (which, incidentally, is another theory challenged in this book). Quantum physicists have learned that the entities of the subatomic world behave sometimes as particles and sometimes as waves; that the more accurately one measures the motion of such an entity, the less accurately he can measure its position, and vice versa; that merely observing some phenomena without interacting with them changes the result; and that decisions carried out by local observers can instantly affect observed results halfway across the universe. Their conclusion is that *there is no deep reality* to the world

---

[b]I am preparing another manuscript about my own experiences in several other fields, which were the basis of my premise that many fields are flawed in their fundamental premises.

[c]In 1990 I founded Meta Research (named after the Meta Model) for the purpose of supporting and encouraging research into astronomical theories which are in accord with observations and experiment, add insight or understanding, and make testable predictions; but which are not otherwise supported because they lie outside the mainstream of theories in Astronomy. The organization is run by a seven-member board and is nonprofit and public-supported. It publishes the quarterly *Meta Research Bulletin,* which specializes in the sort of astronomy covered in this book. Write to Meta Research, P.O. Box 15186, Chevy Chase, MD 20815 for information about receiving the *Bulletin,* which is free to supporting members contributing $25 or more per year.

around us, despite our wish to believe the contrary from reason and the information of our senses.

Those of us who may wish to hang on to our reality are forced to challenge at least this one idea in at least this one field. But why stop there? We have a new scientific methodology to try out. Let's see how far it can take us!

Introduction

● ●

I have always had a strong desire to know, fundamentally, how everything can be the way it is. As with all of us, I found that there came a point in most models where you just couldn't go back any further and keep asking "why." The real fundamentals seemed beyond understanding. But in the last few years I have had the great pleasure of learning how to find answers to some of those truly fundamental questions. If you also have a strong desire to know "how it can be that way," then you too may find pleasure in some of the answers discussed here. But if you have already found your own answers, then you may not enjoy the line of reasoning in this book at all, because it would logically lead to changes in so much of what you think you already know. But please try to find a way to co-exist with those of us who are not satisfied with the answers we now have, and want so much more.

Many people come up with ideas which, if sound, would drastically alter an entire field of scientific inquiry. Almost all such ideas are wrong. Individuals often tend to become either "disputers" or "defenders." Speaking generally, we can identify five stages of progress in the challenge of a paradigm of knowledge (a well-established theory of long standing).

The first stage is *learning*. When we first read about or are taught scientific knowledge, we are impressed with the extent to which humans have learned to describe and understand their environment, and have even succeeded in using this knowledge to make successful predictions. We are awed by the great minds of science, the da Vincis and Einsteins who discovered and taught us so much, whom we could never hope to rival. At this stage, past and present authorities are so numerous, and existing discoveries so definite in their interpretation, that challenges seem inappropriate. Many authority-oriented people lack either the desire or the ability to move beyond stage one. Such people comprise most of the "defenders" of paradigms.

The second stage is *disputation.* Some of the things science accepts and teaches seem inexplicable, contrary to common sense, or inconsistent with new observations or experiments. Well known paradigms that are frequently disputed include the beginnings of the Big Bang theory in cosmology, the twins paradox in relativity, and the lack of objectivity and deep reality in quantum physics. But almost any finding of science can be, and has been, disputed at one time or another. The desire to invent perpetual motion machines will always be with us, no matter how definite the proof that it is impossible. People studying science who are naturally rebellious against authority often progress to this stage, but not often beyond it. These people make up most of the "disputers" of paradigms.

The third stage is *reaffirmation.* In this stage, the body of science successfully defends itself against the dispute. This is usually such an easy process that many scientists disdain to do it properly, preferring to attack the character and competence of the disputers instead. It is argued that the disputer should go "do his homework," that he has no right to consume the time of scientists simply to further his own education. So many people contribute to the body of knowledge over the years that by the time a theory becomes a paradigm, almost every conceivable challenge has already been mounted and answered, and virtually every feasible test undertaken as well. "Explanations" are available for every objection, even if some of these are rather ad hoc. The disputers are generally found wanting in their depth of understanding of the fundamentals of the paradigm to which they object. And almost always they have not appreciated the extent to which their own ideas and many like them have already been thought of and tried in the past. Ordinarily it would be easy to answer the disputed point and send the disputer on to some more productive use of his time and creative energy. However, the tendency of defenders to attack the disputer leads the disputer to believe that substantive arguments do not exist, and that his ideas must have merit if personal attack is the chief response. In my view, personal attacks are unscientific and unwarranted; and all scientists have an obligation to communicate their knowledge freely to other interested persons. A single response to coherent questions, containing a logical argument and/or citations for further reading, should always be in order.

The fourth stage is *crisis*. In this stage the reaffirmation has failed to make the challenge go away, and all essential points in the disputation have been successfully defended. Invariably, the existing paradigm is not contradicted. But its ad hoc supporting hypotheses may be seen as inferior to the explanation of a phenomenon provided by the disputers. The crisis occurs because the disputers generally have the better arguments and the Scientific Method (e.g. Occam's Razor) on their side; whereas the defenders generally have vastly greater numbers and the strong vested interests of many on their side.

A major cause of miscommunication and friction in science is when disputers fail to recognize the difference between stage-one and stage-three defenses of a paradigm; and when defenders fail to recognize the difference between a stage-two and stage-four dispute of a paradigm.

The final stage (five) is *resolution*. Whichever way it goes, it is generally not final; and another round may occur at any later time as new, dynamic personalities come along and begin a disputation. Unfortunately, historical precedent argues that the resolution generally goes in the direction of the survivors, regardless of relative scientific merit. If the chief disputers are too irascible or insufficiently erudite, they may not win enough supporters. Then the defenders only need to outlast them, which is easy, given their greater numbers. On the other hand, if the paradigm is to be overthrown, the disputers will not often convert the strongest defenders. Instead their arguments and tests must persuade the new generation of scientists to learn the new way; and these will eventually come to outnumber and replace the defenders of the old paradigm, who finally die out.

In this book, one of my deductive models will show (as a by-product of reasoning about gravity) a way in which faster-than-light travel can be possible in forward time. Now in today's science, such an idea is so radical that it must be considered crankish. It is certainly to be compared with the notion of inventing a perpetual-motion machine, or with other comparable ideas which fly in the face of well-established laws of physics. So why should you waste time by reading any further?

In answer, let me first point out that such faster-than-light travel in forward time has not been proved physically impossible. What has been established is that it cannot be done within the confines of our existing laws of physics as presently interpreted. And you probably know by now that some of those long and widely accepted "laws" will come in for some challenging in this book.

Secondly, I am a professional astronomer with a 25-year history of work and publishing in the field of astronomy in most of its major journals. That doesn't mean I'm immune from advocating crankish ideas, but it probably means that at least my mistakes are unlikely to be the usual naive ones that come from a lack of background or familiarity with existing work in this area. You have every right to expect that if I am mistaken, it will at least be in some original way. You will not find herein merely a rehash of unsuccessful challenges many others have made before me.

Thirdly, I understand very well why it is that faster-than-light travel in forward time is considered to be quite impossible. I understand the contractions of space and time described in the theory of Special Relativity;[a] and I understand how well these have been experimentally verified. I understand how and why these results imply that time would slow and eventually stop altogether for a body whose speed approached that of light. And I understand that such a body, somehow supplied with infinite energy so that it could be accelerated so fast, would find itself moving backwards in time if it went faster than light; and that this leads to causality violations. (For example, if you could go back in time, you might prevent your grandfather from being born, thereby eliminating your own existence and preventing you from doing what you just did.) So if I truly understand these things, then the new ideas I propose must nonetheless work within these severe constraints without straining plausibility. I believe that they do.

***

[a]Special Relativity is Einstein's theory that predicts, among other things, that communications faster than lightspeed are impossible.

I would go one step further. I have also read a great many of the objections to Special Relativity which have been raised over the years, especially in the form of paradoxes, such as the famous "Twins Paradox," which we will discuss. I believe I understand the resolution of such would-be paradoxes, and I will not be raising new or disguised versions of the same. What you will read herein about the possibility of faster-than-light motion will, I believe, be quite unlike anything you may have encountered previously, and has nothing to do with Relativity paradoxes.

So why should you "waste your time" reading further? Because the new ideas are easy to understand and exciting in their implications; because the subject matter is important; because theories are always subject to revision and possible falsification; because the author is unlikely to make really naive errors, so this challenge should at least be non-trivial; because there really are problems with the conventional theories, which keep getting stranger and stranger; because you are likely to learn some interesting things about the topics discussed and the weaknesses in the accepted models, even if you do not agree with the proposed alternatives; and because the author can explain how one person came upon so many alternative ideas—not through "gifted insight" and not by chance, but by the consistent application of a principle which he proposes as a permanent addition to the Scientific Method. An explanation of the motivation for this principle will be given near the end of this book.

I trust, then, that you will not stop reading merely because this preview is too radical on its face, and that you will likewise give the arguments a fair reading as long as they remain reasonable. I further urge you not to give up at the first point where you disagree. For example, if I introduce a concept which appears to be like a classical "aether," and you know full well the experiments which preclude the existence of such a thing, I ask that you bear with me until I can confront the new concept with the experiments. I cannot reason deductively if I start from the known experiments and generalize. I must let the model go where it deductively must go, then compare its unique implications with reality. Please allow me the latitude to do that much before you judge the plausibility of each model.

"'Type one' error is thinking that something special is happening when nothing special really is happening. 'Type two' error is thinking that nothing special is happening, when in fact something rare or infrequent is happening. Obviously these are at opposite poles, and you increase your probability of avoiding one kind of error by increasing the probability of making the other kind."—Marcello Truzzi

With the supposition that you will not put down this book without giving it a chance after merely reading the following list, let me now preview some of the most interesting points to be proposed or discussed within these pages:

- Faster-than-light motion in forward time is possible.
- Gravitation propagates faster than light.
- The physical universe has five, and only five, dimensions.
- The universe is infinite in extent in all five dimensions.
- There was no Big Bang explosion to start the universe.
- The universe is not expanding.
- The universal microwave radiation is of nearby origin.
- There are no "black holes" in the universe.
- Quasars are associated with our own and nearby galaxies.
- Galaxies are arranged in waves in an immense medium.
- Gravitational shielding is possible.
- The force of gravity is caused by a universal flux.
- The force of gravity has limited range.
- The classical description of quantum entities is incorrect.
- The Bell Inequality in quantum physics should be violated.
- There is no "Oort Cloud" of comets.
- Comets and asteroids are quite similar in nature.
- Comets and asteroids are accompanied by satellites.
- A former major planet exploded between Mars and Jupiter.

- This explosion occurred just three million years ago.
- This explosion was the origin of comets and asteroids.
- This explosion may be connected with the origins of man.
- The Great Pyramids in Egypt are perhaps 9000 years old.
- Artificial structures may exist on the surface of Mars.
- Tidal forces on the Sun and giant planets are significant.
- There may be a sunspot-planet link.
- Solar eclipses are best viewed away from the center line.
- Mercury was originally a moon of Venus.
- Our Moon originated from the Pacific basin of the Earth.
- The Moon no longer shows us the same face it used to.
- The Martian moons are the survivors of a great many moons.
- A great rift on Mars is the impact site of a former moon.
- Jupiter's Red Spot is a floating impact remnant.
- Saturn's rings are only a few million years old.
- Solar system bodies have received black carbon deposits.
- The moons of Neptune were violently disrupted.
- Pluto and Charon are escaped moons of Neptune.
- Another undiscovered planet probably exists beyond Pluto.

The contents of this book indicate that the whole field of astronomy will be greatly revised if a few of these hypotheses are correct, leading to a new vision of the universe, its origin and nature, and our role in it. The book's subtitle might well have been "Forward Thinking in Astronomy," for which I have three meanings in mind. The ideas proposed here will be *forward* in the sense of audacious or presumptuous, and hopefully in the sense of advancing or progressing, but they will also be forward in the sense of chronological or deductive. It is in this last sense that I hope to gain a real advantage over the reasoning often used heretofore in certain areas of astronomy. The method is superior; the question is only one of finding a better starting point. You, the reader, will be the most severe judge of that.

Prologue

● ●

Excitement filled the royal hall. Rumors had been circulating for months. The great blind sage was about to announce his latest findings. At last, the people would know the answer to one of the deepest scientific mysteries remaining on the planet—how light propagates.

Interest in science ran high on planet Krypton. The people had a deep and abiding desire to know about their origins and to understand the nature of the universe around them. So people of science were held in high regard, even more so than the governors. Some said that the great sage, the wisest of all scientists, was even more beloved by the people than the emperor. But then the emperor had that eccentric habit of wearing no clothes during public processions, which cost him some popularity.

Calela was there with her father. From school she knew full well that almost all the mysteries of the universe now had theories to explain them. But the one mystery which had eluded the best efforts of the planet's top scientists concerned the propagation of light. For light seemed to move about in the manner of waves through some medium. Yet no trace of an actual medium had ever been found.

Most puzzling of all, when light came from a moving source, its speed of arrival was found to be no different than when it came from a stationary source. This was in sharp contrast to all non-light material entities, for which the speed of the source affected both the transit time and the measured speed upon arrival. But light must propagate in some truly wondrous way to behave so oddly.

And now, as Calela waited with the others, the great sage was about to reveal to the people how this was possible. "How did the great sage come to be so wise, father?" Calela asked.

"The people say it is because of his blindness," her father replied. "Perhaps his blindness enables him to understand and reason about the wonders of nature more clearly than sighted people can, because of all the distractions which come with ordinary vision."

"That is an odd thing," Calela thought. "How strange that a man who can see no light has been able, by the powers of his mind alone, to understand and explain something about the nature of light which no sighted scientist has been able to do."

Just then a hush came over the royal hall as the emperor himself appeared. Striding to the podium, he was greeted with vigorous, if brief, applause. In his introduction for the great sage, the emperor took pains to point out the support provided by the state to this marvelous man. "The state's support," he assured everyone, "is in no small measure responsible for the success story about to be told!"

All eyes and ears were now focused as one. The great sage himself appeared and was led slowly to the platform. The applause of anticipation and admiration greeted him. Calela and her father joined in. The great sage looked only a bit different than in the recent film about his life and accomplishments. As the applause finally subsided, the great sage began to speak. His words were wondrous.

Space itself, he revealed, was the medium in which light propagated. Bodies with mass were able to curve the space in which they resided, and to slow the rate of progress of time. The greater the mass, the greater the curvature of space and the slowing of clocks. When light came near a mass, its path would be bent because it must follow the curvature of space. Light passing by a mass would be delayed in transit because of the slowing of time.

He went on to explain that when a light source moved, the contraction of space and slowing of time which accompanied it ensured that the speed of light would be the same as measured by all observers, moving or not. "This is a very hard thing for me to understand," Calela whispered to her father. But most of the people had begun to nod in approval of the great sage's wisdom.

"He has indeed done it!" said someone nearby. "Everything about the propagation of light is now explained!" "Nature is even more complex and fascinating than we guessed!" said another. A feeling of great joy came over the royal hall as the solution to the mystery unfolded. The greatest remaining puzzle about the nature of the universe was a puzzle no longer.

As the realization dawned that the great sage had truly done what everyone had hoped for, a thunderous applause broke out. It continued uninterrupted for several minutes. Then the great sage was slowly led away. But the applause grew louder and continued even after the wise man had disappeared from view.

The emperor, applauding with the rest, returned briefly to the platform and spoke just a few more words as soon as the applause had died down a bit. "I will this day nominate the great sage for the Majestic Award, in recognition of this achievement!" The applause erupted again and continued until the people left the royal hall, for the Majestic Award was the most noble prize on the planet.

As the people dispersed, Calela asked her father, "Does everyone understand this new theory? Is there no one who doubts it?"

"What does it matter if we cannot all understand a theory, as long as the great sage and the elder wise men understand it and agree?" said Calela's father. "Besides, even if he weren't the great sage, who would be so unkind as to criticize the life's work of a blind man?"

1

●●●●●●●●●●●●●●●●●●●●●●●●●●●●●

On the Nature of Space, Time, and Matter

Summary: We begin our consideration of the nature of things by ask-ing the most fundamental "why" and "how" questions man has ever asked. Then we adopt our starting point for what we will call the "Meta Model," beginning simply with intuitive meanings for "noth-ing" and its opposite, "substance." We introduce a single unit of sub-stance into a universe containing nothing and develop its properties (the "one-particle universe"). We note that it must be sizeless, posi-tionless, motionless, and even without spin, since these lack mean-ing without a frame of reference (which would require additional substance in order to exist). Then we introduce a second particle of substance and find that we have the property of scale, but only in a relative sense. Even though spin now has meaning, it does not yet have its usual properties. For example, a Foucault Pendulum would retain fixed orientation on its parent particle. Then we examine Zeno's Paradox (that motion is impossible) to see how the paradox can be resolved in this model. The only apparent way is to assume that space and time are infinitely divisible, because the assumption of a mini-mum possible space or time interval would require discontinuities of motion or existence. We note that infinitely divisible intervals may nonetheless have a finite and continuous whole, as may be seen by setting up one-to-one correspondences between them and decimal numbers. Then we see that the same conclusion, infinite divisibility, must apply to mass as well, and we see how one-to-one correspon-

1

dences can resolve the related Zeno-like paradox for mass (that contact is impossible). The relativity of scale shows us that what is infinitely divisible must extend to infinity on the large scale as well. We then see that five and only five dimensions (space, time, and scale) are needed to describe the Meta Model universe, and all must be infinite in both directions. Moreover, space in this model cannot exist without substance to fill it, and time cannot exist without change through collision between substances. We then introduce many particles into our model universe and discover that mutual collisions cause larger particles to grow by acquiring smaller ones. A basic meaning of "force" as the result of such collisions also becomes apparent. But there seems no way to avoid the implication that such forces will have a finite range; and that all dimensions are relative, not absolute. While this Meta Model has some intriguing properties and seems to follow deductively from a minimum of logically necessary starting assumptions, it is not yet apparent at the end of this chapter that the model will resemble the real universe when completed.

Questions and Definitions

What is space? Time? Matter and energy? Why is time irreversible in our experience? Is space or time absolute (able to exist without matter)? Or only relative, and perhaps dependent upon which observer is measuring them? What is the nature of force? In particular, what is gravity? Why do bodies seem able to act on other bodies at a distance? Are space, time, and matter infinitely divisible, or is there a limit to how small a unit of space, time, or matter can be? Or how large? What are the size, age, and mass of the universe?

These fundamental questions are important to us, and a lack of understanding of the fundamentals often causes our science to go astray. Lack of understanding also gives rise to logical paradoxes, such as those of Zeno; e.g. how is motion possible if a moving body is at every instant in some specific place, and at no instant in transition? Although solving all the fundamental mysteries of the universe is beyond the scope of this book, I hope by the following discussion to inject some new insights into the answers to the preceding questions.

The approach here will differ from the discussions of most other authors in one major way: the reasoning will be forward/deductive, not backwards/inductive (the importance of which is elaborated in the chapter "The Scientific Method"). Instead of starting from the observed universe and figuring how it could have come about, we will start with a single unit of substance in an otherwise empty space and step by step build a universe. I will call the resulting model the "Meta Model," since all the meanings of "meta" seem applicable here. (Meta: "later or more highly organized or specialized form of; more comprehensive; transcending; used with the name of a discipline to designate a new but related discipline designed to deal critically with the original one.")

As we develop the model, we will be paying attention to the paradoxes of Zeno and Olbers, as well as the observational data, to determine how well the model universe emulates the real universe. We will arrive at an interesting picture which closely matches reality, despite it bearing little resemblance to the models currently in vogue in astronomy.

We need one more definition before beginning. Is space an absolute thing, existing even without matter in it? Or does it depend upon the existence of matter to give it meaning? Let us define "substance" broadly as anything which exists, whether it takes the form of matter, energy, or "other." In order to answer the question of whether space itself exists in the sense of having substance of any kind, we need to introduce some additional useful properties of substance.

The One-Particle Universe

Let our starting universe remain empty of everything except a single infinitesimal, "stationary" unit of substance, which we will refer to as a "particle." Now imagine the same particle in motion. How fast is it going, and in what direction? There is nothing for it to move relative to, and nothing to provide orientation. All directions are equivalent, and all distances are equivalent. The only way it can be otherwise is if space itself has a sort of "structure" to it, a framework to provide meaning to orientation, scale, and motion. However, we have postulated an empty universe. In it there is no matter,

3

no energy, no substance of any kind except the single particle. How can there be "structure" without substance?

In the real universe there is a frame of reference to provide meaning to distance and direction. The reference frame is provided both by the presence of distant matter in the universe as well as by seas of rapidly moving "agents," such as photons and neutrinos. The essential point is that the reference frame is provided by the presence of substance in the universe. I would not insist that *matter* is needed; but I take it as self-evident that some sort of substance is required, or there can be no reference frame in space. In the absence of other substance in the universe, our lone particle would be incapable of motion, for motion could have no meaning.

Moreover, (and this is something to note), the size of the universe would be indeterminate, even if our lone particle has "finite" dimensions. Indeed, it is impossible to say whether the particle has infinite dimensions, finite dimensions, or is infinitesimal (without size), since there is no scale to measure by. The number of such particles which can fit into the universe around it is infinite in any case.

Our lone particle (see Figure 1.1) would even be incapable of spin. If it had parts, they might move relative to one another. But a uniform, spherical, lone particle cannot spin about any axis, because there is nothing outside the particle to spin relative to. By

Figure 1.1. This particle has a frame of reference: this page. But if it had none at all, there would be no meaning to motion or spin for the particle.

extension, the particle could not be made to exhibit the properties of spin, such as centrifugal force—a tendency to hurl objects off itself due to spin; nor would it tend to flatten from very rapid spin. The origin of these "inertial forces" is surely rooted in the substance which defines the framework of space. Without a framework, without substance (except for the particle), without "agents" to produce forces, surely there could be no meaning to, nor consequences of, "spinning." (The idea that the presence of distant matter in the universe is the origin of inertial forces is known as "Mach's Principle.")

Our example may start to seem a little less hypothetical if we postulate a finite limit to all the substance in the real universe, with nothing beyond. (The "Big Bang" Theory in its simplest form is such a case, in which all substance remains inside a sphere whose surface has expanded at the speed of light since the instant of the original explosion.) Under this assumption, the entire substance of the universe would be like our single particle, and all remarks about its size or motion in a larger infinity of space and time would be fully applicable, i.e., size and motion of the entire universe within its environment would be indeterminate.

The Two-Particle Universe

Consider again our simple lone particle in an empty universe. Now let us imagine a second particle just like the first at another location, not touching. Now, for the first time, we have "scale" in our universe and can measure the dimensions of the particles themselves as a fraction of the distance between them. There is no such thing as "absolute length" in this universe—we cannot tell if the two particles are "close together" or "far apart." Their separation is indeterminate relative to the universe beyond. It can only be measured in terms of the number of particle diameters.

We have also introduced meaning to motion, since the separation measured in particle diameters can vary. But with only two particles, if the separation "varied," we could not tell whether the particles had moved or perhaps only changed diameter (shrunk or expanded)—either would give the same result. We can also now imagine spinning, although we cannot yet tell whether one particle

5

spins or the other orbits. Note that the two particles cannot "see" or influence each other in any way except by collision, since our otherwise empty universe definitely contains no photons or agents to produce forces or actions at a distance, such as electromagnetism or gravitation. Consider a hypothetical pendulum suspended at the "north pole" of one of the two particles, taken as spinning. In the real universe, a suspended pendulum would continue swinging back and forth in the same direction in the universe, ignoring the spin of the body (e.g. the Earth) underneath it (as many museum exhibits of the Foucault Pendulum demonstrate). But our two-particle universe can have no such properties, because there can be no framework to provide a "remembered" preferred orientation for the pendulum. Indeed, the pendulum could not swing at all, because there is no gravity in this imagined universe.

Now imagine the particle on which the pendulum is suspended to have local gravity only, so that the pendulum can swing. But this gravity does not reach out to influence the second particle, so no framework is provided to the universe. Then clearly the pendulum must keep its orientation with respect to the particle it resides on, since that is the only framework it has. (See Figure 1.2.) But as soon as we imagine a sort of universal gravitation, this immediately pro-

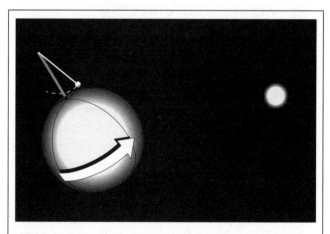

Figure 1.2. A pendulum swinging above a particle without any framework must keep its orientation with respect to the particle. It cannot sense the existence of the second particle, or anything else.

vides a framework for the pendulum. The proximity of the pendulum to a spinning particle is then no longer relevant, since the pendulum "senses" only the universal gravitational framework and must maintain its orientation in that frame. Nothing about the forces acting on the pendulum would tell it that the particle, above which it is suspended, is spinning.

By these constructions, we begin to see the origins of what are called inertial forces, and the importance of a frame of reference to the properties of the universe we live in. We also begin to see why it must be that scale and motion are relative, not absolute, in nature.

We have just seen that absolute motion has no meaning without a frame of reference, and that such a reference frame must logically be provided by some sort of substance. This gives us a basis for looking at a very famous dilemma called "Zeno's Paradox."

Zeno's Paradox

Zeno's Paradox deals with the ultra-small structure of space and time. In its essence, the paradox notes that if a moving body is in a specific place at every instant, then there is no instant when it is in transition from one place to another; and therefore motion is impossible. Since this contradicts everyday experience, it is called a paradox.

The same paradox can be expressed in a different form: to move from point A to point B one must first complete the trip to the midpoint. Having reached that far, one must next reach the new midpoint of the remaining distance. But however far one has traveled, one must first travel half the remaining distance before one can travel all of it. Hence one can never reach point B, because an infinite number of "half-the-distance" steps are required. (See Figure 1.3.)

It might be, of course, that space is not infinitely divisible—that there is a smallest possible increment of distance. But this leads to all sorts of conceptual problems. Consider points X and Y, separated by the smallest possible increment of distance. Now consider another point Z, also separated from X by the minimum possible distance, but in a slightly different direction. Then the distance

Figure 1.3. Zeno's paradox. After traversing half of an interval, half remains. At every step, this remains true. So an infinite number of half-the-distance steps are required, and one can therefore never reach the other side. (Artist: DeVita)

between points Y and Z is less than the minimum possible distance, contradicting the starting assumption. (See Figure 1.4.) But if space were "grid-like," so that adjacent cells had no overlap, then motion in any desired direction would not be possible, unless one took a zigzag path from grid-point to grid-point! Clearly, the postulate of a "minimum possible distance" is problematical.

If time is treated like just another dimension (a "fourth dimension" of space), the same remarks might be extended to include the concept of a "minimum possible time unit." Or we may make a separate argument about time. If there were a minimum possible time unit, then all existing substance would have one condition at one time moment, and some slightly different condition at the next time moment. By hypothesis, there is no possible interval in time, nor any moment in between when anything could have happened to provide a transition from the first condition to the second. It is there-

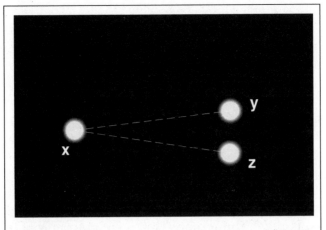

Figure 1.4. If X and Y are separated by the minimum possible distance, and if X and Z are also, then the separation of Y and Z will be less than the minimum possible distance.

fore just exactly as if everything existing at the first time moment ceased to exist, and then was created from nothingness in its new condition at the next time instant.[a] Even imagining a smooth transition from one place to another during a minimum possible time unit does not rescue one from a logical paradox. What if a collision occurs through the intervention of other matter in the middle of the minimum possible time unit? How can the new condition of matter at the end of such a time unit be dependent upon conditions which occur *during* an unresolvably small time unit? There is no logical way for the condition of existing substance to change, let alone change in an orderly way, from one time instant to the next.

To avoid these logical dilemmas, we conclude then that space and time are infinitely divisible. But is this not also ruled out by Zeno's argument? The problem is with our intuitions: while it is easy for us to imagine a finite whole as composed of an infinite number of parts, it is difficult to imagine an infinite number of compo-

---

[a]Although we can imagine that a deity continually recreates the universe to provide the illusion of time passing, there is seemingly no scientifically logical way in which such a scenario could happen naturally without divine intervention.

nents being assembled into a finite whole. As is well known in mathematics, an infinite series *can* have a finite sum. For example, there are an infinite number of possible fractions or decimal numbers between zero and one, yet obviously only a finite interval.

In Gamow's book *One, Two, Three . . . Infinity*,[3] we learn how to count and compare things made up of an infinite number of parts, using one-to-one correspondences. Such a one-to-one correspondence can be set up between points in a space interval, and decimal numbers between zero and one.[b] Since the interval from zero to one is finite by definition, the one-to-one correspondence shows us that the space interval is finite also. With another one-to-one correspondence we also conclude that it is possible to traverse the space interval in a finite time. This is an important point, even though our intuitions do not deal with it easily. The infinite mathematical series $(\frac{1}{2} + \frac{1}{4} + \frac{1}{8} + \frac{1}{16} + \ldots)$, where each new term is half the preceding one, has a finite sum of 1.0.[c] It is clear that in mathematics there exist finite intervals with an infinite number of points between, and infinite series with finite sums. By placing these in one-to-one correspondence with the physical concepts of space and time, we can reason by extension that finite space and time intervals may actually be composed of an infinite number of divisions; and conversely, that an infinite number of divisions may have a finite sum.

What about Zeno's objection that if a moving body is someplace specific at every instant, then at no instant is it moving, making

---

[b]For example, one can take the ratio of the length of a portion of the line segment from the beginning to any point, to the length of the entire line segment, as the decimal number.

[c]This is proved in mathematics by computing limits as the number of terms approaches infinity. To understand it intuitively, a little calculation will show that the sum of the series cannot be made to exceed 1.0, no matter how far the series might be extended. Moreover, if any number less than 1.0 is specified, even if that number be 0.9999 . . . 999 with a thousand nines, the sum will eventually exceed it. Looking at the problem geometrically, the terms of the series have a one-to-one correspondence with locations on the street that our mathematician friend is trying to cross. He must first cross halfway, then half of the remaining distance (or $\frac{1}{4}$ of the way), then half of the new remainder (or $\frac{1}{8}$ of the way), etc., to infinity. Yet all steps put together equal the whole interval, no more and no less.

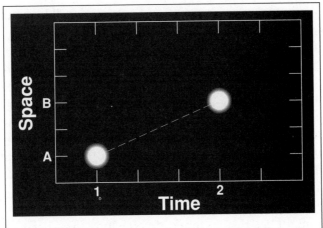

Figure 1.5. Space-time intervals consist of simultaneous motion through space (the y-axis) and time (the x axis).

motion impossible? One way to see the resolution of this paradox is by considering time to be another dimension, just like the three dimensions of space (although admittedly not exactly like a space dimension; e.g. we cannot travel both ways in time). Then a body traveling at a uniform velocity from point A at time 1 to point B at time 2 is traveling on a straight line in this space-time universe. (See Figure 1.5.) To clarify this picture, suppose the body is at rest in space. It nonetheless takes a straight "line" in space-time to connect its position at one time with the same position at a later time— the "line" representing an interval in time, instead of space.

Viewed in this way, it may be seen that the body is at every instant at some specific point on a space-time line. And once again the points in the interval can be put into a one-to-one correspondence with numbers between zero and one. So even though the distance traveled by the body in zero time is zero, it is nonetheless possible to traverse a finite distance in a finite time, each interval consisting of an infinite number of time instants and space points.

To clarify this conclusion, it is possible for substances to be unchanging at every instant, yet changed after a finite interval, *only* if there are an infinite number of steps in the interval!

Zeno-like Paradox for Matter

There is another form of Zeno's Paradox that applies to masses: "If bodies are infinitely divisible, then contact should be impossible." For example, when macroscopic bodies seem to touch, they actually consist of mostly empty space at the atomic level; so it must be their atoms which actually touch. But atoms are themselves composed of smaller particles and mostly empty space, so it must be these smaller constituents which actually touch. But if matter is infinitely divisible, this argument can be prolonged indefinitely, and nothing can ever actually touch.

One might use this argument to conclude that there is a smallest possible unit of matter or substance. Imagine such a "unit particle." It must be utterly uncomposed. It therefore cannot be broken or divided, nor even deformed by spin or collision—since these are properties of bodies composed of yet smaller particles. What then are we to assume will happen when two such unit particles collide? What density will the unit particle have? Indeed, will there be anything inside it at all? (It would seem that the substance in its interior could never contribute in any way to anything in the universe outside the particle, since it can never interact with it.) What would the unit particle's "surface" be like? Could it be hollow inside? With what thickness of shell? Would two colliding unit particles have to stick, since they can't rebound elastically? If they rebounded, with what resultant velocity? What about the slightest of grazing collisions? Would the unit particles be spherical in shape? Why would they have finite space dimensions, yet infinite dimension in time? Or do they come into and go out of existence constantly? Where and when would they appear and disappear?

It should be apparent from these considerations that postulating a "minimum possible unit of substance" is no more logically palatable than a "minimum possible unit of space or time." Substance must be infinitely divisible, as must space and time; or else the paradoxes quickly lead to unresolvable logical dilemmas. But how then can matter ever experience "contact," if everything which might experience contact is itself composed of smaller substances? The resolution of this paradox would seem to be analogous to that for space-time. If the substance of bodies always gets denser (more substance per unit volume) at smaller and smaller scales, then in the limit as dimensions approach zero, density approaches infinity and substances approaching each other must make "contact." (That is, at infinite density, they cannot be "transparent" to other substance). In the real universe, the density of matter greatly increases as scale decreases. Hence the ratio of mass to volume in electrons is enormously greater (about 10^{10} g/cc) than the same ratio for matter in ordinary human experience (of order 1 g/cc), which in turn is enormously greater than the ratio for the entire visible universe (10^{-31} g/cc).[d] "Contact" is therefore possible for infinitely divisible matter, as long as the smaller and smaller particles continue to increase in density with sufficient rapidity, without limit.

Ultimately, this is just another one-to-one correspondence between powers of 10 for a density ratio and decimals between 0 and 1. But I appreciate that it is very difficult for the intuition to grasp this concept. Consider the approach of one minute particle of substance to another. As the outer surfaces approach, the lesser particles (call them "second-level" particles) of which each is composed begin to approach each other. After the original particles traverse only a very small distance, the third-level particles of which the second-level particles are composed begin to approach each other. After an even more minute traverse of distance, and after an ever smaller lapse of time, the fourth-level particles begin to interact.

Although this continues without limit, as we have already seen, the process takes place in a finite time and a finite distance. The penetration of each level of particle into its counterparts in the approaching particle continues until the density of matter in the approaching particle is too great for it to penetrate deeper. Then the smaller particles at the next level penetrate until the density becomes too great for them to make further progress, and so on.

---

[d]Since this density difference of 41 orders of magnitude occurs over a scale difference of 42 orders of magnitude, it would seem a reasonable speculation that the mean density of substance is inversely proportional to scale for all ranges of scales. If it were otherwise, substance would have to fundamentally change in character at extremely large or extremely small scales.

> "If at first you don't
> succeed, find out
> why, THEN try again."
> —James B. Reed

By one-to-one correspondence with terms in our infinite series with a finite sum, we see that the depth of penetration has a finite limit and requires a finite time, after which the original particles react with resistance to the intrusion of new substance into their ranks *just exactly as if there had been a collision!*

By analogy with the proposed resolution of Zeno's paradoxes for space and time, the paradox for mass is resolved, apparently necessarily, by the conclusion that substance must be infinitely divisible and that it must approach infinite density as size decreases toward zero dimensions. This conclusion is reached by reasoning alone; it is reinforced by the observation that matter does in fact increase rapidly in density as scale becomes smaller over a range of more than 40 orders of magnitude in the observable universe.

The Meaning of Space, Time, and Matter

From the preceding considerations it seems altogether reasonable, and in a way compelling, to deduce that space, time, and substance are all infinitely divisible, because the consequences of the alternative are logically absurd. But if they are infinitely divisible on the smaller scale, what about the larger scale?

Recall our earlier argument that the entire visible universe would have undefined scale in space, time, and mass, unless such scale is provided by the presence of other substance in the greater universe beyond. That argument must remain true without limit. So no matter how large a universe we consider, its scale for space, time, and mass must eventually become undefined unless there is a greater universe around it to provide meaning to its dimensions. We conclude that all five dimensions are surely as infinite on the large scale as they must be on the small scale.

Throughout history man has believed that the universe consisted of what he could observe, and a few more things just like the observed ones, but nothing else. At first man thought the stars were "painted" on a hollow sphere perhaps only a few thousand times larger than the Earth. It took a long time to realize how very far away even the nearest star (other than the Sun) is—25 trillion miles! Indeed, the first attempts to measure the distances of the stars met with failure because the astronomers could not allow themselves to believe how far away they really were. And it took a much longer time to recognize that stars are organized into clusters, and then into galaxies. Today we recognize clusters of galaxies, and super-clusters, and "bubbles" or "walls" of super-clusters of galaxies. Does the large-scale structure stop there? Modern-day astronomers believe it does, because they believe the visible universe has a finite age (the "Hubble age") and finite dimensions, and that most of it is visible to us with our largest telescopes. They believe that the speed of light is an upper limit to velocity, and that nothing can be farther away from us than an object traveling at the speed of light for the time the universe appears to have been expanding (its "Hubble age").

But as I will discuss in the chapter "Stars, Galaxies, and the Universe," there are other possible interpretations of the phenomena, such as galactic redshift, which have led to these conclusions. I will also argue (in the chapter "On Gravity") that there exist velocities in the universe which exceed the speed of light, and I will show (in the chapter "On Relativity") how these can be reconciled with relativity theory. In other words, we have taken off the constraints which lead astronomers to believe that, at last, we finally nearly "know it all" about the large-scale structure of the universe. Having removed these constraints, we will be free to draw the conclusions suggested by logic and by the experience of mankind—that the upper limits to the structure of substance, the dimensions of the universe, and the extent of time must all be as unbounded on the high side as they need to be on the small side; and that the Big Bang model of a universe with finite size and age may someday be viewed with the same quaint disdain as the original "stars painted inside a hollow sphere" model. The necessity for this will become clearer as we further examine the nature of substances.

Let us return again to our empty universe which contains no substance, and therefore no frame of reference, except for a single uniform particle of substance. But as we have just seen, the particle must itself be composed of an infinitely divisible variety of subparticles. We could have chosen a single particle at any of an infinite number of sub-levels to be our unit of substance. To avoid the issue of the arbitrary size of the particle we select, let us conceive of it as having zero radius. Although it does not, this conception will allow us to introduce one scale of distance at a time.

As remarked earlier, motion and orientation have no meaning for a single particle in an empty universe. Now introduce a second infinitesimal particle. (See Figure 1.6.) This gives meaning to orientation, since angles can be measured from the line joining the two particles. It also provides a single measurement of length, the distance between the particles. It does not now, as it did before, provide a scale for the empty universe, since the distance cannot be measured in units of particle diameters, which are still being assumed to have no dimensions. Therefore there is no way yet to determine whether our particles are separated by a microscopic or a macroscopic distance. There is as yet still no meaning to motion in this two-particle universe. The two particles cannot change direction, since all directions have meaning only relative to the particle-to-particle direction. And the two particles cannot change distance, since all distances have meaning only relative to the particle-to-particle distance.

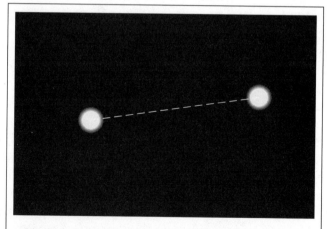

Figure 1.6. A universe consisting of two infinitesimal particles and no reference frame. All positions and all times are equivalent and indistinguishable until the first collision.

In a very real sense, this universe without the possibility of motion or change has no time. Time can have no meaning if there cannot be events or change to mark its progress. Put differently, if there were such a thing as an absolute time which existed somehow in addition to our two particles, the lapse of a microsecond or a million years would be just the same and utterly indistinguishable. But the existence of something with substance, such as an absolute time scale, violates the assumptions of our construction, that nothing exists except our two infinitesimal particles in an empty universe. Remember, we refer to "substance" rather than "matter" to cover *anything* which exists. An absolute scale of time, just like a structure or framework in space, would have substance in this broad definition.

Perhaps you have thought about one possible event or change which might occur in our two-particle universe up to this point. We might imagine that the two particles coincide, which is a distinguishable condition from non-coincidence. It might be fair to say that the first coincidence of the two particles marks the beginning of time; and that the interval between any two coincidences marks an interval of time. This interval still has arbitrary and indeterminate length. We cannot tell if the interval to the next coincidence is longer or shorter than the last (that implies an absolute scale of time to measure against). We can merely mark the progression of time by counting coincidences.

This brings us to an important point of our mental construction. In an empty universe consisting of two elementary units of substance, the ordinary properties of the universe (time, space, matter) do not exist outside the particles and between events of coincidence. It can therefore be said in a logically meaningful way that space and time which are empty of particles and events *do not exist!* This eliminates a logical fallacy we have been skirting around up to now about whether the empty space and time surrounding our particles exist. In our construction they do not. Therefore our use of "substance" to mean "anything which exists" is logically correct, since a true void would not exist (in either space or time), in the operationally defined meaning of the word "exist" as used here.

Of course, for actual particles with finite dimensions, events of coincidence do not occur. Instead we have what may be operationally described as "collisions," in the sense already discussed. Two particles interact "collisionally" when their sub-particles at all levels approach the infinite density limitation and are forced to retreat. Notice, however, that if we were to imagine an infinitesimal volume of space in our real universe within which there were only two uncomposed infinitesimal particles and nothing else (including forces), then all that we have concluded about distance and time not existing between events of coincidence would still be true.[e] No time or time interval would exist until an event occurred, with the only possible events being collisions with other elementary particles of substance.

Therefore, on the most microscopic levels, time must proceed "instantly" from one collision event to the next. Reflection on this construction, which implies the non-existence of space and time between events in a region, begins to provide some insight into why the universe seems to behave as if space and time were relative, not absolute. We have reasoned to the conclusion that they must be.

To emphasize the point that true void implies non-existence, we are asserting that every point in the perceptible universe is at every moment of time filled with contiguous substance at some infinitesimal level. If substance could be imagined to become absent anywhere at any time, time there would cease and the perceptible universe would collapse until the "void" was filled. Put another way, a particle reaching one edge of a "void" would skip instantaneously to the opposite edge, just as if the "void" had zero dimensions, because there is no substance to mark the passage of time inside the "void," and no absolute time without substance.

It is worth emphasizing that in the Meta Model, substance and existence are interchangeable. Where there is substance, there is existence, and vice versa; and where there is no substance, there is no existence, and vice versa. Put differently, at every point of space

---

[e]The rest of the universe cannot have any effect on the two particles, since by construction we have chosen a volume of space so small that no other particles or agents of any kind (including photons and gravitons) from the outside universe are in it. Only the existence of such outside agents interacting collisionally with other particles or agents or substance can provide meaning to scale or interval in space or time.

and time there must be both substance and existence. If either were missing, the other must be also.

It is interesting to note that the universe we have constructed with this model has exactly five dimensions—three in space, one in time, and one in "mass" (i.e., scale: how large or small a space-time volume we wish to consider). "Motion" in the fifth dimension might be conceived of as changes in mass or density or scale. Since these five dimensions encompass all reality as we know it,[f] it seems reasonable to conjecture that there are no other dimensions in reality. Dimensions beyond the fifth probably exist only in the world of mathematics, where there are an infinite number of conceptual dimensions available.

Since most physicists work with four or fewer dimensions, it may be useful to briefly explain the importance of the scale dimension. Given any reference point to serve as an origin for measurements in space and time, at first glance it appears that the coordinates of any point in the universe can be specified uniquely with four parameters: three space coordinates (for example, x, y, and z) and a time coordinate (for example, t). But we have implicitly assumed some constant scale in this description by adopting some units of measurement. Obviously the nature of x, y, z, and t will be quite different if we are measuring the location of a billiard ball on a table, or our position relative to the center of a distant super-cluster of galaxies, or the location of one atomic particle relative to another. That difference is the scale dimension.[g]

---

[f]For example, all constants of physics are measured with dimensions of length, time, and mass or their equivalents.

[g]The units of the dimension of time are different from the units of space. This is circumvented when desired by multiplying a time interval by the speed of light to convert it to a space-like interval. In like manner the dimension of scale is uniquely different from the others. If we adopt, say, the meter as our reference unit, then a scale could be specified by giving the logarithm of the desired unit of length measured in meters. The logarithm is desirable to normalize the range from minus infinity to infinity, as for the other dimensions, and because useful variations of scale are obviously exponential, not linear.

The Many-Particle Universe

Now let's jump forward just a bit by introducing a small but indefinite number of additional particles. We wish the particles to be of comparable size so that no one of them dominates all the others. But there is no need for the particles to be identical. Now these particles would certainly disperse immediately into the void around them if they could. So to prevent that, we will imagine a spherical barrier to contain the particles. Any particle encountering the barrier will simply reflect from it and continue moving inside the sphere without suffering any effect from the barrier. It's condition will then be equivalent to the particle having left the sphere and another having come in from outside to replace it.

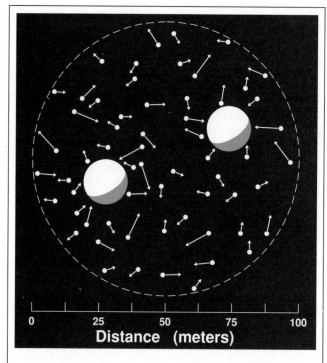

Figure 1.7. A many-particle universe within a 100-meter spherical barrier. Fixed particles A and B, when 50 meters apart, feel little or no net force from the random impacts on them.

To make the visualization more specific, let's picture the limiting sphere as 100 meters in diameter, giving it a volume of 523,599 cubic meters. And imagine that it contains 523,599,000 small particles—each, say, about 1 centimeter in diameter. On the average there will be 1000 particles per cubic meter, with a mean separation of about 0.1 meters (10 centimeters) between each. Then the particles will move about, occasionally colliding with one another and rebounding, with their state of motion eventually becoming completely random.

Now imagine two particles fixed in place within the sphere. Let each be 10 centimeters in diameter (1000 times the volume of the moving particles), and let's position them 50 meters apart and 25 meters from the barrier. (See Figure 1.7.) As long as all the particles are quite small in comparison with the barrier sphere, collisions between either of the two fixed particles and all the moving ones will occur nearly equally on all sides. The frequency of the collisions will be a function of the average speed and size of the moving particles. Although the fixed particles will feel "pressure" from the collisions and receive many tiny pushes in different directions from them, the average of all the collisions would tend toward zero net push in any particular direction.

However, the situation would be different if we placed the centers of the same two fixed particles only 12 cm apart, such that their surfaces were only 2 cm apart. (See Figure 1.8.) What has changed is that the fixed particles now shadow each other on one side from some collisions with the moving particles. And as a direct result of that shadowing, the fixed particles will feel forces tending to push them toward one another because of the excess numbers of collisions on the more exposed surfaces of each.

From this picture we conclude that in any sea of particles of indefinite size, the larger and slower-moving particles which happen by chance to come close to one another will feel apparent forces of attraction toward one another. Those which happen to come into contact will tend to "stick" because of the continuing pressure applied to them in collisions with the smaller, faster particles in the vicinity. Such accretion will continue for a while, with the larger particles absorbing the smaller, slow-moving ones which come into contact. The accretion will stop only when almost all the smaller, slow-moving particles have been accreted by larger masses, and what remains are particles moving too fast to be accreted in collisions. Alternatively, the larger particles could eventually reach a condition where collisions eject as much of their old mass as gets accreted as new mass, so that they tend to remain nearly fixed in size.

In this way we begin to see why the particles in a universe would form themselves into masses, and the circumstances under which such masses would appear to attract one another, i.e., exhibit "force." Note that the range of any such force as this is necessarily finite, since its effect diminishes rapidly over distances much greater than the mean free path between collisions of the nearby moving particles. This is an important point which will come up later when we discuss gravity. All forces which originate in this way have a finite range.

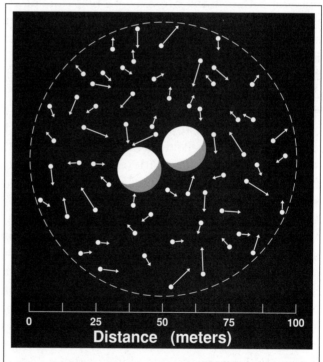

Figure 1.8. If particles A and B are much closer together than the mean distance between particle collisions, they will feel a net push toward one another caused by impacts from the other particles.

The counterpart of forces of attraction caused by external collisions and shadowing is forces of repulsion, which logically would be produced when a mass begins to emit some of its small, accreted components back into the space surrounding it. For example, when our Sun had accreted to a certain size, it began to radiate light, which is known to have a repelling force on high-volume, low-mass bodies, such as balloon satellites of the Earth.

Besides these phenomena of collision, accretion, attraction, and repulsion, we might also consider the case of a large mass which itself moves with speeds comparable to or faster than the speeds of the particles in its environment. The high relative speed would prevent accretion. The essentially simultaneous collisions of the large mass with many small particles at high speed would create a "wave" propagating outward from the large mass. I mention waves here only for completeness. We will discuss the properties of waves, and what starts them, in the chapter "On Relativity."

Implications

Pausing for a moment to digest some implications of our reasoning, it would be fair to conclude that the only logically imaginable way in this model in which substance can come into, or pass out of, existence (as opposed to changing form) is for it to "enter" or "leave" the region of collisional interactions with other substance. But if there were such regions where matter density is so low that no collisional interactions between units of substance occurred, then all substance on the edge of such regions would instantly dissipate into the non-interacting regions, followed by substance slightly further in, and so on. All substance in this universe would dissipate immediately into the void. We suppose that solid bodies as well as particles are held together by the action of agents which would disperse if not continually held together by the presence of other substances, so that even solids would dissolve. Since this does not happen, we conclude that the universe has no such regions where collisional interactions between units of substance do not occur.

The conclusion is not avoided by introducing curved universes or curved space-times, because there cannot exist curvatures or borders or reference frames except through the action of substance of some sort. Moreover, space curvature is a meaningful concept only if we postulate another space-like dimension for it to be curved in. It should therefore be true that the universe is as infinite in extent, and filled with substance throughout, on the large scale as on the small scale. The average density of substance must continue to decrease as the volume under consideration increases; but local densities must approach infinity at every point throughout all of infinite space.

The same reasoning applies to time. A cessation of collisional events would bring a cessation of time; but with matter existing everywhere with sufficient density for collisions, it follows that time continues forever, in both the future and the past.[h] But couldn't substance redistribute itself so that densities no longer approach infinity anywhere, thereby ending collisional events? By analogy with the dissipation of substance in space, if it could so dissipate (for example, if the amount of substance in the universe were finite), it would have already happened, quite immediately. Conversely, if substance does not start out with density which approaches infinity as dimension approaches zero, it could not assemble itself into such an infinite-density configuration in a finite time. We may therefore be reasonably certain that the "universe" (in our model) is infinite in space, time, and mass or scale. It does *not* follow that the form which substance takes need necessarily be the same in widely differing parts of this universe—for example, assembling itself into the familiar matter with gravitation, electricity and magnetism, protons and electrons, stars and galaxies.

It must be the case that every bit of space is occupied at all times by a continuum of substance; and that wherever substance is not, existence of time, space, and matter is not. The substances whose presence "define" space-time must be infinitesimal compared to the substances in our experience, such as baryons or photons, or even neutrinos. What we call "energy" is usually just substance in the form of waves.

---

[h]Since substance would disperse if given the opportunity, it follows that the substance of the universe could not have arrived at such a condition at any past time unless it had always been in such a condition.

Since dimensions are unlimited in space and time, the Big Bang theory of the origin of our universe (according to this line of reasoning) can, at best, refer only to a local "large-scale" event in our region of the universe. More likely, some other explanation exists for the redshift of distant light and the microwave background radiation than a big initial explosion of all matter, and we will derive some such ideas in the chapter "Stars, Galaxies, and the Universe." A clear prediction from this discussion, however, is that matter will likely continue to be discovered at ever higher redshifts, rather than disappearing in favor of pure energy, as the lookback time of the astronomers' telescopes approaches the age of the Big Bang universe. We will discover once again that the observable universe is not the complete universe, but represents merely the limitations of our detectors at the present epoch. Ideally the Hubble Space Telescope will greatly extend the range of our observations.

Distance scales must be purely relative, with no absolute meaning to "large" or "small." Likewise we should not be surprised by very large velocities. I will argue in the chapter "On Gravity" that the agents which propagate gravity act much faster than the speed of light. It seems likely to be the case that neither the speed of light nor any other speed is a physical upper limit to the velocity of substance. Indeed, it follows from our construction that two isolated "units" of substance would interact instantaneously, and therefore with infinite apparent velocity. Although true "units" of substance do not exist, it does follow that apparent velocities of interaction would approach infinity as scale approaches infinitesimal. I believe the discussion in the chapter "On Relativity" shows that no contradiction with Relativity Theory need exist on this account, although obviously this is a crucial point for the viability of the entire model.

We can also formulate a principle about scale. Since scale is infinite, large and small, our own scale level must be quite arbitrary. It follows that certain physical properties—such as the nature of motion, change, collision, matter, energy, waves, and forces—should be essentially the same at any scale, with only accidental differences. So we introduce the following new axiom: "The universe should look essentially the same at all scales." But in applying this axiom, one must not be overly impressed with the enormous variety of forms available as one moves through a finite range of scales. One could be impressed by the obvious differences in any finite time or space if one did not stand back, look from a broader perspective, and take note of fundamental similarities, such as particles and waves.

The axiom is not meant to imply that blocks of space, air, land, and water would look essentially the same. Rather, it implies that such forms are not unique to our scale, and similar structures will be found at vastly different scales. Conversely, the large structures we see at our scale, such as stars, galaxies, walls, and voids, are not necessarily the same structures we might find in a different part of the infinite universe at our scale. In this connection, it may be sobering to appreciate that there are as many atoms in a single drop of water as there are stars in all the galaxies in the visible universe. Yet just outside that single drop of water, the structure of the universe changes drastically—for example, to fast-moving air molecules.

We are building a model of the universe: the Meta Model. We have adopted a starting point and are reasoning deductively. The hypothetical model universe has some interesting properties, provides a resolution of Zeno's Paradoxes, has no boundaries, and lacks a need to invoke *creation ex nihilo*[i] at any time or scale. Yet there are many ways in which it appears to be inconsistent with experiment, observation, or logic, such as its somewhat "aether"-like quality, faster-than-light velocities, and especially the implication that no scale is unique, only different in the details. But we have no choice but to build the model one step at a time. So I must ask your continued forbearance, while offering the assurance that these "problems" will be resolved in an uncontrived (if unexpected) way as the model develops.

---

[i]Creation out of nothing.

2

· ·

On Gravity

Summary: We review the properties of Newton's Law of Universal Gravitation, and for each property, we ask "why?" To answer this question we postulate that "action at a distance" in its purest form, with no agents passing between the acting body and the affected one, must logically be impossible. But if such agents exist, they must propagate and interact in order to have an effect. Gravity would then be an inverse square force, because whatever propagates spreads out in two dimensions while moving in a third. If the action of the agents results from collisions, then their source must be external to the acting body; because if they came from inside, the force of their collisions would be repulsive. For gravity to be a "universal" force, the universe must be filled with a flux of such agents. To affect every atom of matter in a body, the agents must be small enough to be able to pass through ordinary matter with ease. And the mean distance between mutual collisions of agents with each other must be large compared to the distances separating the acting and affected bodies, or the flux would behave like a "perfect gas" and produce no force between separate bodies. But if these conditions are met, bodies would "shadow" one another from some of this universal flux, resulting in a net force toward each other which would behave exactly like Newton's gravitation. Some common objections to this type of flux model for gravitation are discussed. We then call the flux particles which give rise to gravitation "C-gravitons" (CGs). We also name the medium through which light propagates the "light-carrying medium" (LCM). And we name the largest entities through which CGs cannot pass "matter *ingredients" (MIs). Inertia, or the resistance of bodies to changes in their state of motion, may arise from the continuum which defines space, so it may be the same for all forces at all scales. Inertial masses would appear to approach infinity as bodies approach the speed of light only because electromagnetic forces cannot propagate faster than light, and hence, their ability to "push" approaches zero at lightspeed. Forces from gravitation may have no such limitations if gravity operates faster than light, as we conclude after a short discussion of the properties of media in general. We then note that, operationally, dynamicists are obliged to assume instant propagation of gravity for the equations of motion of bodies to work correctly, even though the light from those same bodies has a significant delay in time of arrival. An experiment using the Sun-Earth-Moon system shows that the direction of the Sun's gravitational force and the direction of its arriving photons at the Earth differ by an angle of 20 ± 1 arc seconds, implying that gravity travels at least 20 times faster than light. But the absence of accelerations of contact binary stars sets the strongest lower limit to the speed of gravity at 1010 times that of light. Gravity must behave differently than in Newton's laws in a second way in this model: if all the space is removed between the MIs in a body, the CG flux can no longer penetrate, setting an upper limit to the strength of a body's gravitational field, regardless of how much mass it contains. This would eliminate the singularity (zero divisor) in present gravitational theory, and cancel its prediction that "black holes" exist in the physical universe. Instead, the sudden collapse of super-massive bodies would predict dual-lobed features not unlike those of radio galaxies, and nearby objects of high gravitational redshift not unlike quasars. Other possible tests of gravitational shielding are discussed, but applications to Relativity are saved for the next chapter.*

The Properties of Gravitation

"Every two particles of matter in the universe attract each other with a force which acts in the line joining them, and whose intensity varies as the product of their masses and inversely as the square of their distance apart." (Newton's Law of Universal Gravitation)

Why is any of this true? Modern physics has come to understand something of the nature of light and sound, of matter and energy,

28

of force and motion. We know that heat is a phenomenon caused by the motion of molecules. Matter is composed of molecules, which are composed of atoms, which are composed of baryons, etc. Forces are understood as something pushing against something else, or as action and reaction. But our understanding of gravity is at a far more primitive level. We can describe operationally *how* gravity acts, and the gravitational laws of motion must be among the most exactly measured and confirmed laws in physics. But we really know very little at all about the *why* of gravity.[a] This is primarily because of its remarkable properties, which seem to defy all understanding.

"Every two particles of matter in the universe ... "—regardless of chemical composition, regardless of atomic makeup, regardless of charge or spin or any other property—surely a remarkable thing. "Attract each other"—other forces of nature have both attractive and repulsive manifestations, but gravity always attracts. Why?

"Inversely as the square of their distance apart"—this is perhaps the easiest property of gravity to understand, since it is true of so many other physical manifestations. As something propagates (light, sound, energy), it spreads out in two dimensions as it moves forward in a third dimension and in time. This causes an inverse square weakening, simply because the "area" of the propagating entity increases with the square of distance, so its "density" (substance per unit area) must decrease with the square of distance. (See Figure 2.1.)

"With a force which acts in the line joining them"—this seems a trivial point until one considers that it remains true even if the particles are moving at high speed or accelerating. It means that the force acts without detectable delay, which is remarkable. As fast as light travels, there is a significant delay for it to traverse the interval between two bodies; and we see only images of bodies as they were when the light left them, not as they are at the instant their light arrives. But the opposite is the case with gravity. We will

[a]The General Theory of Relativity postulates that gravity is the result of a curvature of space-time in the presence of mass. But that tells us nothing about why gravity exists in the present context. It merely changes the question from "Why do objects attract each other?" to "Why do masses cause a curvature in spacetime?"

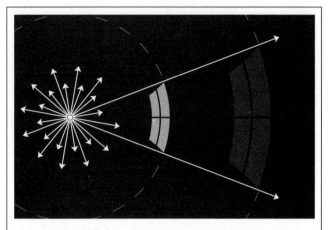

Figure 2.1. Anything which spreads in two space dimensions while propagating through a third attenuates in an "inverse square" fashion. At twice the distance, the propagating substance will spread over four times the surface area.

return to this point, the apparent "instantaneous" nature of the action of gravity, later in this discussion.

Although not spelled out explicitly in the universal law of gravitation, there is one other property which needs elaboration before we can begin thinking about why there is universal gravity. It is the question of "action at a distance." Can one object act upon another at a distance without some agent passing between them? In the case of atomic forces, there certainly are such agents, said to be photons traveling at the speed of light. However, in the case of gravity, it is sometimes supposed that there is no agent.

Action at a Distance

Sir Isaac Newton is credited as the first to make a remark that I personally find compelling: "That one body may act upon another at a distance through a vacuum without the mediation of anything else ... is to me so great an absurdity, that I believe no man, who has in philosophical matters a competent faculty for thinking, can ever fall into." Although Newton would on that account perhaps be dis-

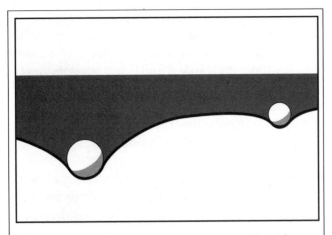

Figure 2.2. Curved space-time is like a rubber sheet on which masses may roll freely, and affect each other's motion without actually touching. The agent carrying the apparent force is the rubber.

appointed in twentieth-century physics, he was surely right that it must be impossible for one body to influence another at a distance without the action of some agent passing between them. Forces such as gravity or magnetism, which appear to act at a distance, must actually consist of *something* which passes between the source body and the affected body. In other words, "action at a distance" in its purest form, where something local affects something remote without any causative agent passing between the two, must logically be impossible.[b] In the cases of gravity and magnetism, this postulate is reinforced by the observation that the force exists at all distances from the source, dropping in strength with the square of distance, suggesting an outward propagation from that source.

Sometimes physicists talk about the "curvature of space-time" near a massive body, predicted by Einstein's Relativity Theory, as an example of action at a distance. (See Figure 2.2.) But *something*

[b]For quantum physics experts reading this, we will address quantum "non-locality" and the way other quantum problems interface with this model in a separate chapter. At this point we are presenting a postulate of logic, not of physics.

must act to maintain the so-called "curvature of space-time" at a distance. Moreover, if the massive body is suddenly accelerated, it must take a finite time (however small) for the accompanying "curvature of space-time" to respond and begin accelerating too. If the massive body were to cease to exist, there must likewise be a finite time before the "curvature" also ceased to exist. This is merely restating the first principle, that there must exist some agent which passes between to accomplish any action; and this agent cannot act instantaneously, because its velocity must be finite. (Note, however, that there is nothing in the field of logic which compels us to set any upper limit on the speed of such hypothetical agents; it particular, logic alone does not place any requirement that they travel at the velocity of light or slower.)

Every force of every type must ultimately be produced by some form of agents which transmit the force by contacting the affected body. There may be a variety of different agents. But for a force to act without any such agents would be magical. The agents which must pass between bodies are responsible for all known types of forces, whether they be gravitational or electromagnetic, thermal or mechanical, produced by visible agents or invisible ones, of known or unknown types.

The Agents of Gravity

The agents which produce forces must exist; therefore they must be tangible in some way. Everything existing is classified by physics as either matter or energy, and ultimately all matter and energy are interchangeable, according to modern-day physics. For purposes of this discussion, it is unimportant whether the "agents" that give rise to forces are matter or energy, or "something else"; but it will be convenient to think of them as having "substance," at least on some infinitesimal scale.

Therefore I suppose, and feel no doubt in my supposition, that gravity acts by means of some sort of agents making contact with matter, despite the fact that no such agents are yet known to physicists. Conceptually, the only way that "agents" have to act on bodies is by means of collisions. (I am not aware of any conjecture about how gravity is supposed to bring about the "curvature of space-time," spoken of in Relativity theory.) If an agent does not come into contact with a body to influence it, then we have another "action at a distance" dilemma, once removed. "Collision" here is still a broad concept, encompassing many possibilities. At this stage of the discussion, I will rely upon an intuitive meaning associated with the term: contact, followed by elastic deformation, followed by rebound. "Collisions" which lead to sticking, or to destruction of the target body, may be thought of as consisting of numerous elastic, non-destructive collisions occurring at a more microscopic level.

We might then imagine two possibilities: the agents come from within the matter which attracts, or the agents originate outside the matter. Our first impulse is to assume an origin from within, but it is not easy to see intuitively how agents coming from within one body, then traveling to and making contact with a second body, can give rise to a force of attraction between the two bodies. Such a force would logically be "pushing," or repulsive. On the other hand, a sea of rapidly moving agents everywhere outside a body would tend to push down on the surface of the body, giving rise to an apparent force of attraction toward the center of the body. Moreover, two bodies would shadow each other from some of the agents, giving rise to an apparent force of attraction between the bodies (since fewer agents would be available to "push" from the shadowed side than from the opposite side of each body). Models of gravitation using such an external universal flux were first proposed by Boscovich.[4]

We have already seen how the Meta Model requires that just such forces would arise within a universe with a sufficient number of particles at any scale. Such a force would be always attractive, as gravity is. If the universe is filled with such "agents," the force would be universal. The force would be inverse square, as would any force from agents which diverge in two dimensions while moving in a third and have a sufficiently great mean distance between collisions with each other.

And lastly, assume that the agents are sufficiently small that most of them can easily pass entirely through large solid bodies without contact. (Recall that at the atomic level, ordinary matter is mostly empty space anyway.) Then every atom of matter, even the ones near the center of the body, will contribute its share to the net "gravity" force exerted by the body, because the occasional collision

33

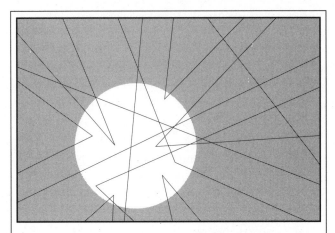

Figure 2.3. A mass in the sea of agents. While many agents pass through the mass unnoticed, some press the surface layers towards the center of the mass.

between an agent and an atom of matter in the body would be equally likely to occur for every unit of mass. (The agents which pass through without contact contribute no force at all. Matter which deflects agents then shields matter behind it from the possibility of collision with the same agents, which results in an imbalance of collisions on one side.)

To summarize, consider a spherical body of ponderable mass. Although the hypothetical agents are flying through it all the time, some of them are always colliding with the atomic particles making up the body, producing push-like forces. (See Figure 2.3.) When a collision occurs, the agent rebounds and therefore is not available to collide with other atomic particles deeper in the spherical body. This means that more agents strike every atom from above than from below, because of the shielding effect of the nearby matter. The resultant of all such collisions must therefore be that every particle of the spherical body is "pushed" in the net direction toward the center of the mass, where the most shielding from push-collisions occurs.

If the agents were absorbed during collision instead of deflected, a net force would still occur; but all bodies would be continually increasing the total amount of their substance. It remains possible in this model that bodies do in fact increase the total amount of their substance over very long times. For example, stars continually radiate light into space over billions of years without losing appreciable mass, so the converse could be equally true. But for the moment we will apply Occam's Razor and assume a conservation of agents absorbed and reradiated into space, unless some compelling reason arises to deviate from that assumption.

If the picture is not yet clear, take it to the logical extreme: suppose the matter in the spherical body was so dense that no agent could penetrate, and every agent reflected off the surface of the body. Then all collisions of agents with the spherical body would serve to cause a downward force at the surface of the body pushing toward the center. The body seems to have "gravity" and would be held together, even though its atoms do not, in this concept, actually attract one another.

Now suppose we have two spherical bodies of ponderable mass some distance apart. Each shields the other from some collisions by the omni-present agents (again assuming that the mean distance between agent collisions with each other is much greater than the separation of the spherical bodies). (See Figure 2.4.) The result is that each body experiences more "pushes" from one side than from

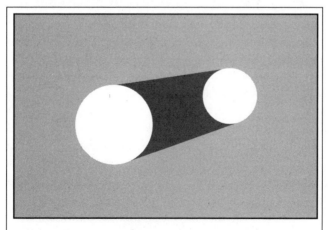

Figure 2.4. Masses in the sea of gravitons "shadow" each other from some graviton collisions, resulting in an apparent attraction.

the side toward the other body. It is just as if the two bodies somehow magically attracted one another from a distance—but all the action is produced by the pushing collisional forces of the supposed universal agents.

Since the spherical bodies are nearly transparent to the rapidly moving agents, every particle of matter within them helps contribute to the "force" experienced by the remote body. Moreover, since the angle subtended by the remote body decreases with the square of the distance from the shielding body, the force it experiences is inversely proportional to the square of the distance between the bodies. In other words, the hypothetical force we have just constructed exactly mimics Newton's Law of Universal Gravitation.

Objections to Agents of Gravity

If the basic model is clear, let me now address various objections which have been raised to it. One claim is that the hypothetical "sea of agents" should act like an "ideal gas." This means that it should apply pressures equally on all sides of every particle. There should then be no more of a tendency for two bodies in space to attract each other because of collisions with agents than there is for two bodies in air to be pushed together by collisions from air molecules.

The answer to this objection is that the behavior of the "sea of agents" depends upon the mean distance between collisions. If it is small compared to the separation of bodies as is true for air molecules, then the "sea" should indeed behave as an ideal gas. But if it is much greater, then the bodies must shadow one another, and "feel" attraction. This objection is correct, however, in indicating that gravitational forces from such a "sea of agents" cannot have the infinite range that Newton's Law requires. There must be some distance, however large, in excess of which gravity no longer behaves in the accustomed manner, but will start to behave like an ideal gas.

A second objection comes from considering an infinite, superdense wall through which no agents can pass.[5] Since every agent reflects off such a wall, the outbound flux should equal the inbound flux, giving no net force toward an effectively "infinite" mass. The answer is that if a superdense particle approaches the wall, and the mean distance between agent collisions is much greater than this approach distance, then the superdense particle casts a "shadow" on the wall which represents a net force toward the wall. This second objection, however, goes on to state that the force felt by the superdense particle under these circumstances would be independent of its distance from the wall. But that is the case in classical physics as well. Most of the force of the infinite wall is directed sideways, and is canceled out by symmetry. But consider any solid angle subtended at the particle and extending toward the wall. The solid angle encompasses a certain quantity of mass. If the particle distance is doubled, then the same solid angle will encompass four times as much mass, each unit of which will exert one-fourth as much pull. So the net force is indeed constant and distance-independent, contrary to intuition.

A third objection[6] is that two perfectly reflecting spheres in a universe filled with a flux of photons do not cast shadows on each other. And since they do not, they become invisible. By implication, the "sea of agents" for gravity ought to behave in the same way as the photons. The answer to this objection is that light does not propagate as particles, but rather as waves. So particle-like properties, such as a conservation of the number of agents in the flux, do not apply to light analogies. The ability of each point of reflection on each sphere to become the origin of a new lightwave, no matter how close the spheres get to one another, effectively eliminates the possibility of shadowing and makes light behave more nearly as an ideal gas would. This objection is also how we deduce that gravitational agents must be particles, not waves.

A final, classic objection to all "sea of agents" models is that the sea would produce drag, or resistance to motion, for all masses moving through it. If agent velocities were limited to the speed of light or less, this would indeed be an obvious problem for masses moving at near-light velocities. But as we will discuss below, no such limitation applies to mean gravity-agent speeds. The obvious answer to this objection is then as follows: The momentum transferred to a mass by a gravity agent is proportional to the agent's speed. The drag produced is proportional to the speed of the moving mass. If the ratio of these two speeds (mass speed over agent speed) is sufficiently small, then the drag produced will be too small to be measurable with the accuracy of modern observations. As we will see shortly, this ratio actually is very small indeed, so that the hypothesized drag is likewise exceedingly small.

Matter Ingredients
and the Light-Carrying Medium

Let us give a name to the entities in this "sea of agents" which are responsible for gravitation. I will call them "C-gravitons"[7] ("C" for "classical") to distinguish them from the hypothetical spin 2 "gravitons" of quantum physics, which are the supposed carriers of the gravitational force in that field. As a shorthand notation, I will refer to C-gravitons simply as "CGs."

These proposed C-gravitons must have some typical size and density. It is clear by observation that the mean distance between collisions of the C-gravitons must be larger than the solar system, since gravity seems to behave like an inverse square force for distance scales at least that great.[c] And the individual C-gravitons must be small enough to fly through most matter without contact. So they really cannot be the main constituents of the universal continuum which we have argued must fill all space and time in the Meta Model.[8]

This is not a surprising result, since the continuum which defines space and time must be infinitesimal in scale in comparison with C-gravitons. The CGs should then be just another medium of the universe, of great significance at our particular scale, but of no special significance to the structure of the larger universe. (At some small scale, the C-gravitons may play a role analogous to that which galaxies play for us.) The continuum defining space and time must consist of all entities throughout an infinity of size ranges, including those infinitesimal in comparison with C-gravitons. Yet another identifiable ingredient in this continuum must be a "light-carrying medium" (LCM), whose natural wave velocity is the speed of light.[d]

---

[c]We will propose in a later chapter that this mean distance between collisions is about 2 kiloparsecs, or about 10,000,000 times the size of the solar system.

[d]Well-known objections to the existence of such a hypothetical medium for the transmission of light, called the "aether," will be dealt with at the appropriate time. The model must be further developed first.

But the C-graviton medium does not have the right properties (such as speed and density) to itself be the LCM, as we shall soon see.

These C-gravitons must have a finite size; so although they flow through ordinary matter rather freely because they are so small, they cannot be small enough to flow through everything. At some level, some constituents of matter will stop them cold and be 100% reflective to C-gravitons.

Let me use the term "matter ingredients" (MIs) for the largest constituents of ordinary matter that are small enough to be impervious to C-gravitons. Then CGs will apply pressure to MIs, just as an ideal gas applies pressure to any boundary. But they cannot penetrate MIs. Although MIs must be much smaller than the quantum particles of today's physics, they are in no sense the ultimate units from which everything else is composed, since in the Meta Model there can be no such ultimate unit. Everything is infinitely divisible.

Now this is the important point: any two MIs will shadow each other from some CG impacts, resulting in a net force toward one another. And all larger masses are ultimately made up of MIs. So large masses will behave like collections of a huge number of individual MIs, each of which "feels" an inverse square attraction toward every other MI. (See Figure 2.5.) And this is why every particle of mass seems to attract every other particle of mass. As long as our definition of mass is equivalent to counting the number of MIs in a body—whether an atom, a molecule, a planet, or a star—then the force these bodies generate (which we call "gravity") must be proportional to the number of MIs within.

Masses also exhibit a property called "inertia," which is a tendency to maintain a state of either rest or motion indefinitely, until some other force acts to change it. This inertia, and the resistance of a mass to any acceleration, are the same regardless of whether the force applied is gravitational or electromagnetic. This implies that inertia originates from some other, finer medium in the continuum, and not from the CG medium or the LCM.[e] In effect, iner-

---

[e]If a body moves, then all its constituents on all scales down to infinitesimal must also move. So moving a body causes an infinite number of interactions with an infinite number of media on an infinite number of small scales, right down to the infinitesimal substances which define the

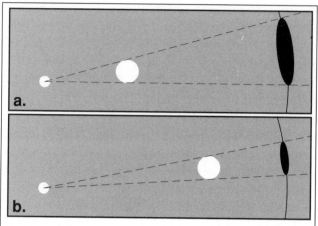

Figure 2.5. The force of an MI on a particle attenuates in an inverse square fashion. This is because the solid angle subtended by the remote body declines in proportion to the square of its distance.

tia senses the substance which must be present at every point of space in order for that space to exist. So it is possible that inertia may exist at all scales, not just those we are examining. But as long as all MIs are equally affected by it, both the gravitational and the inertial masses of bodies will be equivalent, as observed,[f] because each is proportional to the number of MIs in a body. (Later we will consider the possibility that some MIs in large, superdense bodies might not contribute to the body's gravitational mass.)

We are then led to ask why masses are observed to resist acceleration to velocities greater than that of light. It would seem necessary that electromagnetic forces, which themselves depend upon motion through the LCM and therefore can propagate no faster than the speed of light, would be unable on that account to "push"

---

existence of the space the body moves in. One old objection to the existence of an "aether" permeating space was that it had to be a continuum (like a solid body), not separate particles (like air molecules) in order to produce transverse-type waves for light. We see that the Meta Model indeed meets this objection, in that there exists such a continuum in space.

[f]This equality of gravitational and inertial masses of bodies is called "The Equivalence Principle."

anything else faster than that speed. Indeed, the ability of such forces to push faster at all must necessarily diminish toward zero as motions approach lightspeed, which is consistent with what is observed.[g] Since the C-graviton medium is different

> "Everything should be as simple as possible, but no simpler."
> —Albert Einstein

from the LCM, it may be possible (as we shall soon discuss) that CGs themselves propagate faster than light. If so, then CGs would in principle be able to accelerate masses to velocities faster than light, even though electromagnetic forces cannot.

The Behavior of Media in General

Let us speak briefly about the nature of motion itself. It is difficult to picture a continuum which covers an infinite range of scale. But in the Meta Model, any finite range of scale is about as good as any other. So the scale range we are familiar with in the observable universe should be qualitatively the same as any other scale range, including ranges thousands of orders of magnitude smaller than the observable range.

In our observable range, space must contain a variety of media. One of these must be the LCM, in which light and other electromagnetic phenomena propagate. Smaller still is the CG medium which gives rise to gravity. On the large-scale side, stars and galax-

---

[g]In physics it is said that the inertial mass of a body approaches infinity as its speed approaches lightspeed. This is exactly equivalent to what we have just described: the ability of a force to accelerate a mass moving near lightspeed diminishes more and more because the force cannot propagate faster than light. This appears to the observer as if the inertial mass of the body is increasing, making the force less and less effective. This is analogous to a propeller-driven aircraft approaching the speed of sound. The speed of sound is the natural wave velocity of air. A propeller-driven aircraft uses displacement of the air medium (waves of air) for propulsion, and so can never drive itself faster than the speed of sound, even with infinite energy and infinite propeller speed, because those waves cannot be made to travel at any velocity other than the natural wave velocity of the medium (the speed of sound).

ies can both be considered media in their own right, operating on time scales as long as their size is large in comparison with the LCM or CG constituents.

In general, when a mass moves through a medium, several conditions are possible. If the medium is dense enough, the mass will feel resistance to motion. If the medium is thin enough, no resistance at all may be detectable (although in principle it always exists at some minute level). If a thin medium has large-enough constituents, the mass will sense individual collisions and tend to random-walk rather than move smoothly. If the constituents are too small, they will be unable to affect the mass. They will be like neutrinos moving through a galaxy, taking virtually no notice of being surrounded by a large mass as they pass through. So masses only have to contend with media whose constituents are large enough to affect them.[h]

For dense media, there are other possible effects. A moving mass will set off a series of spherical wavefronts in the medium. And if the constituents of the medium are large enough and the mass's motion fast enough, the mass may even be eroded as it moves. This is reminiscent of the decay of certain atomic particles.

Of course, different media can affect each other. For example, gravitation can cause the interstellar medium to condense. If one medium changes the density of another, it also changes its characteristic velocity of propagation. Or one medium may simply retard waves in another without changing the density, which would affect wavelength but not wave velocity. Nature provides us with examples of all these possible phenomena.

In particular, we note that the CG medium appears to interact with the LCM (light-carrying medium) in a number of ways. The LCM in the vicinity of masses appears to be compacted in density, slowing the propagation of light and producing other refraction phenomena, such as increased light bending. We will develop this further in the chapter "On Relativity." On a larger scale, lightwaves seem to be retarded (redshifted) by resistance from the CG medium,

---

[h]MIs must have far smaller collisional cross-sectional areas than neutrinos, for which that area is about 10-43 cm2. CGs must be many orders of magnitude smaller yet.

with the amount continually increasing with the distance light travels. We will develop this further in the chapter "Stars, Galaxies, and the Universe." And the LCM must be a relatively stationary medium in comparison with the sea of gravitons, since C-gravitons must move about far faster than light (see next section).

We conclude that a sea of agents such as the C-graviton medium could produce forces which have all the properties of gravity. Since the existence of some such agents seems required to avoid "action at a distance" paradoxes, we conclude that this is an operational description of the "how" and "why" of gravity. It requires the existence of a universal sea of minute substances, so small that large solid bodies are virtually transparent to them. In the chapter "On Relativity" we will see how this "sea" differs from the old "aether" theory, and take up the question of how this model may be developed to include Relativistic properties. At this stage, the model operates exactly as does classical Newtonian gravitation.

The "Instantaneous" Action of Gravity

The advantages of the underlying concept I have just described, which has been discussed by numerous authors since the eighteenth century, is that it provides an intuitively understandable construct to explain why there is universal gravitation, how bodies can act on one another at a distance, why the force is always attractive, and why it behaves in an inverse square fashion. The other remarkable property of gravity not explicitly stated in Newton's Law of Universal Gravitation is that gravity is assumed to act instantaneously over all distances. In the equations of motion of Celestial Mechanics, for example, each body in the solar system affects every other body from its instantaneous true position. By contrast, solar system bodies are not *seen* in their instantaneous true positions. Rather they appear in the positions they occupied when they emitted the light just reaching the observer.

Take as an example the case of the Sun and Earth. It takes light nearly 500 seconds, or 8.3 minutes, to travel the 150,000,000 kilometers between the two bodies. When we look at the Sun in the sky, we do not see it where it is now, but rather where it was 8.3 minutes ago. This amounts to a displacement of about 20 arc sec-

43

onds on average—an astronomically large angle, impossible to mistake. Despite the almost unimaginably fast speed of light, it is not fast enough to allow the Sun, planets, or stars to appear in their present locations. In the case of some distant stars, we see them where they were thousands of years ago.

Astronomical observations are accurate enough to permit us to measure the direction of the force acting on the Earth caused by the Sun. Do you suppose that direction corresponds with the Sun's apparent position in the sky (which it really occupied 8.3 minutes ago, and is the position from which light now appears to come), or with the Sun's true instantaneous position now (which we won't be able to see until 8.3 minutes in the future)? Although the astronomers who calculate the motions of solar system bodies use equations with instantaneous action of gravity, not gravity acting at the speed of light, what would be the observable consequences of assuming a finite propagation speed for gravity?

In fact, the Sun's gravity emanates from its instantaneous true position, as opposed to the direction from which its light seems to come. If gravity propagated at the speed of light, it would act to accelerate the orbital speed of bodies.[i] By observation, no such acceleration exists down to the level of about one arc second per century squared for the Earth's orbit. The absence of the acceleration implies that the gravitational lines of force arriving at the Earth from the Sun are not parallel to the paths of its arriving photons, but rather have directions which differ by about 20 arc seconds. This is true for any model of gravitation.

To be clear, we are arguing here that gravity acts faster than light. If the force of gravity is carried by entities called C-gravitons, these entities must move faster than light. This is a radical proposal because Einstein's Theory of Special Relativity postulates that the speed of light is the upper limit for the speed of anything with substance in nature. There are a variety of supporting arguments for

---

[i]This is analogous to the so-called "Poynting-Robertson" effect: light, which pushes instead of attracting, acts to decelerate the orbital speed of bodies, though ever so slightly, since "light pressure" is a relatively weak force. This happens precisely because the action of light is much slower than the action of gravity.

this postulate, some of which are quite strong. Before we examine these arguments, let us see first if indeed we must violate the postulate. Then if we should be forced to conclude that something acting faster than light exists, we can re-examine the postulate about the speed of light in that context. For now, it is enough that the existence of the postulate that nothing can travel faster than light should not hinder us from looking at the evidence objectively. Because this point is so important, so central to the whole model under discussion, yet so contrary to conventional thinking, I will develop the same point in eight different ways. The reader may wish to examine only one or two of these.

1. Eddington[9] explains the dilemma for classical gravitation with these words: "If the Sun attracts Jupiter towards its present position S, and Jupiter attracts the Sun towards its present position J, the two forces are in the same line and balance. But if the Sun attracts Jupiter toward its previous position S', and Jupiter attracts the Sun towards its previous position J', when the force of attraction started out to cross the gulf, then the two forces give a couple. This couple will tend to increase the angular momentum of the system, and, acting cumulatively, will soon cause an appreciable change of period, disagreeing with observations if the speed is at all comparable with that of light." (See Figure 2.6.)

2. Consider a vertically falling rain encountered by a rapidly moving train. The faster the train moves, the more slanted from the forward direction the rainfall appears. The faster the Earth's motion, the more slanted in the forward direction the sunlight (and by extension, its gravity, if it traveled at finite speed) would appear to be. The Sun would then always have a forward-pulling component to its force which would accelerate the Earth. The absence of an observed orbital acceleration of the Earth about the Sun places a lower limit to the speed of propagation of hypothetical gravitational agents between the Sun and Earth. This lower limit is about 8 times the speed of light.

3. Relativists argue that the existence of the Sun's mass produces a curve in space-time which bends the motion of bodies near it, producing what appears to be a gravitational force. Since the space-time field at the Earth's distance is already pre-curved by the Sun's mass, the Earth simply encounters the already curved field and

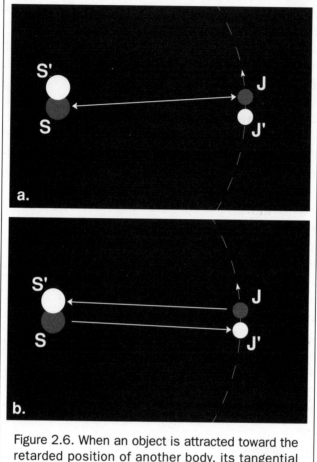

Figure 2.6. When an object is attracted toward the retarded position of another body, its tangential motion is accelerated.

responds to it instantaneously. In this view, the apparent gravitational force is produced by the Earth's encounter with the space-time curvature, not by its encounter with gravitational agents from the Sun which produce the curvature; so the propagation velocity of the agents, which is assumed to be the speed of light, is said to be irrelevant. In this view, if the Sun suddenly ceased to exist, its field at the Earth's distance would survive it by 8.3 minutes. The effects of any acceleration of the Sun would likewise take 8.3 minutes to modify the field. But uniform linear velocity in Relativity

Theory is always relative, and the Sun's field should share the Sun's linear velocity with no lag.

In point of fact, I believe the reasoning in such a construction is defective. If the agents maintaining the curved space-time propagate with the velocity of light, then the directions of lines of force in the field must still suffer "aberration," just as light does. (See Figure 2.7.) If the Earth moves through the field with a velocity of 30 km/s or 10^{-4} the speed of light, then the field lines must seem to stream somewhat toward the Earth, bent by 10^{-4} radians (about 20 arc seconds). Just as for light, this effect arises from the relative velocity of the Sun and Earth, and is not dependent upon which is thought to be "moving" and which "stationary." So the ratio of the speed of a moving body to the speed of regeneration of the local space-time curvature determines the resultant direction of the force lines. The absence of observed acceleration of the Earth then requires that the lines of gravitational force affecting the Earth are regenerated faster than light.

4. Either the Sun regenerates its field instantly ("action at a distance"), or it takes a finite time to regenerate its field at, say, the Earth's distance of one astronomical unit. In the latter case, the

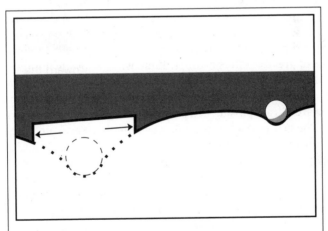

Figure 2.7. In the rubber-sheet analogy of curved space-time, if one body suddenly vanished, the field disturbance must propagate at a finite velocity and suffer aberration due to the motion of the other body, just as light does.

time delay between the regeneration of the field at 0.9 astronomical units and 1.0 astronomical units would necessarily affect the apparent direction of the force which acts upon the Earth. The size of the effect would depend upon the relative speeds of the Earth and the outward propagation of the field regeneration. We are really back to our starting postulate—that some sort of agents must pass between Sun and Earth in order to transmit the force, since action at a distance is logically impossible. But those transmitting agents must *move,* and that motion is the necessary and sufficient condition to produce aberration. (The vector sum of two velocities, the Earth's and the agents', gives the apparent direction of origin of the force, even though the actual direction is toward the Sun. So even if the field is pre-existing at the Earth's orbit, the Earth's motion makes it appear to come from a slightly advanced direction.)ʲ Since the motion of something is essential both to the continual regeneration of the field and to its inverse square nature (spreading in two dimensions while moving in a third), the aberration is inescapable.

ʲThis point about the necessity of the aberration of forces (apparent change in their direction of application) as a result of the motion of the affected body has caused much confusion in the literature. The reason for the confusion is simple: astronomers have felt compelled to explain why the force of gravity suffers no aberration, while allowing nothing involved in producing that force to move faster than light. To visualize aberration at work, consider the flight of an arrow from a source (analogous to the Sun) toward a train passing in a perpendicular direction (analogous to the Earth). The arrow at all instants moves radially away from the Sun, both before, during, and after its encounter with the moving train. Now visualize the path of the arrow as it passes through an open window, through the train, and out another window on the other side, without meeting any obstruction. As seen by passengers on the train, the flight path through the passenger cabin has a rearward component due to the forward motion of the train. Indeed, if the arrow interacted with the train by striking it, it would apply a slight decelerating force to the train. (A pulling force like gravity would have a slight accelerating component acting on the Earth.) So even though the arrow does not in fact change its direction of flight, it is unavoidable that a moving observer will see the arrow acting in a direction which is influenced by the observer's own motion.

5. Consider an "Earth" of negligible mass moving in a circular orbit around a massive "Sun." If the mass of this Sun is imagined to be a very large value, the orbital velocity of the Earth-particle required maintain a circular orbit may be close to the velocity of light. The true Sun is in the direction perpendicular to the Earth's motion; but the apparent Sun is seen out in front of the Earth, because the light of the Sun and stars all seem to stream toward the Earth from in front of it (just as vertically falling rain splashes into the face of a fast-moving observer). Mathematically, the force of the Sun's gravity is said to be "the gradient of the potential" of the Sun, meaning that it is in a direction which slopes toward the Sun. But since it is the Earth, not the Sun, which moves, how can the direction of that gradient or force from the Sun not also be shifted out in front of the Earth, just as all other directions are? (Answer: it must be so shifted unless it propagates so fast that the Earth's motion is negligible during its transit from the Sun.) And if it is shifted out in front, as the apparent Sun is, then the gradient or force on the Earth is always somewhat in the forward direction and tends to constantly accelerate the Earth. But this contradicts observations. The only escape from this dilemma is that gravity propagates far faster than light.

6. The same point may be extended to the mutual interactions of three or more bodies. Consider the Sun-Earth-Moon system. The Moon's orbit around the Earth is approximately an ellipse, but one which is quite distorted by the Sun's gravitation. I myself have analyzed observations of the Sun and Moon to solve for the direction of the force exerted by the Sun on the Moon's orbit. The solution showed that the Sun's force comes from its true, instantaneous position rather than its apparent, aberrated position, to a precision of one arc second. (The two positions differ by 20 arc seconds.) This solution alone constrains the speed of propagation of the Sun's force to be at least 20 times that of light.[k] No relativist has yet, to my

---

[k]For those interested in the technical details, I analyzed occultation observations to solve for any correction which might exist to perturbations of the Moon's orbit which depend upon the elongation angle D between the Earth and Sun. For example, D must be corrected by about 20 arc seconds to give the apparent angle between the two bodies because

knowledge, devised a theory to explain how it can be that the direction of the Sun's gravitational force on the Earth and the direction of the photons arriving from the Sun are not parallel.[l]

7. Perhaps contact binary star systems place the tightest constraints on a lower limit to the speed of propagation of gravity. Unless the speed of gravity exceeds 10^{10} times the speed of light, such systems would fly apart within a few hundred years. Moreover, since the centers of mass of the two nearby massive bodies are accelerating, not merely moving linearly at high speed, we know from such examples that even the response of a gravitational field to an acceleration (not merely a motion) of its source body must propagate faster than light.[m] Extrapolated retarded positions cannot be made to work. Even though such massive bodies are severely distorted in shape and must evolve to synchronous rotational locks with each other under the influence of tidal friction, this would not prevent the outward orbital evolution; it would simply rob the bodies of spin.

8. Let a high-speed mass with charge approach a neutral test particle from infinity. Let its linear trajectory pass by at a known distance from the test particle; and let its initial and final directions

---

of the finite speed of light. However, gravitationally, the correction to D in my analysis was measured to be zero to within the uncertainty of plus or minus one arc second, which places a minimum propagation velocity for the force of the Sun acting on the Moon of 20 times the speed of light. Although this constraint is far less severe than the lower limit derived earlier, it is a different kind of test utilizing the angle between two bodies instead of the offset of one body; yet it still constrains the speed of gravitational interaction to exceed the speed of light.

[l]Again, the resultant directions in which forces act are modified by the velocities of the bodies they act on. This is intrinsic to the dynamic nature of forces. Since the Earth moves at a velocity of 0.0001 c, the direction of the Sun's force must be modified by that motion, even if the force is already present at the Earth's orbit and just waiting for the Earth itself to arrive. A static (unmoving, unchanging) force could not push the Earth toward the Sun, but only retard its motion. Not could it respond to changes in the Sun's motion, either instantly (as is observed to happen) or with an 8.3-minute delay, because that would require a moving or changing force.

[m]By extension, this implies that if a body ceased to exist, its gravitational field at a distance would disappear long before the last light from the body at that distance disappeared.

at infinity be known. Its gravitation produces a net impulse on the test particle. Long after the passage, consider in what direction the test particle will be moving due to that impulse. If the gravitational effects of the charged mass act instantaneously, the answer is easy: perpendicular to the trajectory of the charged mass. That is also the answer implied by experimental results in the solar system. But in relativity, in order to get the correct answer, we must assume that the curved space-time associated with the charged mass is felt instantaneously by the test particle, without lighttime delay. So the test particle will feel an acceleration toward this net impulse direction when the charged mass is actually in that direction, even though its light is still arriving from a direction offset toward the direction of approach.

Now we can create the following paradox for special relativity. Consider an instant one lighttime interval before the true moment of closest approach. At that instant, use a negligible-mass magnet to deflect the path of the charged mass, so that it veers away from the test particle. Then at what would have been the moment of closest approach between the two, the test particle must sense an acceleration either toward the position the charged mass would have had if undeflected, or toward its true position. In the latter case, if the test particle responded instantaneously to the changes in the charged mass's trajectory, this would permit signaling of information faster than the speed of light, which is supposed to be forbidden by special relativity. In the former case, where there is delay in the test particle sensing where the charged mass has moved, then the test particle will experience a force toward a position that the charged mass will never actually occupy! This would constitute an effect without a cause. Moreover, after the lighttime interval has elapsed, the test particle will suddenly sense the deviation of the charged mass's motion away from the trajectory it formerly occupied. This would cause a discontinuity in the acceleration felt by the test particle, which would presumably suddenly start to feel acceleration from where it thinks the charged mass is now, ignoring its effects along its actual trajectory during the lighttime.

The conclusion of the eight preceding considerations is that whatever agents propagate the force of gravity from the source body to its field must travel at least 10^{10} times faster than light. It might seem that the thrust of the argument is that the action must be instantaneous. This would be another form of action at a distance: action which propagates at infinite speed. I do not at all propose that the velocity of propagation is infinite; far from it. A velocity of a mere 10^{10} times lightspeed, or across the observable universe in 1.5 years, is a very far cry indeed from infinite velocity, especially in an infinite universe. Whenever a new very large physical number is discovered, there is a tendency to disbelieve it as "too large to be plausible." However, even the largest numbers we can imagine are infinitely far below infinity.

This disbelief was manifested when the velocity of light was itself first measured. It took a very long time to accept that a velocity of 300,000 km/s, or seven times around the Earth in one second, was real; it had always been assumed up to that time that light propagated instantaneously throughout the universe. It was likewise very difficult to accept the initial discovery that stars were, after all, at a finite distance, although the nearest of them was 25 trillion miles away! Later it was difficult to accept the dimensions of our galaxy, or the Hubble age of the universe. Each time our knowledge of the size and age of the universe was extended, the initial reaction was disbelief. Then, when these new limits were finally accepted, each time there was a tendency to believe that the new limits were truly *limits*, not merely the latest extension of our growing knowledge of the universe.

The same is true of the composition of matter—the discovery of each new layer of building blocks is treated as if we had, at last, found the truly fundamental building blocks of all substance. Looked at with one eye to history and the other toward human psychology, claims to have discovered the size or age or mass of the universe, or minimum or maximum possible units of time, distance, mass, or velocity, should always be treated with skepticism. If it turns out that the observable universe is only an infinitesimal portion of the full universe, then it would not be at all remarkable to find velocities of agents operating at speeds of 10^{10} times lightspeed. Indeed, the Meta Model tells us that the smaller the agents, the more transparent substances will be to them; so the faster they would tend to move about, on average. Such agents can then have very high number densities while having low space densities.

52

New Properties of Gravitation

So the picture of gravity we have arrived at here demands a universe filled with gravitational agents moving at velocities much faster than light, in order to explain the nearly instantaneous action of gravity on the local scale.[n] But the Meta Model also predicts additional properties for gravitation which are not a part of the Newtonian or Einstein models. One of these is that there must be a limited range for gravitational fields, corresponding to the mean distance between mutual collisions of C-gravitons. We will discuss this further in the chapter "Stars, Galaxies, and the Universe."

Another new property is "shielding." If matter exhibits gravitation because of the shadowing of other matter from the action of a sea of agents, it follows that at some density the shielding is complete, and no gravitational agents can penetrate at all. If a sphere of matter were to collapse to such a high density that no gravitational agents could penetrate (e.g. all the space between MIs was removed), then only the surface layers would reflect the gravitational agents. None of the matter in the interior of the body would make any contribution to the strength of its gravitational field. It follows that a mathematical singularity could not exist in gravitation, since the force exerted by a finite body cannot approach infinity at its surface as the body collapses.

Moreover, since massive bodies would contain interior material which does not contribute to their gravitational fields because of complete shielding, this would help explain several astronomical mysteries. For example, there is an observed deficiency in the output of neutrinos from the Sun. If there were additional mass in the Sun's interior than is exhibited in its gravity field, this would increase the density in present models of stellar interiors, increase lifetime estimates, and lower the calculated flux of solar neutrinos. So the observed neutrino flux might be used to estimate the amount of such excess interior solar mass predicted by this model.

---

[n] How this can be reconciled with the constraints of the theory of Relativity—that nothing can go faster than light—are addressed in the chapter "On Relativity."

53

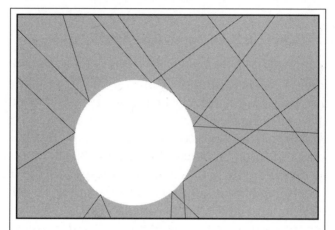

Figure 2.8. A superdense mass reflects all CGs from its surface. Interior mass does not contribute to the external gravity field.

Can a body exist with a density or mass so great that escape velocity exceeds the speed of light, thereby preventing light from escaping? Recall that in our model, gravitation does not arise from within the dense body, but rather from the C-gravitons near it. As a body gets denser, it still has a finite limit to its gravitational field: the limit when all CGs are reflected, and none penetrate. (See Figure 2.8.) At this limit, presumably, escape velocity would be just exactly equal to the velocity of light, since all gravitons interact with a photon from one side and none from the other side. No greater redshift than this would be imaginable. So the concept of "black holes" is physically impossible in the Meta Model.°

One further interesting corollary of the new picture of the behavior of collapsed bodies is that the objection to the existence of very massive "stellar" bodies is removed. There may exist objects of indefinitely large mass without correspondingly large gravitational fields (because of the gravitational shielding effects of sufficiently

---

°We will examine in a later chapter the sort of object which would result from the collapse of a massive star that became a supernova. This is just the sort of object that the conventional theory expects to become a "black hole."

dense matter). Moreover, as such bodies accreted mass and tended to become denser, they would develop very rapid spins. This is because any spinning, contracting body must spin faster, and an expanding body must spin slower, to preserve their spin energies.

If such a supermassive stellar body were to suddenly collapse, the result might resemble a supernova. The result of collapse would be increased spin without a commensurate increase in the gravitational binding because of shielding. Such an object would fly apart explosively, with two lobes on opposite sides leading the way. We now know what a supernova remnant looks like up close, since the ROSAT X-ray satellite observed details of the Crab Nebula in Taurus (a known supernova remnant, observed to explode in 1054 A.D.). The Crab Nebula clearly appears as a torus with jets emanating from a central pulsar at right angles to the torus plane. The resulting phenomena would seem to resemble certain jets and lobe features of radio galaxies and quasars which have caused astrophysicists to develop some wild ad hoc theories in recent years. But the idea just developed for supermassive star-like objects did not arise from an attempt to fit the astrophysical observations; rather it came out as a natural corollary of a general description of the properties of supermassive bodies in the context of our present discussion. It is always reassuring when a model under development makes predictions which resemble reality.

When very large masses undergo collapse, the collapse is naturally limited because the gravitational field has a finite limit. So "black holes" in the classical sense (collapse to a singularity) cannot form. Instead, one would expect the result of collapse to be an object with a very intense gravitational field. Light leaving such an object might be highly redshifted. Its predicted properties would not in any obvious way differ from the observed properties of quasars, which may be just such highly redshifted objects (to be discussed in more detail in the chapter "Stars, Galaxies, and the Universe").

And what of ordinary stars in the 3 to 10 solar mass range, if they should collapse? Without redoing all of stellar evolution theory, it seems clear that a finite gravitational field will result from the collapse, regardless of the remaining mass content. The strength of this finite field will therefore depend more on the size of the collapsed star (specifically, its surface area) than on its mass. It therefore comes as no surprise to learn that pulsars, which are believed to be remnants of supernovas, often have measured masses close to 1.4 solar masses. In standard theory this is coincidence. But in the Meta Model, we see that it is not truly mass we are measuring, but collapsed surface area. If revised stellar evolution theory under Meta Model premises predicts just such a constant-area plateau for a variety of original-mass collapsed stars, this would have to be counted as a successful prediction of the model.

Direct observational tests for the existence of shielded mass within large bodies would not be easy, because large bodies reveal their mass only through their gravitation. The easiest method would seem to arise in a three-body case. For example, suppose the Earth were massive enough so as to block some C-gravitons from passing through its core regions. Then at the times of a total eclipse of the Moon, some of the Sun's gravitation should also be blocked from reaching the Moon.[p] This would produce an outward radial impulse on the Moon, lasting about as long as the eclipse.[q] Perhaps observational accuracy will eventually improve to the point where we can learn if short-lived accelerations do in fact occur at times of lunar eclipse.

Better yet, a suitable artificial satellite of the Earth would show up the effects sooner because it would spend far more time in the Earth's shadow. The *Lageos I* satellite may be just such an object, since it was launched into an orbit high enough to avoid most of the Earth's atmosphere and other non-gravitational forces. It is covered with corner reflectors so that its orbit can be determined with

---

[p]Note that blocking part of the Sun's gravitation means allowing more C-gravitons to hit the Moon from the Sun's direction than would otherwise occur. The gravitational force from the Sun and Earth combined is somewhat less than the sum of the two forces acting separately, because C-gravitons already blocked by one of the two bodies cannot also be blocked by the other. The more transparent the two bodies are, the more perfectly their combined forces add. The more opaque they are, the closer they come to behaving as one body when acting from the same direction.

[q]I am grateful to Victor Slabinski for correcting an error in my original development of this point.

extraordinary precision by bouncing laser beams from it. During "eclipse seasons" when its orbit goes through the Earth's shadow, we would predict an anomalous radial acceleration during part of each orbit varying with the mass-density of the Earth along a line joining the satellite and the Sun. At other times when its orbit does not pass through the Earth's shadow, no such anomaly should be seen. In fact, an anomaly with just such a qualitative description is known to exist in the *Lageos* orbital data. A detailed test using a specific, quantitative prediction of when and how strong the anomalous accelerations should occur has the potential to lead to the discovery of a real gravitational shielding effect, as well as to provide an important test of the Meta Model. The results of this test will be known in the near future.

The Big Bang theory, the physical limitation of the speed of light, the existence of "black holes"—three fundamental tenets of present-day cosmological research. There are reasons to believe that none of them is correct as customarily interpreted. We have also examined an alternative theory which, at this stage of development, has a comparable number of objections to it as the Big Bang theory, or perhaps fewer. In the other chapters I have proposed that fundamental tenets in many other fields of astronomical research are no more valid. These conclusions are deductive, not inductive. So they can be invalidated only by faulty reasoning or an incorrect starting point or assumptions. If they add understanding and make successful predictions, I argue that is sufficient for them to be worthy of consideration *as hypotheses* in the field of astronomy.

This completes the extension of the Meta Model to explain the "why" for all the remarkable properties of Newtonian gravitation. Surely the ultimate model we seek must also have this virtue of explaining why. We must still discuss how the model may be reconciled with Special and General Relativity Theory. And we still have more implications and applications to develop. But as with any model, its most important functions are to predict things we do not yet know but may discover in the future, and to aid our understanding of phenomena. If such predictions are fulfilled and our understanding is improved, then the model is said to have value—even if it is not the ultimate and complete explanation for everything.

3

• •

On Relativity

Summary: In physics we study longitudinal and transverse waves. Light and other electromagnetic phenomena propagate as three-dimensional waves, with properties more nearly like underwater waves. Gravity influences the density of the light-carrying medium (LCM) near matter ingredients (MIs), which in turn can change the speed of propagation of light and electromagnetic forces. Their behavior follows the laws of refraction for light moving through a medium of higher density: propagation slows, directions of propagation bend, and wavelengths shift toward the red. This is why, in the Meta Model, light bends near the Sun, radar beams to the planets slow their round-trip travel times, and light escaping a gravitational field gets red-shifted. The refraction model likewise can exactly predict the advance of Mercury's perihelion, as has been known since Eddington. These are the famous tests of Einstein's General Relativity Theory, which are clearly all obeyed in a natural way by the Meta Model, but without the need for "curved space-time." Einstein's Special Relativity Theory predicts not only that all motion is relative, which is required in the Meta Model, but also that space and time will seem to contract for moving observers. To see these features of reality as natural consequences of the Meta Model, we construct a "sound analogy" in which all matter is made of special atoms whose electrons propagate through air, and where all communications are limited to the speed of sound. We discover that we can reproduce all the important experiments of physics pertaining to the speed of light using the sound analogy instead. In particular, as a moving observer approaches the speed of sound, the sound waves in front of him get compressed, making it appear that space has contracted. The orbital period for electrons in this "sound" universe is likewise increased, making it appear that clocks have slowed down. Yet all observers in this analog universe attempting to measure the speed of sound will get the same answer, regardless of their state of motion, as in the famous Michelson-Morley experiment. If a body composed of "sound" atoms in this universe were forced to travel faster than sound, the electrons around its special atoms would reverse their direction of motion, making it appear that time was going backwards. Nonetheless, it is possible to define a "meta-time" which is not affected when the observer's atoms reverse, showing how causality violations may be avoided. We discuss how the gravity field of a binary pulsar might be used to define a "meta-time" in the real universe which would not be affected, even if an observer were to move faster than light, because of the superluminal propagation of its gravity field. Finally, we note that only a model which is true to reality could reveal so many new insights into the nature of things.

The Nature of Waves

One cannot study the nature of things for very long before an understanding of waves and their properties becomes an essential tool. When substance is disturbed, individual particles may scatter or behave "randomly"; but the surrounding medium communicates the effects of the disturbance outward by means of organized motions of its own constituent particles. These organized motions in a medium are called "waves."

Waves are pulses, sometimes in the same direction as the wave motion (called "longitudinal" waves; e.g. sound waves in air), and sometimes perpendicular to the direction of the wave motion (called "transverse" waves; e.g. water waves, also light). (See Figure 3.1.) Dissimilar waves from different sources pass through one another without lasting effects—i.e., they do not exhibit the property of collision, as particles do (although a barrier can be made to reflect them).

When water is the medium of transmission, individual molecules of water merely move up and down as the wave passes; they do not

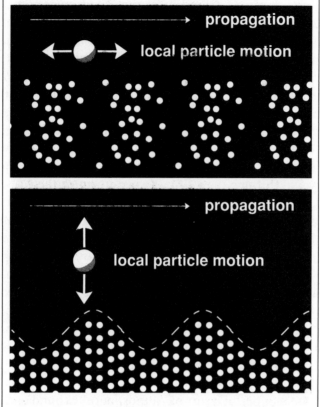

Figure 3.1. Longitudinal waves (e.g. sound) on the left. Transverse waves (e.g. water) on the right.

themselves advance with the wave. When air is the medium, individual molecules move at high velocities, faster than the wave itself, colliding with other molecules frequently. The passing wave is merely a statistical tendency for the molecules to collide more frequently in certain locations ("condensations"), and less frequently in others ("rarefactions"). Information about the time and place of some source disturbance is transmitted by the wave, although the molecules comprising it do not themselves share that information. The propagation velocity of the wave is a function of the density of the medium and the speed and mean distance between collisions of the individual particles comprising it.

On Relativity

The hypothetical CG and LCM media we have postulated in earlier discussions, both pervading the universe, can likewise transmit information by means of waves—information not shared by individual entities within each medium. Although waves in such entity seas are not exactly analogous to either of the other kinds of waves mentioned, their behavior will bear many similarities. My son Michael pointed out the need for more experimental study of water-like waves in three dimensions—that is, waves through water, not just on the surface. For example, underwater bubbles or explosions send out such waves. These would be more nearly analogous to lightwaves through the LCM. If waves through the CG medium exist, they must be longitudinal, analogous to sound waves, because that medium is made up of discrete entities and is not continuous.

The light-carrying medium must pervade all space where light can be transmitted. This would seem to be everywhere except inside "matter ingredients," which are presumably impenetrable to light as well as to C-gravitons. Indeed, CGs must be capable of collisions with the LCM constituents, since gravity does influence the LCM. The LCM must be present in the immediate vicinity of each MI, just as it is everywhere else. But since MIs reflect all CGs, MIs must have relatively strong gravitational fields near their surfaces. So the LCM is not merely present near MIs, but tends to get concentrated there in the manner of a sort of "atmosphere" around each MI. In short, the density of the LCM increases with decreasing distance from an MI.

This increased density of the LCM near MIs would only be significant for a relatively short distance from the MI. However, in the vicinity of a huge concentration of MIs, as in an ordinary massive body such as a star or planet, their combined gravity field is strong enough to increase the density of the LCM even at a considerable distance from the body.

The Three Tests of General Relativity

As a lightwave approaches the limb of the Sun, it is passing from the ordinary LCM into a region of higher-density LCM. The behavior of waves propagating through a medium is well-studied and understood. In particular, as a wave moves from a medium of lower

62

density to one of higher density, its propagation slows, its wave-length shortens, and it undergoes "refraction," which is a bending of its path toward the denser medium.[a] The bending of lightwaves which pass close to the Sun's limb is one of the original three tests of Einstein's Theory of General Relativity.

It has been shown by many authors that this famous "light-bend-ing" effect can be derived exactly in a model which assumes a flat space-time with refraction in a medium whose wave velocity is c. It even gives correctly the time delay of radar waves in the solar system as a consequence of the slight slowing of the speed of light when traveling near the Sun through denser LCM. (It is of course already well known that light appears to slow down when travel-ing in any denser media, such as water.) Although this refraction analogy[10] gives precisely the correct amount of bending and has been known almost since the General Relativity theory was first published, the "curved space-time" model has received wide accep-tance over the "refraction" model for these phenomena because of the failure of experiments to detect the presence of a medium within

---

[a]Ordinary refraction, such as when light or sound passes from one medium into another, is "chromatic"—that is, different wavelengths or colors are affected differently. In current theory, the change in the speed of propagation of the wave is caused by its repeated absorption and re-emission as it travels. For example, as light travels through glass, its speed never changes from "the speed of light in a vacuum"; but it is delayed fre-quently along its path by the absorption and re-emission of photons by the atoms of the glass, making it appear to propagate more slowly. The frequency of such absorptions varies with wavelength because the cross-section of the absorbing atoms more easily absorbs large-wavelength waves than small.

Gravity bends and slows light in an "achromatic" way—that is, the effect is the same at all different wavelengths. This makes good sense because the cause of the refraction is not absorption and re-emission (C-gravitons are far too small for that). Rather it is the change in the den-sity of the LCM, the wave-carrying medium itself, caused by the action of C-gravitons on it. This necessarily affects all wavelengths equally because the speed of light itself actually changes while it traverses the denser medium, and returns to its original value in open space. Of course such a change in the speed of light can be detected only with clocks and rulers which do not themselves undergo the same changes as light.

which light propagates. This has to do with the "Special Relativity" theory, which we will examine in a moment.

The presence of concentrated LCM around every MI also has one other effect. Bodies will resist acceleration to velocities faster than light, because that is the wave velocity of the LCM. Faster-than-light travel may be seen in this construction, therefore, not as physically impossible, but as requiring forces which do not themselves draw upon waves in the LCM to provide the impetus (as all electromagnetic forces do). A good analogy would be the use of propeller-driven aircraft trying to exceed the speed of sound. No matter how fast the propellers spin, they cannot push the air, nor therefore the aircraft, faster than the wave velocity of that medium (the velocity of sound). Applying additional energy accomplishes little, just as if the aircraft's mass were increasing to resist further acceleration, approaching infinite inertial mass as the velocity of the aircraft approaches the velocity of sound.

If a wave traveling at the velocity c approaches a massive body, the gravitational force of the massive body tries to make the wave travel faster than c. But since the number of wavefronts passing any point in any given time (the "frequency" of the wave) does not change, the wave must actually decrease in both velocity and wavelength as it approaches a massive body and enters LCM of increased density. We may apply this result immediately to lightwaves traveling away from a massive body. The light will experience a "redshift" (an increase in wavelength, which represents a loss of energy) as the wave climbs from denser LCM to less dense LCM. This is the so-called "gravitational redshift" of light, another of the three tests of Einstein's General Relativity Theory. Note that we achieved this result in an intuitive, geometric way without the need to "curve spacetime."

An alternative way of viewing the gravitational redshift phenomenon is the slowing of atomic clocks in a gravitational field. This is again a reflection of the slowed propagation of all electromagnetic phenomena in such a field, because of the increased LCM density.

The third classical test of General Relativity is the excess rotation of Mercury's elliptical orbit, which has been accurately verified. This, too, may be seen as merely a consequence of the behavior of bodies becoming more "wave-like," including the bending of their paths by refraction rather than by acceleration as they approach the speed of light. Specifically, the contraction of space and time, which are consequences of Special Relativity (to be discussed next), will result in a greater force from the Sun when Mercury is at perihelion (closest point to the Sun) than at aphelion (farthest from the Sun).[b] As is well known in Celestial Mechanics, applying a radial perturbation to an orbit which augments the central force at perihelion, and decrements it at aphelion, has the effect of rotating the direction of perihelion in the forward direction. Again, it has been known since Eddington's time that the predicted size of the effect in this refraction model is exactly the same as in the "curved space-time" model for how General Relativity operates. In the Meta Model, space is a dimension and cannot be curved or distorted; only its contents can.

Einstein's theory is also said to predict the existence of a phenomenon called "gravitational radiation" or "gravity waves." These are ripples in the fabric of space-time caused by sudden alterations of mass on a large scale—for example, a supernova explosion. Einstein himself wavered back and forth over the question of whether or not such entities should exist. The prediction is based on an assumed analogy between gravity and electromagnetism (EM). However, such an analogy is defective in several particulars. Both gravity and EM give rise to an inverse square force, but there the similarity ends. EM forces are both attractive and repulsive, gravity is attractive only. A body's own charge affects its motion in EM, but its own mass does not affect its own acceleration in gravity. There is no Equivalence Principle[c] in EM, and no analog of magnetism or Maxwell's equations[d] for gravity. EM forces between two bodies act with lighttime delay, while gravity acts with no detectable delay. Under gravity, masses are free to move wherever the forces

---

[b]Refraction in the LCM medium has the effect of increasing the radius of curvature at perihelion, where LCM densities and planet velocities are higher, and decreasing it at aphelion, where the reverse is true. Increasing the radius of curvature is effectively increasing the central force.

[c]The equivalence of gravitational and inertial masses.

[d]Describing electric and magnetic fields in EM.

direct them; but electrons are confined to discrete energy levels, and cannot stably orbit at intermediate levels. And the relative strengths of the two forces differ by 40 orders of magnitude.

Today it is often forgotten that gravitational radiation is a theory, not a fact. This is largely due to a supposed "detection" of gravitational radiation in the binary pulsars 1534+12 and 1913+16. But a recent paper by Damour[11] pointed out that only a relationship among the parameters of pericenter motion, bending/delay, and gravitational radiation is determined by these pulsars. The gravitational radiation itself is *not* uniquely separable from the other two, and a zero value would permit an equally good fit to the observations by adjusting the other parameters. The original finding amounts to saying that the observations are consistent with theory if one throws in gravitational radiation, but cannot be said to require it for the best fit.

In any case, there is still much controversy over how to calculate the predicted amount of gravitational radiation in this hypothetical analogy, since it involves the "permeability of free space" as an adjustable parameter of unknown size. As things now stand, one really couldn't tell if an orbital deceleration of a pulsar system were due to gravitational radiation or any of several other possible causes, such as tides or mass exchange.

To better visualize how gravity waves might or might not fit into the Meta Model, we will consider the following analogy. Imagine an asteroid striking the Earth at a high velocity. The speed and energy of the asteroid impact are loosely the analog of gravitational force. But as the asteroid flies through the Earth's atmosphere it creates a wave disturbance in the air. We experience this disturbance shortly after the asteroid impact as a sonic boom. The wave disturbance and boom are the analog of gravity waves—miniscule in their effect when compared to gravity itself.

In the Meta Model, "gravity waves" would be ripples or disturbances in the LCM, not in the fabric of space-time. They would indeed propagate with the speed of light, the characteristic speed appropriate to the LCM. However, waves in the LCM are a familiar phenomenon which we call "light." In view of our analogy, we see that the only way to generate a phenomenon of a new kind would be for a body to travel faster than light through the LCM, which would then cause a sort of "sonic boom" in the LCM. One would presume that such a phenomenon would manifest itself as a brilliant burst of photons. This might be visible as ordinary light. But if the frequencies generated were higher, it might be an X-ray or gamma-ray burst; or if lower, a radio noise burst.[e]

For completeness we should mention here one other possible manifestation of gravity waves: virtual photons. These entities are invoked in quantum physics to explain a host of electric and magnetic phenomena, including the binding force between electrons and atomic nuclei, the field lines in magnets, etc. Virtual photons propagate at the speed of light, but can pass through matter and are not visible as light.

If we examine the details of wave propagation through a contiguous medium such as the LCM, we see that such media can oscillate in any of *three* dimensions: two transverse, and one radial. When LCM waves oscillate in either transverse (perpendicular) direction, we see them as light or photons at other wavelengths, which are known to be transverse waves. But what about oscillations in the radial direction (the direction of propagation), which must be equally possible? I suggest this phenomenon as the "virtual photon," and as a possible way gravity waves might be expressed in nature.

Special Relativity and the Twin Paradox

Why do clocks slow down when the speed of a body approaches the speed of light? Clocks, change, aging, and all measurements of time ultimately depend upon the structure of the matter they are made out of. To focus on just one aspect of this, consider the revolution of electrons around atomic nuclei. Suppose every electron in every orbit around every atom took twice as long to complete a revolution (or any motion). Then clocks, aging, and indeed time itself for observers made of such "slow atoms" would slow to half the usual rate.

---

[e]For example, if other civilizations exist and have solved the problem of space travel at "warp speed," their spacecraft might create brief flashes of high electromagnetic energy as they accelerate past the speed of light.

A reason that electrons might "slow down" while moving at high velocities is that it takes longer for them to complete a revolution when their atoms are moving near the speed of light than when their atoms are stationary. This is true of any body traveling in a moving medium.[f]

Like General Relativity, the theory of Special Relativity needs some discussion when confronted with our alternative model of the fundamental nature of the universe. Although an in-depth discussion of the theory of Special Relativity would be quite beyond what we can hope to accomplish in this book, we may be able to understand the experimental results in a way which permits the existence of faster-than-light entities in forward time, but which does not violate causality.

The essence of Special Relativity is that all motion is relative. It is supposed that there is no measurement which can decide that one body is "really moving" and another is not, since the opposite point of view is equally valid. The theory then goes on to propose that moving bodies undergo an apparent contraction of space and time, as seen from a stationary frame: distances seem to be compressed in the direction of motion of the body, and clocks traveling with the body seem to tick more slowly.

Although the contraction of space and time is negligible at ordinary velocities, it becomes indefinitely great as the velocity of the body approaches c. This is often dramatized with an example of two newly born twins. It is supposed that one of the twins remains on Earth, while the other is placed on a spacecraft moving toward a nearby star (Alpha Centauri) with a speed of 99% of the speed

---

[f]Suppose a canoe can travel at 12 miles per hour (mph) in a river with no current. Then it can travel 1 mile "upstream" in 5 minutes ($\frac{1}{12}$ hour), and would take another 5 minutes to make the same trip back "downstream," for a round-trip time of 10 minutes. Now imagine the stream has a current of 8 mph. During the canoe's upstream trip, it makes progress at a net rate of 4 mph (12 – 8), requiring 15 minutes to gain 1 mile. Downstream again, its net rate is 20 mph (12 + 8), requiring just 3 minutes to return that 1 mile. Round-trip time is therefore 18 minutes (15 + 3). The canoe exerted the same amount of energy and attempted to travel at the same speed (12 mph) in both cases (stream with and without current). But it took longer in the moving frame.

of light, c. We further suppose that the nearby star is about four lightyears away, so that the one-way journey takes just a little over four years, as measured by Earth clocks. We then imagine that the traveling twin turns around and returns to Earth. According to Special Relativity theory, the twin who stayed on Earth will be over eight years old when the two are reunited; whereas the traveling twin will have aged only a little over one year and will still be a baby, because of slowing of the rate of progress of time for a body traveling with a velocity of 99% of c. Traveling atomic clocks have been successful in showing that such effects really do occur, and that traveling bodies age more slowly.[g,12]

---

[g]This is called the "Twin Paradox" because it seems at first glance (and maybe even at second and third glance) that the situation is symmetric for both twins, so their aging should not differ. Even the turn-around of one twin can be avoided to improve the symmetry. Although almost all authors on the subject try to show how the paradox is resolved, most such resolutions do not truly, in my view, get at the essence of the paradox, since they rely on symmetry-breaking in some manner. For those interested in the technical details, let us keep the twins symmetric: no turn-arounds, no accelerations, no switching inertial frames. The paradox can still be resolved.

Setup: Observer E1 remains on Earth. Observer E2 is on Alpha Centauri (AC), exactly 4 lightyears away as measured in the Earth's frame of reference. Observers E1 and E2 are in a common reference frame, communicate continually with each other, and both note that they are at every moment the same age and have synchronized clocks in their own reference frame. (They could come together at slow velocities to verify this, then slowly separate again, without suffering significant time dilation.) Observer T1 is in a spaceship whose journey will be monitored from the moment it passes the Earth, heading toward AC at 99% of the speed of light. To parallel the twins paradox, assume that observers E1 and T1 are born at the instant they are simultaneously at the Earth. Indeed, all observers will agree about the simultaneity of two birth events which occur at a common place and time.

Now consider the later instant when T1 passes AC, where E2 resides. As promised, there has been no turn-around of T1, no acceleration, and no change of reference frame. Calculating entirely within the common reference frame of E1 and E2, it is easy to compute that E2 will be about 4.04 years old when T1 arrives (4 lightyears/99%). The question is, how old will T1 be?

> "A friend of mine once held that time and space were illusions. I told him to meet me at the coffee shop in two hours to discuss it. He was never seen or heard from again."
> —Joel Frahm, as quoted by Mark Bradford

Now the essence of the paradox becomes clearer! If one answers "4.04 years old," then the time dilation predicted by relativity has not yet occurred, but the traveling twin is already older than he should be upon his return. On the other hand, if one answers "7 months old" (the relativity value), then we can truly demand to know what gave E1 and E2 the right to claim that T1 traveled. According to relativity, T1 may view himself as stationary, with E1 and E2 doing the traveling. So why should he show up at AC younger than E2, and not vice versa?

Many people try to answer this dilemma by fixating on any lack of symmetry between T1 and E2. But that is a mistake. The resolution of the paradox does not lie in any lack of symmetry. To prove this, let us complete the symmetry and make it perfect. Introduce T2: another observer aboard a spaceship in T1's reference frame, but stationary relative to him, and 4 lightyears away in his frame in the direction back toward the receding Earth. Then T1 and T2 both note that they are the same age and ensure that their clocks are synchronized with each other. At the moment of T1's arrival at AC, T1 (still moving at high speed and 7 months old) compares his clocks and age with E2. T1 and his clocks read 7 months; E2 and his clocks read roughly 4 years.

It is true that under the rules of relativity, observers E1 and E2 will not agree that T1 and T2 are the same age; nor will observers T1 and T2 agree that E1 and E2 are the same age. Separated observers in a moving frame do not appear to be synchronized. That fact is important to any true understanding of relativity.

To be sure we have perfect symmetry, consider now the situation when T2 arrives at AC. E2 will say that only another 7 months have elapsed since T1 went by; and E2's age will be about 4 years and 7 months. In the T-frame-of-reference, on the other hand, both T1 and T2 are stationary, while the Earth and AC move. Both T1 and T2 must be 7 months old in their frame when E2 passes T1. By symmetry, T2 will measure a time interval of 4 years in his frame for the flight of E2 from T1 to T2; so he also will be 4 years and 7 months old when E2 passes him. Therefore both E2 and T2 will agree that E2 aged only 7 months while T2 aged 4 years during E2's journey from T1 to T2. The age and clocks of E2 and T2 will

We have always known that we could use the average position and velocity of all bodies in a given vicinity as a reference frame for both position and motion. And if some velocity greatly exceeds the motion of any individual body in the vicinity, such a velocity is both detectable and has physical consequences. Only in that sense can it be called an "absolute" velocity. In the universe as a whole, there would be asymmetries in the amount of visible matter in the

---

agree with each other when they pass, just as the age and clocks of E1 and T1 agreed when they were passing one another.

To recap the four events:

T1 meets E1: both are age zero.

T1 meets E2: T1 is age 7 months, E2 is age 4 years.

T2 meets E1: T2 is age 4 years, E1 is age 7 months.

T2 meets E2: both are age 4 years plus 7 months.

So the situation is perfectly symmetric for both frames. Understanding this is the principal key to resolving the logical paradox, and for a true understanding of relativity. Naturally, neither the E-frame nor the T-frame runs systematically slower or faster than the other, since they are equivalent. The reason that the twins can be perfectly symmetric yet show different aging is this: In any frame, the apparent rate of progress of time (and distance) for a fast-moving traveler is quite different when the traveler is moving away, from what it is for an approaching traveler.

The preceding fact means that as T1 travels from E1 to E2, his apparent rate of aging is slower as seen by E1 from whom he is receding, and is faster as seen by E2 whom he is approaching. In combination with the earlier fact that T1 does not see E1 and E2 as synchronized, the aging asymmetry can exist without logical contradiction with the postulate that all motion is relative—even in a perfectly symmetric setup!

As a final exercise, suppose one twin travels outward, then turns around in an instant and retraces his path. When the Earth twin sees the turn-around (somewhat later than it actually happened, because of light-time delay), there is no discontinuity in the apparent distance of the traveling twin; but the inferred true distance changes, because the Earth twin has just learned that the traveling twin's motion was not continuous in one direction. But at the moment of the turn-around, the traveling twin sees the Earth alter its apparent distance from 0.564 lightyears (ly) to 55.9 ly, with no change in the inferred true distance. This asymmetry for the case where one twin turns around also serves to illustrate why there are different results for approaching and receding twins, even when the symmetry remains perfect.

forward and aft directions; and the "cosmic microwave radiation" would be redshifted in the direction of motion and blueshifted in the opposite direction. These likewise would enable us to define a local standard of rest, but only in a statistical sense.[h]

With these concepts in mind, let us examine by analogy exactly how and why space and time contract in our model as velocities approach the speed of light, and most importantly, how it is possible for substance to travel faster than the speed of light without violating Special Relativity, and without moving backwards in time, thereby violating causality.[i]

The Sound Analogy

Consider an alternate universe containing "atoms" of unspecified size and mass, each consisting of a "nucleus" exerting some attractive force, and "electrons" in orbit around that nucleus, similar to the Bohr model for the Hydrogen atom. Now let the universe be filled with a continuous medium having the properties of air, and let the electrons of our hypothetical atom propagate through this medium in their orbits around their nucleus just as sound propagates through air. Let the Bohr radius of an imitation "Hydrogen atom" in this universe provide the unit of length; and let the elapsed interval needed for the corresponding electron to circle its nucleus provide a unit of time in this universe.

The essential difference between this model and the real universe is that all motion in this model is via wave propagation through a medium in which the limiting propagation velocity is the speed of sound.[j] We will find the implications of this variation familiar.

---

[h]This is a somewhat greater problem in the Big Bang theory, where in principle one can measure the absolute velocity of anything with respect to the cosmic microwave radiation, presumed to come from the "background."

[i]"Violating causality" means, for example, deciding that if some "trigger" event happens within a certain interval, you will travel backwards through time to prevent the trigger event from happening; but if it doesn't happen in the selected interval, you will travel backwards through time to ensure that it will happen.

[j]Note that there is nothing about this analogy special to the choice of

Suppose that an airplane composed of these alternate atoms flies through the air-like medium (assuming no gravity) by means of propellers. Since its means of propulsion is by pushing against the medium (rather than action-reaction, as in jets or rockets), the speed of the airplane is limited to the speed of sound. (The speed of sound is the maximum speed at which waves or pressure can propagate in a medium.) As ever more energy is applied to make the propellers spin faster, the airplane's speed will approach the speed of sound ever closer; but it can never quite reach it, except with infinite energy and infinite propeller speed.

To a physicist in this alternate universe, it appears as if the airplane's inertial mass is increasing as its velocity increases. The airplane seems to resist further acceleration as the energy applied approaches infinity because the airplane's inertial mass seems to approach infinity. This is precisely analogous to the way in which the inertial mass of a body in the real universe seems to approach infinity as its velocity approaches the speed of light.

As the airplane's velocity approaches the speed of sound, the sound waves emanating from it in the direction of motion get bunched up closer and closer together, because their velocity *relative to the airplane* gets less and less. For precisely the same reason, the orbits of the electrons in the airplane get compressed in the direction of motion, because they too propagate like sound waves in our special universe. But since the dimensions of the electron orbits provide the unit of length in this universe, a physicist in this universe would conclude that distances contract in the direction of motion as bodies approach the speed of sound. Indeed, he would derive precisely the well-known "Lorentz contraction" formula[k] to represent the amount of this contraction. In the real universe, distances seem to be contracted in the direction of motion in accord with the Lorentz formula as bodies approach the speed of light.

---

air as the medium and sound as the waves. Any medium with any form of waves would serve as well.

[k] The Lorentz contraction factor for a moving body is $c/\sqrt{(c^2 - v^2)}$, where c is the speed of light and v is the velocity of the body.

Moreover, if the matter is judged by a stationary observer,[l] the electrons will take more time to complete their orbits, because the round-trip time for any particle moving upstream and downstream in a moving current is greater than the round-trip time in a stationary medium. This "time dilation" for the moving electrons of the airplane also follows the Lorentz formula, because the revolution time for the electron approaches infinity as the velocity of the airplane approaches the speed of sound. In the real universe, the clocks of moving observers seem to slow down with respect to those of stationary observers as their relative velocity approaches the speed of light.

The contractions of the units of length and time are exactly analogous in the alternate universe with respect to the speed of sound to what they are in the real universe with respect to the speed of light. So it follows that all observers in the alternate universe performing "Michelson-Morley" experiments,[m] or trying to measure the speed of sound, will get the same constant answer regardless of their state of motion with respect to the air medium, just as that happens for light in the real universe. In fact, all experiments performed in the two universes would be analogous. Even a moving biological twin being made of such hypothetical "sound" atoms would age more slowly than his non-moving identical brother, because the "sound" atoms of which he is comprised slow down in all respects. The situation is, of course, reciprocal for "moving" and "stationary" observers (i.e., each "sees" the clocks of the other slow down and distances contract, but via waves traveling at the speed of sound, not light).

It is possible in principle to measure the average motion of all air molecules in a given volume, and to adopt that average as a stan-

---

[l]Of course, neither "stationary" observer nor "moving" airplane can tell who is really stationary and who is really moving, if only sound waves are allowed for communication. Such a distinction could only be made by someone who can "see" both via light, or anything traveling much faster than sound.

[m]Michelson-Morley measured the velocity of light in all directions, finding it constant. It is apparently unaffected by the motion of the Earth through space.

dard of rest. Of course there might be a "breeze" blowing through our entire adopted volume, so that it does not provide an "absolute" standard of rest for the alternate universe. In the real universe, we could make the same remark with respect to the LCM.

Meta Clocks and Meta Time

There is one more important point to consider. In the real universe it is concluded that faster-than-light communications would violate causality because they would propagate backwards in time. In our alternate universe we may see a similar line of reasoning if all communications were limited to the speed of sound. The fact that atoms and clocks would slow down as they approached the speed of sound, and that the electrons would *reverse direction* if the speed of sound were exceeded, does not alter the forward flow of "meta-time" as kept by clocks fixed with respect to the local standard of rest. Indeed, the phenomenon of "slowed time" may be seen as a consequence of using imperfect clocks which depend upon the speed of propagation of waves through a medium. An observer could choose to use "meta-clocks" which do not depend upon the speed of sound or the properties of the medium they reside in. Against such meta-clocks the observer could measure the slowing of his own imperfect clocks and of his own biological processes as his velocity increased.

In the real universe, gravity could be used to measure this "meta-time" even in classical Special Relativity. For example, one might observe the moments of peaks and minima in the dipole component[n] of the gravity field of a binary pulsar. The passage of these could be used to synchronize meta-clocks for all observers, since they would be unaffected for all practical purposes by the state of motion of the observers. This would not alter the apparent lack of simultaneity for the observed or inferred peaks and minima based on *light* received from such a binary pulsar. Some ordinary clocks might even show events appearing to occur backwards in time for

---

[n]The dipole component of the combined gravity field is the principal deviation from what would exist if all the mass were concentrated at the center of mass.

some observers relative to meta-clocks. This is analogous to hearing a sonic boom, then hearing the sound of a jet receding toward the direction it came from.

If a physicist in the alternate universe could devise a way to construct an enclosure out of matter from our real universe, it would not be subject to the speed of sound limitations in his universe. Such an enclosure could fly through his air medium at any speed whatever, shielding occupants within (still composed of "sound" atoms) from experiencing space and time contractions. By analogy, if real physicists could find a way to construct an enclosure out of substance (such as pure MIs) which was not subject to the limitations of ordinary matter (all electromagnetic forces propagate at the speed of light), then they too could move through the universe faster than light without suffering space-time contractions—or violating causality!

If the reader accepts this analogy, then we have demonstrated that wondrous things, such as faster-than-light travel, are possible. And if there truly are CGs and an LCM, then there will be no such thing as "black holes" in the usual sense, nor singularities in nature. Dense masses will be capable of shielding some of the matter in their interiors from acting directly on the external universe (a violation of the "Universal" Law of Gravitation), which would prevent escape velocities for such dense masses from ever reaching or exceeding the speed of light. There may come a day when we master the utilization of CGs, using them for communications as easily as we now use sound or light.

Although these interpretations may alter the way we teach and understand Relativity Theory, they do not truly alter the theory itself, but only extend it. In a manner of speaking, the only significant difference from traditional relativity introduced with the Meta Model is a new relativity of a fifth dimension, scale, to go along with the relativity of the other four dimensions. Traditional theory has always assumed that scale was somehow absolute, and that there were entities which were the smallest and others which were the largest in the entire universe. In this new picture, the human scale is relative and arbitrary. The phenomena of nature occur on other scales as well: the unimaginably large and the inconceivably small. There is no such thing as absolute size.

76

The "sound analogy," which shows how it can be that Special Relativity is valid and yet faster-than-light communication in forward time is still possible, is at the heart of the Meta Theory. To my knowledge, no one had ever previously thought of a way that could be true, myself included. It is important to realize that I did not one day get a flash of inspiration and think of the sound analogy. It came out of the Meta Model, simply by deductively developing the model's logical consequences. This is the principal reason why I feel such confidence that the model is basically correct in its descriptions of reality. It provides marvelous insights into the nature of things, such as a natural, unforced explanation of why space and time seem to contract for moving observers, and why the speed of light seems constant in all frames of reference, all done in normal, uncurved space-time. As a by-product, it shows us a way to communicate faster than light which no one had previously thought of. The model has no "intelligence," so the only plausible explanation for these amazing and most improbable insights must be that the model is indeed an accurate description of reality. The probability would seem to be negligible that a false model would reveal so many new insights into the "how" and "why" of the phenomena around us.

4

••••••••••••••••••••••••••••••

Stars, Galaxies, and the Universe

Summary: We jump to the galactic scale and note the Meta Model's insistence that gravity, like all forces, must have a finite range, limited by the mean distance between collisions of C-gravitons. Over greater distances, C-gravitons should start to behave like a perfect gas, with no net force. Interestingly, this is just how galaxies actually behave at distances over 2 kiloparsecs. Their rotation velocities remain constant at all distances from the center, in defiance of Newton's laws, but just as a perfect gas would do. The existence of structure in the universe at the largest observable scales then implies the existence of forces other than gravitation operating on those scales. Indeed, the largest scale structure presently observable, a series of "walls" of galaxies extending out to nearly half the radius of the visible universe, much resembles wave patterns, as the Meta Model might expect. Next we examine the principal observational facts about the universe, which have been interpreted in terms of the Big Bang cosmology up to now. In the Meta Model, the redshift of starlight is an energy-loss phenomenon due to LCM waves attempting to propagate through the resisting C-graviton medium. The loss of energy of photons traveling great distances then explains "Olbers' Paradox," or why the night sky is dark. But if space itself expands, as in the Big Bang theory, then observations within the solar system that show a lack of such expansion at the Hubble rate violate the spirit of that theory. The observed cosmic microwave radiation could be produced, as

79

one possibility, by any uniform explosion fireball which has since encompassed the Earth—for example, the "Planet K" explosion discussed in later chapters. Indeed it appears that the theoretical equilibrium temperature of the interstellar medium is quite close to the observed 2.7-degree radiation. This seems to imply a possible source for the "background" radiation within our own galaxy, as well as other sources within other galaxies. I then argue that gravitational lenses would not preserve the uniformity of the background radiation, providing another test of cosmologies. Finally, we review observational evidence that quasars are not at cosmological distances and show that the Meta Model predicts the existence of just such high-redshift quasi-stellar collapsed objects as quasars. These appear in place of "black holes," which cannot exist in the Meta Model.

The Limited Range of Gravity

On a galactic scale, if a "universal" inverse square force is the only force operative and most of the mass is in the form of stars, then the velocity of the stars *must* drop off as distance from the galactic center increases, just as it does for planets orbiting the Sun. The star velocity does drop off close to the centers of galaxies. Yet it is an observed fact that the rotational velocities of the stars in galaxies are nearly constant (sometimes even slightly increasing) at all distances well away from their centers, even out to the edges of visible matter at enormous distances from the galaxy centers.[a] In one study of radio emissions from a galaxy, the rotational velocities appeared to remain nearly constant out to ten times the visible radius of the galaxy. There is generally not a tendency for rotational velocities in galaxies to drop off well away from the central regions.[13] *This observed fact cannot be true if Newtonian gravity alone is the dominant force operative in galaxies,* unless one hypothesizes "invisible mass" in ever increasing amounts with distance from the galac-

---

[a]Stars in galaxies have, on the average, a roughly constant linear velocity. A galaxy does not turn like a rigid wheel, which requires a constant angular velocity. Instead, a constant linear velocity implies that stars further from the center will have longer paths and take longer to revolve around the center than stars further in.

tic center in just the right quantities to hold the star velocities constant. Incredibly, this ad hoc swidget[b] is often mentioned in current textbooks as a likely explanation of the velocity problem. The alternatives to this ad hoc hypothesis are considered too problematical to deal with.

But is it reasonable to assume that gravity operates in the same way on galactic distance scales as it does on planetary scales? Our galaxy is 10^{11} times more massive than our Sun, and we are 10^9 times further from the galactic center than the Earth is from the Sun. If gravity is produced by the pushing action of C-gravitons, as we have conjectured in the Meta Model, then it must have a limited range. This limit of range is approximately given by the mean distance[c] between mutual collisions of CGs with one another. Note that this does not imply that the CG medium is tenuous, but only that CGs are individually quite small.

Let us refer to this mean distance with the symbol R_G. Well beyond R_G, the force of gravity must become omni-directional, in the manner of a perfect gas. The gravity from more distant masses, however large in the aggregate, would not be able to make itself felt. At any given place, only masses closer than R_G would contribute in a normal inverse square way to the local gravitational field. Given the observed fact of constant velocity away from the center of galaxies, it seems likely that this is caused by the limited range of gravity. The pattern of velocity drop-off in galaxies, and the fact that galaxy rotation curves go flat about 4 or so kiloparsecs from the center for widely different galaxy types, implies that R_G is about 2 kiloparsecs.[d] The force law would be similar to that discussed by Richard Liboff.[14]

---

[b]Swidget: an idea contrived to save a theory, rather than to explain some observational evidence or data. The term was coined by the author as short for "scientific widget." "Widget" refers to a useless commercial product.
[c]This is called the "root mean square" or "rms" distance.
[d]Two kiloparsecs is about 4×10^8 astronomical units, or 6×10^{16} km. Perhaps star orbits are actually constant-velocity spirals away from the galactic center, rather than closed orbits. This would give rise in a very natural way to the puzzling spiral structure of galaxies—the spiral arms would be paths along which the stars escape into intergalactic space! If this conjecture were correct, it would seem likely that galactic centers

Our conjecture would have other implications. For example, galaxies with higher rotation velocities should have more mass within each sector of radius R_G, and therefore would be intrinsically more luminous. This is precisely what is observed.[15] And our conjecture implies that some unusual behavior may occur in galaxies in the transition region from inverse square gravity to "perfect gas" gravity. As three Australian astronomers have recently discussed,[16] the mass-to-light ratios from spiral galaxies up to large clusters of galaxies seem to increase with the size of the structures involved. Put another way, the amount of "missing mass" required to keep everything in balance increases with scale until it reaches nearly a factor of 1000 for superclusters. But the inferred masses and the mass-to-light ratios drop dramatically if gravity is no longer inverse square over such distances, and the need for invisible mass completely disappears. The Australian astronomers' calculations show that when galaxies interact, the results from using an inverse linear law are, if anything, in better agreement with observations than those using an inverse square law.[e]

---

would be huge masses constantly accreting new MIs and creating new stars to spiral outward until lost into intergalactic space. In any case, the local force of gravity somewhere in a galaxy would be principally due to the stars in a sector toward the galactic center with radius R_G, lessened by the similar outward force from a similar sector of stars toward the galactic anti-center. It is easy to visualize that for spiral star orbits, the force difference between such sectors could remain constant at all distances from the center, giving rise to the constant rotational velocities. This would imply that galactic "edges" are actually very gradual, not at all like sharp boundaries; and that galaxies extend far beyond their visible dimensions from stars too faint to be seen in the aggregate.

[e]It might not be clear why a finite range for gravity would appear to imitate an inverse linear force law over distances greater than R_G. Consider the location of the Sun, about 10 kpc from the center of our own galaxy. Call this distance R_S. The Sun does not feel significant force from the galactic center, which is too far away. But it does feel the effects of all stars within the distance R_G of the Sun. Since there are more stars in a sector toward the galactic center than in an equal sector away from it, the Sun feels a net force toward the galactic center.

Consider what would happen if all the stars between distances $R_S - R_G$ and $R_S + R_G$ were moved out to some new distance from the galactic

Perpendicular to a galactic plane, the situation is similar. Interestingly, galactic thicknesses are typically about 2 kpc. Contiguous three-dimensional structures with thickness much greater than plus or minus R_G could not be supported, which is what we observe throughout the visible universe. In our own galaxy, the stellar densities and velocities closely follow theoretical drop-off curves out to near 1 kpc, then begin to deviate seriously in the sense that the velocities are too high and the implied densities begin to greatly exceed the observed densities.[17] This is also perfectly in accord with our hypothesis of an R_G characteristic scale for the range of gravitation. Along the same lines, it is considered a mystery in the conventional view why outlying clusters and high-velocity hydrogen clouds still tend to lie close to the galactic plane.[18]

At the center of our own galaxy it has been established that there is a huge "bar" structure, similar to what is observed in many other galaxies. The bar serves as a transition between the compact mass at the galactic center and the spiral structure beyond. Also at our galactic center is an object identified by the name "Sagittarius A," which has an angular diameter of less than 0.001 seconds of arc, or about 10^9 km (about the size of Jupiter's orbit), and which gives off intense radio emissions. Its size, intensity, and relatively constant radiation make it unique among the objects in our galaxy.[19] The motions of stars and gas near this object behave as if the region within one or two lightyears from the center encompasses three or four million solar masses, with most of that concentrated in the Sagittarius A object.

---

center. These stars would spread out in longitude, but not in latitude or radially. So at twice the distance from the galactic center, the density of stars would everywhere be half of what it was at R_S. Then the apparent force of attraction toward the galactic center would also have half the strength. This is precisely the force required to keep the stars in circular orbits at twice their former distance.

Consistent with this image that stars occupy twice the volume of space at twice the distance from the center, the diameters of globular clusters are known to increase on average in precisely this linear way with distance from the center, both in our galaxy and in other nearby ones. Indeed, it has been a mystery to astronomers up to now why there are no small, dense globular clusters in the halo of our galaxy.

It is a mystery in conventional theory why so much mass is not seen in visible light, unless it has formed a "black hole." But then one should see radiation from energetic infalling material. The region does give off intense ultraviolet radiation, also unexplained because if infalling material were responsible, intense infrared radiation would be observed also, and it is not. These phenomena are easily understood with our new picture: there is no conceptual difficulty with the existence of a mass so large as that inferred from the motions of the stars and gas. Such a mass would cause extreme redshifting of radiation at all wavelengths. Gamma rays would be shifted into the ultraviolet region of the spectrum, and visible light would be redshifted into the radio spectrum.

Another traditional problem for the understanding of galaxies is their spiral structure. Stars in spiral arms do not stay in place, moving around the galaxy as if the spiral arm were a coherent unit. If that were true, the arms would wind up more and more tightly as the galaxy rotated, because the stars in the outer parts of spiral arms must travel a much longer path to complete a revolution than the more central stars. Current thinking is that "density waves" collect more star-forming gas in these arm regions, leading to increased star formation there. As older stars spread around the disk of the galaxy, new stars continue to form mainly in the arms. However, this ad hoc theory is unnecessary if most star formation occurs in the galactic center regions, and huge agglomerations of stars stream away from the center in spiral patterns because of the limited range of the gravitational field of the galactic center.

What is the effect of a finite range for gravity within the solar system? To a first approximation, the number of additional C-gravitons which scatter into the gravitational "shadow" of the Sun, diluting its inverse square force, would increase linearly with distance. Each such scattered C-graviton would make it appear that the Sun was less massive than it is. The apparent loss of effective mass, as we have deduced from galaxies, becomes complete at about 2 kiloparsecs' distance. From this we conclude that masses lose their effectiveness at a rate of 100% in 2000 parsecs $= 4 \times 10^8$ astronomical units (au), which is about 2.5×10^{-9} per au. Within our solar system, this implies that the Sun's mass would appear to be slightly less for, say, Neptune than for Earth. The first place this effect would show up is in how well the planets obey Kepler's third law, $a^3 = P^2M$, where a is the mean distance of a planet from the Sun measured in au, P is its period of revolution measured in years, and M is the mass of the Sun, taken as 1 solar mass when measured from the Earth's orbit at a distance of 1 au. The values of period, P, for the planets are known from optical observations over the past 150 years. The mass of the Sun is assumed constant in conventional gravitation, and the mean distances of the planets are calculated from Kepler's law.

The recent *Voyager* spacecraft mission to the outer planets was able to check the calculated planetary distances. The round-trip travel time for radio communications with the spacecraft gives an accurate measure of the true mean distances of the planets. The Meta Model predicts for Neptune at 30 au an expected error of 30 parts in 4×10^8 in the effective solar mass, which translates into a calculated mean distance of Neptune which is too large by about 110 km when compared with the observed distance. *Voyager* found a range error of about 4000 km. This means that systematic errors in the old optical observations (as Standish[20] suggests) or due to "Planet X" (see the chapter of that title) are having a greater effect than the one we are seeking. However, even though the size of the effect is 30 times smaller at the orbit of the Earth, the accuracy of radar, laser, and spacecraft ranging observations is such that we can probably now detect such an effect in the inner solar system, if it exists.[f]

---

[f]For the Earth's orbit, ranging observations are so much more accurate than old optical data that the size of the Earth's orbit is set by distance observations, which in turn fixes its period. But a small but significant discrepancy has arisen with the optical data, which seems to want the Earth's period to be about 5×10^{-9} different from that preferred by the radar data. This is currently considered an unsolved mystery. But it will immediately be recognized as qualitatively the same as, and quantitatively similar to, the effect the Meta Model would predict. A reasonable conjecture is that the observed discrepancy is due to a combination of Relativity and Meta Model effects. An new analysis of the orbits of the four inner planets with this model in mind could soon resolve this question.

The Large-Scale Structure of the Universe

On larger scales than galaxies there are even more severe problems with forces and structure. Galaxies tend to exist in clusters. Clusters of galaxies tend to be organized into superclusters. (All this would be natural enough if gravity were the dominant force, but for the problem that the orbital periods of clusters within superclusters would likely be greater than the Hubble "age of the universe.") But superclusters tend to exist in large structures separated by large regions of space which are essentially void of visible matter. Such an organization of matter cannot be stable under the laws of gravitation—even if one hypothesizes that the structures are actually "bubbles" with a super-massive "black hole" at the center of each. (A ring could be stable, but not a shell.)

In the popular "Big Bang" theory for the origin of the universe, the largest structures don't have to be stable, since 15 billion years is too short a time for stability considerations to matter. But if it turns out, as I have argued, that the universe is infinitely old, then these large-scale features are surely stable; and in the Meta Model this may then be taken as proof of the existence of another force of nature operating on super-large distance scales.

Related problems for the Big Bang theory are that the distribution of matter on the largest scales is supposed to be uniform, and the highest redshift galaxies should consist of only very young stars. But the highest redshift (z) galaxy to date, $z = 1.02$, and the highest redshift quasar to date, $z = 4.9$, both have ordinary spectra, implying roughly the same materials and evolution as later galaxies (in the Big Bang interpretation, where quasar redshifts are velocity indicators). And the smoothness of the cosmic background radiation ("the heat left over from the creation of the universe") contrasts with the lumpiness of matter in galaxies, clusters, superclusters, and larger structures.[21]

A remark attributed to astronomer M. Geller is that for every galaxy survey, "structures appear as large as the survey." Structures such as the "Great Wall" of galaxies with dimensions of hundreds of Megaparsecs (Mpc) don't fit well into any version of the Big Bang theory. And now we have a new statistical study of galaxies based on a combination of four other surveys in narrow sky zones roughly 6 Mpc wide and 2000 Mpc long (1000 Mpc to each side of us), containing 900 galaxies. Two of the four surveys were toward our north and south galactic poles. When the redshift distributions are combined, a distinctive pattern emerges of clustering into groups of 20 to 30 galaxies at about every 130 Mpc, which is evident through at least nine full cycles, with relative void regions in between.

The first and largest peak in the distribution, at about 130 Mpc, is what is called "The Great Wall." Such a feature has now been found in two opposite directions from us, one in the northern and one in the southern hemisphere. These peaks alone are said to be incompatible with all galaxy formation mechanisms. The existence of numerous other possible "great walls" out to the limits of the surveys merely compounds the problems for theorists.

In the latest related work,[22] 13 evenly spaced "walls" of galaxies were found, each 420 lightyears apart, covering a total distance of seven billion lightyears. A line of sight passing through a random pattern of "bubbles" has less than a 2% chance of producing the observed sequence, which implies that the observations don't fit a random-cell pattern. (See Figure 4.1.)

Big Bang theoreticians don't know what to make of this structure yet. But using the Meta Model axiom that the universe should look essentially the same at any scale, it would be a reasonable conjecture that we are looking at *waves* on a huge scale. The so-called "walls" would be like wavefronts, with alternating condensation and rarefaction intervals. Indeed, in the Meta Model it would be clearly unreasonable to postulate that the "light-carrying medium" (LCM) and the sea of gravitons are uniform and homogeneous throughout an infinite universe. Any large-scale disturbance in these media must propagate through them in the manner of waves. Waves in the LCM would mean changes in its density, which would affect the speed of light and produce both redshifts and blueshifts of light passing through. In that connection, it is interesting to note the work of Tifft,[23,24] who points to both periodicity and variability in the redshifts of galaxies—something clearly impossible for times as short as decades in the Big Bang cosmology.

Using this idea of wave structure, we might hazard some of the following predictions (made 10/91):

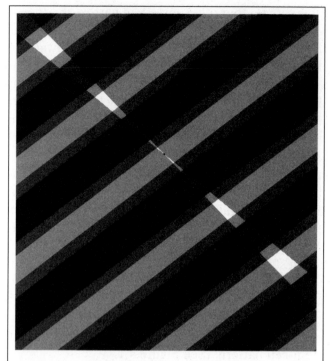

Figure 4.1. Deep-sky galaxy-redshift surveys in opposite directions have found that galaxies seem to cluster in "walls", or possibly waves, on the largest scales we can now observe.

1. The nearest "great wall" to the north and the nearest one to the south will have no physical connection, since each would be an independent wavefront separated by the wavefront our galaxy is in.[g]

2. Our own galaxy will be found to reside within another "great wall" which we are viewing from the inside. If we look in the correct directions within our own wall, the uniform alternating "wall-void" structure seen at great distances in other directions will not be found.

---

[g]The latest observations, still unpublished as this book goes to press, suggest this may be correct.

Figure 4.2. The same cosmic "walls" or waves viewed along other directions will change their appearance drastically.

3. If we look just slightly off that internal line of sight, at a steep slanting angle through the wavefronts, we will see enormous voids separating enormously thick galaxy walls. (See Figure 4.2.)

4. The wall-void pattern will continue well beyond the distance where the Big Bang theory says that no galaxies should yet have formed.

5. The non-expansion "random" motions of the individual galaxy superclusters will be consistent with particle motion within a wavefront; that is, it will depend upon position within the wave, showing a regular pattern of compression and rarefaction.[h,25,26]

[h]Thinking entirely in conventional terms, D. Lynden-Bell and O. Lahav (see next reference) have discussed the question of galaxy motions. From

Our examination of the large-scale structure of the universe would not be complete without adding some obvious corollaries of the assumption that it is infinite in extent, time, and scale, as developed in the chapter "On the Nature of Space, Time, and Matter." At some level of scale, whether that be the "great wall" features or well beyond, the structure may become non-uniform in the extreme. It may appear at first that there are limits to the matter in the universe, but we will eventually discover that other such super-super structures exist at vast distances. It will be analogous to finding the limits of stars within our own galaxy, later to discover that there are entire other galaxies at vast distances beyond ours. Moreover, the fundamental forces of nature operating over such vast distances over such long time scales are likely to be other than the ones we presently know about. Just as gravity turned out not to be a significant force at atomic levels, we may expect that it will likewise cease to be the most important force at some super-large-scale level.

---

their summary: "If the apparent large-scale coherence of the velocity field of galaxies out to 3500 km/s is not a chance superposition, the gravity that causes it must arise from distant sources such as the Great Attractor." (The "Great Attractor" is an invisible, hypothetical source of enormous gravitation imagined to explain this coherence of galaxy velocities in one direction.)

Looking at a slightly broader picture, we still see nothing to dissuade us of the notion of wave motion. A. Yahil (see second following reference) writes that "the picture of peculiar gravity which emerges ... is dominated by two large mass concentrations, ... one in the direction of Hydra-Centaurus (the Great Attractor), and the other around Perseus-Pisces (in roughly the opposite direction). As a result, the gravitational field bifurcates not far from the position of the Local Group." The latest data do not support that picture, but are consistent with the Meta Model picture just described.

It now appears likely that the so-called large-scale streaming of galaxies is not due to "great attractors", but is an artifact of measuring peculiar velocities of galaxies relative to the cosmic microwave radiation. If that radiation is not coming from the "background" (a Big Bang idea), then we have no reason to adopt it as a standard of rest for velocity measurements, and the inferred galaxy streaming would vanish.

Comparison with the Big Bang Theory

If the universe is infinite in extent, duration, and mass, how can such an idea be reconciled with the Big Bang theory, or with the observed "expansion of the universe," or with the universe's inferred age?

All of modern cosmology is based ultimately upon a very small number of observed facts, the chief of which is that the further away a galaxy is, the more its light is redshifted. For lack of any better explanation, the redshift of galaxies has been assumed to be due to a velocity of recession. Hence, the further away a galaxy is, the faster it is receding from us (and from all other galaxies). A trace-back of these fleeing galaxies with their "observed velocities" tells us the "age of the universe"—the time when this expansion began. The theory which explains the beginning of the expansion of the universe in an explosive event is called the Big Bang theory.[i]

We also observe a "cosmic microwave radiation" nearly uniformly around the sky, with a peak temperature of 2.78 degrees Kelvin, which is interpreted as the remnants of the "fireball" from the Big Bang explosion.

A third observation useful to cosmologists is that the number of radio galaxies and the number of faint, blue, optical galaxies both increase with redshift at a rate which implies that the number of such galaxies per unit volume of space increases as one goes fur-

---

[i]This might be a good place to note that the modern Big Bang hypothesis does not propose an explosion in space, because that would have a definite location and a specific center, and would place us at or close to that center, since everything seems to be moving away from us. To avoid placing ourselves in a special place in the universe, and to adhere to the notion that the universe would look essentially the same from anyplace else, it is supposed that the Big Bang was an explosion of space, and also of time. The galaxies are not moving rapidly through space. Rather, space itself expands, carrying galaxies with it, causing the observed redshift. While you are digesting that information, you might also note that the "cause" of the explosion is supposed to be a "quantum fluctuation," which is basically the spontaneous emergence of matter from nothingness without any specific cause. One interpretation of quantum physics is that such events are observed to occur at the quantum level.

ther out into the universe.

Finally, the abundance of the elements of nature in stars is similar to what one would predict from the Big Bang theory, given the temperatures at which matter would form in that theory.

The redshifts, the microwave background radiation, the number of radio galaxies versus redshift, and the abundance of the elements in stars are observed facts. It is easy to forget that their interpretation as velocities, fireball remnants, increased space density of galaxies, and condensates from a fireball, respectively, is theory. There is nothing compelling about these interpretations; they were merely the best available explanations at the time they were conceived of. We must continually evaluate whether or not these theories remain valuable (i.e., make useful predictions), and whether they continue to be supported by newer observational data.

Halton ("Chip") Arp's book, *Quasars, Redshifts, and Controversies*[27] offers compelling evidence from many different sources that at least some galactic and quasar redshifts are not due to velocity. The fact that redshifts occur preferentially at certain values, even within single clusters of galaxies, reinforces the view that there must be more to redshift than velocity, since velocity could produce redshifts of any value.[28] Still other lines of evidence have been developed by Geoff Burbidge *et al.*[29,30] But if some large redshifts are not due exclusively to velocity, then we must question whether any of them are. Indeed, we must question whether it is reasonable to continue assuming that the universe is expanding at all. Even if Arp, Burbidge, and others were wrong about all the evidence they present, it would still be reasonable to question the velocity interpretation of redshifts. There is, after all, next to nothing in the way of evidence that the redshifts *are* due to velocities. It is merely the case that objections have been raised to the other possibilities proposed to date.

The essential property which must be present to produce a redshift of light is a loss of energy. The most common way to produce a loss of light energy is a recessional velocity. Another way is by having the light climb out of a strong gravitational field (a "gravitational redshift"). Still another way is travel through a resisting medium. For example, resistance caused by the sea of gravitons would be provided to lightwaves propagating through the light-carrying medium; this alone would alter both the frequency and wavelength of traveling light through energy loss.[j] Still another, more exotic way to produce this energy loss is the proposal that hydrogen atoms in distant galaxies start out with less energy than our own present-day hydrogen atoms, perhaps because all atoms in the universe are gaining energy with time. Of course we see distant galaxies as they were in the past, when their light left them.

The abstract idea that photons of light lose energy as they travel through space, redshifting the light, is called the "tired light" theory. The principal objection to it is that if the energy losses are due to interaction with particles in space, the resulting "scattering" effect on the photons would prevent images of distant objects from being sharp in our telescopes. However, consider a sea of gravitons traveling many orders of magnitude faster than light, consisting of "particles" many orders of magnitude smaller than known quantum particles, as proposed in the chapter "On Gravity." Such a medium would not be subject to this scattering objection, because the energy losses in lightwaves would be slow, gradual, and continuous, since CGs are so much smaller than the particles contemplated in the scattering argument. In the Meta Model, the redshift of light propagating in the LCM because of loss of energy to the resisting C-graviton medium is as unavoidable as the loss of energy by ocean waves moving through a resisting medium of air.

Indeed, in an infinite universe, there must be some such loss of energy by photons, forcing them out of the range of visible light. If there were not, then Olbers' Paradox would come into play: in an infinite universe, a line drawn in any direction would eventually intersect a star from which photons are emerging; hence the sky would be everywhere bright. The shift of photons out of the visible range through this "frictional" energy loss with the graviton sea

---

[j]Recall that in the Meta Model, change occurs on every scale. It would not be reasonable to postulate that either the light-carrying medium or the sea of gravitons were everywhere perfectly uniform. At some scale, they must have waves, which are the natural result of disturbances in any medium. So for example, our entire visible universe might just now be slowly being emptied of light-carrying medium as a wave of even larger scale passes through it.

can explain why the sky is dark, and it would cause a redshift of the light of galaxies without any expansion of the universe.[k]

It will eventually be possible to distinguish directly between the two possible causes of redshift: high velocity, in the Big Bang theory, or energy loss from propagation through a resisting medium, in the Meta Model.[l] In the meantime a good indirect test can be done. Measurements of the angular size versus redshift relationship for galaxies is now in full agreement with the Meta Model explanation of redshift. In order for the Big Bang theory to accommodate the observed relationship, it must be postulated that galaxies have grown considerably in average size since galaxies originally condensed. Presently only an ad hoc galaxy growth correction is available in the Big Bang, since we do not yet know a way to predict galaxy growth at the required rate.

Another consideration is that in the Big Bang theory, matter does not form into galaxies for about a billion years after the originating explosion, so there is a maximum possible redshift for the youngest galaxies we can ever observe. "Proto-galaxies" should already start to look pretty strange well before this maximum redshift. We note that all the hypothetical steps between the microwave radiation and full normal galaxies required by the Big Bang theory are currently missing from the observations. In particular, another predicted cosmic background radiation at infrared wavelengths has yet to show any signs of its existence.

In the Meta Model there will be no such limit to the redshift of ordinary galaxies, which will be ever more abundant as one observes fainter and fainter, perhaps without limit. Since quasars are not galaxies, the current most distant objects seen would be the galaxies with redshifts just over 1.0.

---

[k]The energy lost by lightwaves would return to the sea of gravitons, from which energy is derived when light is emitted; so energy is conserved.

[l]Of the three commonest mechanisms (velocity, gravitation, resistance) that can produce energy loss—and therefore redshift the light of galaxies—only travel through a resisting, energy-dissipating medium is ordinarily and necessarily proportional to distance traveled. One must introduce an additional ad hoc assumption, universal expansion, to make the velocity mechanism proportional to distance.

Another possible test of cosmologies is provided by radio galaxies and faint, blue, optical galaxies, whose space density seems to increase with distance. By optical magnitude 28, the excess is an order of magnitude.[31] In the Meta Model, this is not an "evolutionary effect," as it is in the Big Bang theory.[m] The Meta Model predicts that the volume of space at redshift three is 8.0 times what it is at redshift one. But in the Big Bang, the same volume ratio is only 3.2, so the inferred volumes of space at each redshift are much smaller, and the inferred galaxy densities are greater.[n] No change in the Meta Model space density of galaxies is expected until some distance is reached where the universe changes fundamentally in character.[o] In fact, the number of normal galaxies increases about as expected if brightness is used as the distance indicator instead of redshift and one assumes an infinite universe. This is fully in accord with Meta Model expectations, and is a simpler interpretation of the data than is required by the Big Bang.

In the Big Bang theory, the original explosion is the origin of space and time. Neither existed before the event. So the explosion is one *of space itself,* not an explosion *into* space.[p] Galaxies have only relatively slow motions within space, but the space they reside

---

[m]And radio galaxies, like quasars, are not at their redshift distances in the Meta Model, as we will discuss.

[n]In the Big Bang, the redshift-distance relationship is: $d = [(1+z)^2 - 1] / [(1+z)^2 + 1]$ c/H, where d = distance in megaparsecs (Mpc), z = redshift, c = velocity of light in km/s, and H = Hubble constant (approximately 75 km/s/Mpc). In the Meta Model, the relationship is: $d = [\ln(1+z)]$ c/H, where ln = natural logarithm.

[o]There are some indications of such a change of character beginning around magnitude 30, near the limit of present technology. The background sky does not seem to continue to fill in densely with ever fainter sources. We know this must be true at some magnitude, or the night sky would be bright, because every possible line of sight would eventually encounter a star (Olbers' paradox).

[p]If the Big Bang were simply an explosion of matter into space, then there would be a center for the explosion which we could locate, and the velocities of expansion would be different in different directions, unless we were fortuitously located just at the center. Since this is contrary to observation, the Big Bang is said to be an explosion of space and time,

in expands at rates approaching the speed of light. Indeed, it is even allowed in the theory that the expansion of space may exceed the speed of light. However, I believe there is direct observational evidence against this idea that space itself expands.

> "Scientists say that no experiment is a failure, since even a mistake advances the evolution of understanding."
> —Dr. Catherine Pulaski, *U.S.S. Enterprise*

Suppose we start simply with the requirement that light must take longer and longer to move a unit distance as space expands. One such unit distance is the Bohr radius of the hydrogen atom. Either it expands too, or it doesn't. Either its frequency changes too, or it doesn't. Correspondingly, time either expands with space, or it doesn't. We wind up with roughly four distinguishable cases that I can see:

1. Nothing changes on the scale of atoms, which I believe contradicts the meaning of "space itself expands." 2. The speed of light changes, which contradicts some other assumptions in the Big Bang theory. 3. The gravitational constant changes, which allows galaxies and gravitating systems to change relative to electromagnetically bound systems such as atoms. 4. Both distance and time scales change, in which case we could detect no change (i.e., there would be no redshifts of galaxies because as space expands, so do the units of length for measuring the change). It looks to me as though only 3. is useful for the Big Bang theory. But it is observationally in poor

---

not an explosion into space and time.

The Meta Model illustrates one of the fallacies of such reasoning: it makes no sense to have change without time, or time without change. So there is no way to get such a process started. Moreover, the Big Bang presumes a pre-existing sense of scale to the universe, which the Meta Model does not. Finally, it should be pointed out that in the Big Bang theory, the universe appears to have enough mass to be a "black hole." If it doesn't have quite enough mass now, it certainly did in the past, when the same mass occupied a smaller volume. But a black hole must have a singularity at its center. This would require the existence of a specific and definite center, despite all the effort invested in avoiding such a thing in the Big Bang theory.

standing right now, based on radar ranging observations of the planets and planet-orbiting spacecraft, which show no expansion of distance scales within the solar system at anywhere near the rate at which the universe expands.

At the moment, I don't see a way out of this dilemma for the Big Bang idea that "space itself expands." How can it possibly be that things bigger than galaxies expand, while galaxies, star clusters, solar systems, and smaller things do not?[q] Radar ranging observations that the solar system is not expanding at the Hubble rate clearly imply that if galaxy redshifts are due to velocities, then galaxies are moving apart *in space,* with no change in space itself.

Another related problem for the Big Bang model is that it is in the nature of an explosion that the density of matter (or space) near the explosion site is at every instant greater than the density of matter near the leading edge of the expanding shock wave, with a gradual change in density in between. This is simply because the volume enclosed keeps increasing more rapidly for the shock wave than for matter farther in. So one can avoid the implication that the density of matter in the real universe should point the way to the center of the explosion only by assuming a uniform density distribution before the explosion, which was retained during the explosion! But an explosion of that description could never form galaxies or clusters of galaxies. They would have to exist pre-formed before the explosion, then simply expand as space expanded. Such a thing is con-

---

[q]It is sometimes argued that gravity prevents the expansion of space within structures as small as galaxies. But this implies that gravity has a different strength, or a different kind of effect, on small scales from what it has on large scales. For if gravity has only the strength and effect we know about, then a simple calculation shows that its known effects on local space-time are not so great as to be able to hide or completely cancel the Hubble expansion effect on local spacetime.

It may also be seen that if gravity prevents galaxies from expanding, then when galaxies collide there must be a transition from sharing in the expansion of space to no longer sharing in it. Where is that transition region and what causes it? Would the Big Bang also advocate that gravity has a finite range? Or is gravity with a certain strength required? If so, what strength? In my opinion, this "swidget" (see Glossary) does not stand up to close scrutiny.

trary to many observations; for example, some galaxies contain only very young stars, whose apparent age is less than one per cent of the Hubble age of the universe.

We might also ask the question, if space itself expands, it expands into what? Obviously to say that it expands into space is circular reasoning. It must expand into another dimension. But such a dimension so far exists only in the math. I do not see that this concept, however elegant mathematically, can survive close logical or physical scrutiny.

One argument sometimes quoted as supporting the Big Bang theory is its prediction of the primordial abundances of certain elements. But a particular value must be arbitrarily assumed for the starting abundance of light relative to matter to get this result. And other cosmologies make similar predictions.[32] Moreover, for the heavy elements, even the Big Bang must rely on the assumption that these were created by many generations of stars converting hydrogen to helium and heavier elements. And for the lighter elements, the Big Bang predictions are not in any better overall standing than are alternative cosmologies, which must invoke cosmic ray processes to produce certain lighter elements. For example, the beryllium abundance is perhaps a factor of 1000 greater than the predicted Big Bang value.[33] So this argument cannot be regarded as being of strong significance for choosing between cosmological models.[r]

---

[r]In the Meta Model the predicted abundances are those which would result after an infinite cycle of star and galaxy formation, nucleosynthesis, and explosion back into the interstellar and intergalactic media, as continually modified by ongoing processes such as cosmic ray spallation. It is already clear from work done on the Big Bang that what I have just described is very close to what is observed. However, detailed calculations will undoubtedly turn up some surprises. It is important that such calculations include the effects of mass in the interior of stars that, because of shielding, does not contribute to the external gravity field of the star. This is the major difference from existing models. One might begin with the assumption that galaxy birth starts with pure hydrogen, thereby preserving the idea that metal-poor stars are quite young, and that stars become metal-rich after several generations. However, it is not obvious to me that any of these assumptions have any deductive validity in the

Still another logical dilemma with the Big Bang theory is that it must give up one of the postulates of Relativity theory—that the speed of light is constant in all reference frames. In particular, the speed of light must be retarded by expanding space, in the sense that the speed of the source does affect the net speed of light toward us. If this were not so, then galaxies 14 billion lightyears away from us but only 1 billion years old could not possibly have expanded that far in so short a time.

Although the Big Bang (BB) theory is still the most widely advocated cosmological theory today, many astronomers do find various aspects of it objectionable. For example, *Nature* magazine ran an editorial[34] to the effect that the Big Bang philosophy is no longer an acceptable one. But the alternatives up to now have not found favor, either. Bondi & Gold's "Steady State" (SS) theory conserves the density of the universe, but not matter. In it, new matter is constantly created as old matter expands to make way for it. The lack of a source for the continual creation of new matter made this theory unpopular. Later, its lack of accommodation of the cosmic background radiation caused it to lose many supporters. More recently a theory called "Plasma Cosmology" (PC) has time which runs from minus infinity to plus infinity, and a universe that is filled with a hot plasma. Although this is similar to certain parts of the Meta Model (MM), an essential feature of the latter is that a fifth dimension, scale, also runs through an infinite range in both the large and the small directions. And the Meta Model has numerous other fundamental differences, such as a finite range for gravity, and propagation faster than light. Plasma cosmology depends upon electromagnetic forces to explain many of the universe's observed properties.

---

model. Unfortunately, in order to approach the task in the right way, deductively, we would be led to expect that forces other than gravity operate on still-larger scales. Until we establish observationally the properties of at least one such force, such that we can make deductions about the life cycle of galaxies, clusters, walls and voids, we are in no position to reliably guess the starting conditions for galaxy formation. Aesthetic guesses such as "galaxies start from pure hydrogen" may be the best we can do for the moment.

Many additional arguments against the Big Bang, as well as historical details, and a discussion of Plasma cosmology as an alternative, may be found in an important new book by Eric Lerner.[35] Additional arguments of a more technical nature have been published by Arp and Van Flandern.[36]

The Cosmic Microwave Radiation

The "cosmic microwave radiation" (sometimes called "background" radiation) is a uniform flux of microwaves from all over the sky. In the Big Bang theory, it is the predicted fireball remnant left over from the original explosion of the whole universe. The radiation is near half a centimeter wavelength, which corresponds to a redshift of ordinary light of about 10,000. However, the radiation's remarkable uniformity currently is causing some difficulty for the Big Bang theory. To surmount this difficulty, theoreticians need to "discover" a structure-forming mechanism that creates features as large as 5% of the size of the whole universe from perturbations in the density of matter that was uniform to a few parts in 100,000 at a few hundred thousand years after the Big Bang.

As William H. Press of the Center for Astrophysics in Cambridge, MA, put it: "If it weren't for the microwave background, you could just say the structure is what it is, and you could work your way backward to find out what the initial conditions were."[37] David N. Spergel of Princeton commented: "If there were an alternative model that explained the microwave background and the nucleosynthesis abundances observed, and produced galaxies, then people would start thinking about it." Ivars Peterson, writing for *Science News,* said: "In its simplest form, the Big Bang scenario doesn't look like a good way to form galaxies. It allows too little time for the force of gravity by itself to gather ordinary matter— neutrons, protons, electrons—into the patterns of galaxies seen today. Yet the idea survives for want of a better idea."

Recently, a new specific problem has arisen with the idea that the microwave radiation comes from a great distance. The amount of radiation emitted by distant galaxies falls with increasing wavelengths, as expected if the longer wavelengths are scattered by the intergalactic medium.[38] For example, the brightness ratio of radio galaxies at infrared and radio wavelengths changes with distance in a way that implies absorption. Basically, this means that the longer wavelengths are more easily absorbed by material between the galaxies. But then the microwave radiation should be absorbed even more easily by that medium too, and has no chance to reach us from great distances, or to remain perfectly uniform while doing so. It therefore must result from the re-emission of microwaves from the relatively nearby intergalactic medium. This argument alone implies that the microwaves could not be coming directly to us from a distance beyond all the galaxies, and therefore that the Big Bang theory cannot be correct.

The spectrum of the cosmic microwave radiation has been determined to be quite close to that of a "blackbody," which is a type of spectrum requiring a uniform temperature source in equilibrium with its environment. The "surface" of a fireball remnant is assumed to meet the conditions needed for a blackbody spectrum. So if the microwave radiation were indeed "background," i.e., coming from beyond the most remote galaxies, then it surely is what the Big Bang theoreticians have hypothesized: the remnant of a gigantic explosion involving much or all of the visible universe.

But there are other possibilities, such as the re-emission by the nearby intergalactic medium already mentioned. As another example, note that any fireball remnant which surrounds us would produce almost exactly the same type of spectrum. If a supernova in our part of the galaxy exploded in the past, its fireball would eventually encompass us. Once inside, we would see a blackbody spectrum coming uniformly from all directions in the sky. This would inevitably cool to thermal equilibrium with the interstellar environment, which happens to be about 3 degrees Kelvin.[39] It would look just like the cosmic microwave radiation, because any source in thermal equilibrium with its environment will radiate a blackbody spectrum.

The reason for the uniform appearance to an observer not near the center of the remnant may need some explanation. It is well known in physics that any inverse square field emanating from a spherical shell will produce a uniform effect everywhere inside the shell. (For example, the gravitational potential inside a massive spherical shell is constant.) To see why, consider the radiation into

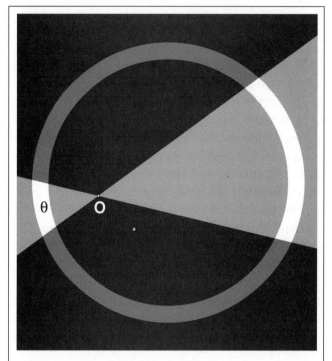

Figure 4.3. An observer O anywhere within a sphere radiating an inverse square field will find the flux equal in all directions, regardless of distance to the sphere.

a certain solid angle arriving at an observer some distance inside the shell. The flux seen by the observer will vary inversely with the square of the distance, but the area of the shell emitting into that solid angle will increase with distance squared. The two effects exactly compensate, keeping the flux at the observer constant regardless of the distance to the shell wall. (See Figure 4.3.) It follows that observers anywhere inside a spherical fireball remnant would continue to be irradiated by it at some constant flux level no matter how large the fireball expanded, but for the fact that the fireball cools and gradually emits less (and longer wavelength) flux with time.

In the chapters on the solar system, we explore the hypothesis that a major explosion occurred within our own solar system in the astronomically recent past (the "exploded planet" hypothesis). Perhaps this is the event which also gave rise to the microwave blackbody radiation. The principal objection might be that the asymmetry of the "fireball remnant" implies that we are moving at several hundred km/s relative to it. However, that asymmetry might also have originated from the natural ellipticity of the fireball due to the motion of the explosion source (a planet) relative to the Sun. Although that relative velocity would be only on the order of 18 km/s, the ellipticity of the resulting remnant would look similar to the observed asymmetry of the microwave radiation.

The distance of the microwave radiation is difficult to determine. But our new "COsmic Background Explorer" (COBE) satellite has found some evidence in mapping the microwave emissions from over the entire sky. Although gravitational lensing effects might tend to produce bright spots in the background, and COBE might have seen the outlines of bubbles and walls and other large-scale features of the universe if the radiation source were more distant than those, no such patterns were seen. Instead, the radiation map clearly showed our own galaxy and a trace of the Large Magellanic Cloud (our nearest neighbor galaxy). Otherwise, the radiation was uniform from all directions.[s,40]

Measurements of cyanogen absorption lines in certain distant stars have been used as evidence that the microwave radiation is approximately the same at other locations within our galaxy. This is not surprising because, as already noted, 3 degrees Kelvin is the calculated equilibrium temperature in the interstellar environment of our galaxy. This means that interstellar particles must eventually cool to that temperature, and then can get no cooler, because that is the temperature at which absorption of photons from starlight and emission of microwave heat are just exactly balanced. Equilibrium temperatures will be higher in regions of great stellar density, such as near galactic cores.

But the normal equilibrium temperature in our galaxy and most others is about 3 degrees Kelvin. So the Meta Model expects just

---

[s]More recently, small temperature variations (less than a hundred-thousandth of a degree) may have been detected. The next reference discusses this newer data critically.

this temperature for the bath of equilibrium radiation which surrounds us, whatever the distance of its origin from us. And its spectrum must be that of a blackbody because of thermal equilibrium (temperature balance with the environment). The fact that nearly the same equilibrium temperature would apply to other galaxies as well would explain certain observed X-ray anomalies associated with galactic clusters,[t] which some astronomers have taken as "proof" that the microwave radiation originates farther away than those galaxies. With our new interpretation, we see that no such conclusion may be drawn—rather the contrary, as we shall now see.

The Effect of Gravitational Lenses on a Background

The majority of astronomers are of the opinion that a uniform background would still look uniform, even in the presence of gravitational lenses. The arguments for this viewpoint are based primarily on a conservation law for photons. But photons do not propagate as discrete entities; light always propagates as waves, and its intensity is not conserved. Lenses, of course, interrupt the inverse square intensity decrease of light by refocusing it; and that seems to be the source of the extra intensity seen by the observer. In the several independent arguments which follow, I will be careful to use "lightwaves" instead of "photons" to emphasize this point.

The importance of this argument is that a uniform background such as the cosmic "background" radiation either will or will not continue to look uniform when observed through clusters and superclusters of galaxies. I maintain here that any uniform background should be distorted by such foreground clusters. Specifically, grav-

---

[t]This so-called Sunyaev-Zeldovich effect, in which the temperature of the microwave radiation is locally changed by interaction with hot X-rays from galactic clusters, is very difficult to interpret because it has so far been observed at only one frequency and only in a handful to spots on the sky. Observations at enough frequencies to define the blackbody shape of the radiation, and to determine its spatial distribution, are needed before one might conclude that the radiation source is beyond these galaxy clusters.

itational lensing should make it look brighter. And since the microwave blackbody radiation does not appear distorted or significantly brighter in spots near clusters of galaxies, it cannot be coming from the background.

The casual reader may only be interested in one or two of these eight parallel arguments:

1. Consider a gravitational lens in direction X, and a bright spot on a uniform background in direction Y, where Y is far from X. If there were no lens, the only lightwaves we would receive from Y are those which travel in the line of sight direct to us. With the lens, we still receive all those direct lightwaves from Y to us. In addition, we receive an image of Y (some additional lightwaves from Y) through the lens.[u] More total light reaches us because the lens focuses lightwaves.

2. Consider a cone containing a small solid angle extending from its vertex at the observer to a small area on the sky. The brightness of the background seen within that solid angle will depend only on its area. Now trace the same cone from the observer toward the sky if it passes close by a gravitational lens. The side of the cone farthest from the lens is bent least; that closest is bent most. The distorted cone now intercepts a larger area on the sky than it did without the lens. The observer sees a larger area, and therefore more light, in that conical solid angle if it goes by a gravitational lens than if it does not. Therefore the sky must appear brighter within that cone when a lens is present.

3. Consider an "observer" who sends out light uniformly in all directions that illuminates a background uniformly. Now add a gravitational lens between the observer and the background in some direction. We direct our attention to the light which passes from the observer outward through the lens. This light is then spread over a wide area of the background, with little or no light reaching the background along the optical axis of the lens. Basically, the lens produces a "dark spot" on the background behind it, with darkness increasing toward its center. We began with completely uniform

---

[u] A gravitational lens images a wide angle on the sky behind it. A strong-enough gravitational lens would image the entire sky, because lightwaves from every point on it can be bent toward the observer.

light in all directions from the observer, and ended with a non-uniformly lit background. It follows that reversing every light ray from such a non-uniform background back to the observer, with some rays going direct and others through the lens, will produce what appears to the observer to be a perfectly uniform sky brightness. Then adding light behind the lens to make the starting background uniform will make the background appear brighter through the lens.

4. The observer sees a sky around him with an area of 4 pi steradians (the area of the surface of a sphere). If there is a gravitational lens in one direction, then through the lens he sees an area of the sky much greater than the area taken up by the lens itself. So counting the area seen through the lens (which enables him to see many points on the sky which he can also see directly), the observer sees a total area much in excess of 4 pi steradians, with correspondingly greater intensity than if he could only see 4 pi steradians.

5. Think of a telescope objective lens looking at the background, with an observer at its focus. Clearly the intensity of the background, seen through the lens, will increase. But it increases by robbing light which would have gone to other places off-axis, and concentrating it all on-axis for the lens. The total brightness is conserved because the area of the lightwaves passing through the lens and the distances they travel are unchanged; they are merely focused. But if the lens were gravitational instead of flat optical, lightwaves from all directions (not merely those behind the lens) would enter and get focused; so there is truly more "light energy" (in the inverse square sense) directed toward the observer than when the gravitational lens is absent.

6. The "retro-reflectors" placed on the Moon by astronauts are special mirrors which always reflect light back in the direction it came from, even if that direction is off-axis. Imagine the gravitational lens being replaced by a sphere made of perfect retro-reflectors (an "R-sphere"). Then instead of focusing the light, the R-sphere would do the opposite: "defocus" and disperse it. An observer looking in the direction of such an R-sphere would see much less light than would come from the background in its absence; yet the "photon conservation" argument is no less applicable. Move the R-sphere from the center out towards one surface of the sky to see the point more clearly.

7. Suppose that instead of a single gravitational lens, the uniform background were shielded from the observer by a sky filled densely with gravitational lenses in every direction. Let these lenses be close to the background, and the observer in the center. All the light gets refocused from a low-intensity big sphere (the background) to a high-intensity small sphere (near the observer). If one layer of lenses is insufficient to see the point, then add another layer of gravitational lenses all over the sky in front of the first one, then another, etc., until the universe is filled with lenses symmetrically placed around the observer. Then all the light of all the background would get focused at the observer instead of being spread throughout the universe.

8. It is supposed to be true of the cosmic microwave radiation, and of any spherical shell emitting radiation which obeys an inverse square law, that the intensity of that radiation is uniform everywhere within the spherical shell—whether near the shell surface or near its center. This is because an observer close to the shell, looking within a certain solid angle, sees only a small area which is bright by virtue of its closeness. Looking at the far side of the shell within a solid angle of the same size, the area he views will be greater by the ratio of distances squared; but each unit area will appear fainter by the same factor because of its greater distance. Nonetheless, the product of area times brightness per unit area will be everywhere the same, and this is what produces the uniform intensity at the observer. This means that if you look at the wall of the shell where it is quite close to you, you are looking at fewer points. If you were to associate one photon per point, that would mean fewer photons. But that isn't physically correct because light doesn't propagate as photons, which would maintain their brightness. It propagates as waves, which are constantly attenuating as they move. The brightness of a unit of area is not conserved. It depends on how far away you are.

In the conventional models, it must be the case that the cosmic microwave radiation will show the effects of gravitational lenses, superclusters, voids, bubbles, cosmic strings, "great attractors," and other sources of concentrated gravitation in space, if it is truly background in nature. If such effects do not show up in mappings of the background, we may confidently conclude that the radiation has a more local origin.

Quasars

It is easy to make a case that the very high-redshift quasars are not at the cosmological distances implied when their redshifts are interpreted in the Big Bang theory. If these objects are at such great distances, then we have the following dilemmas, which would not exist if quasars were "local":[41]

1. There must exist an unknown energy mechanism to produce such intrinsically high-luminosity objects, enabling them to be so bright at such great distances. Energies are often equivalent to thousands of supernovas per year.

2. There appears to be no continuous X-ray background from the sky at currently detectable levels. Many of the main discrete X-ray sources are within our own galaxy. Most of the others are quasars and related objects. A mechanism is needed for producing detectable X-rays from extremely nearby and extremely far away objects, but not from objects at intermediate distances or from the background. (The same problem occurs in the extreme ultraviolet, which cannot penetrate the local interstellar medium. So quasars and "active galactic nuclei" seen emitting extreme ultraviolet must be visible through holes in the interstellar and intergalactic media, or they must be local.)

3. The existence of rapid light variations implies that most quasar light must come from a small source, of solar-system dimensions. Light variations could not be coordinated in different parts of a larger object, because that would require faster-than-light communication. Yet some quasars which can be resolved are seen to be as big as giant galaxies (if assumed to be at great distances).[42]

4. An X-ray flare from one quasar was observed to increase its brightness by 67% in just 3 minutes.[43] At its redshift of $z=0.137$, the implied rate of brightness change exceeds what is physically possible, unless the X-rays were relativistically directed our way in a narrow beam. Even then, the beam had to be a short-lived one, since the event was not repeated.

5. Quasar jets would have to be the largest contiguous structures in the universe.

6. Jets from quasars seem to expand faster than light (up to ten times faster). Statistics argue against this being due to deceptive geometry, so "relativistic beaming" is invoked as a possible explanation.

7. The calculated density of charged particles is so high in some quasars that there is a theoretical problem with how to get the photons, by which we see the objects, out from the interior. (See Arp, p. 3.)[27]

8. The number of quasars versus redshift, z, is nearly flat, with a slight drop out to $z = 2$, then a sharp drop. So they do not increase in number as space increases in volume with redshift. This is explained by assuming a variable number of quasars as the universe evolved and expanded.

9. Quasars near our part of the universe (i.e., with small redshifts) are quite rare, seeming to imply that most of the universe's quasars died out long ago. What we see now would be the light of quasars which existed long ago that is just now reaching us.

10. Sources are "quasi-stellar" by definition, implying little visible angular extent of the sort that galaxies have. Yet quasars must have galaxy-like masses to produce so much energy (if they are far away).

11. Some low-redshift galaxies have associated quasars. In the first four cases with multiple quasar associations, all have redshifts less than about 0.02. The same sort of low-redshift association exists for three quasars apparently "connected" to galaxies.

12. Similarly, very faint galaxies tend to be clustered around high-redshift quasars at very small separations.[44] This trend continues even for quasars with redshifts approaching 3, for which the clustered galaxies need to be absurdly overluminous to be visible.[45] Elsewhere on the sky, galaxies of this brightness have mean redshifts of only about 0.4.

13. Where distant clusters of galaxies are observed, quasars are generally not found in them. Only a few examples of such associations are presently known.

14. The magnitudes and angular separations of quasar-galaxy pairs are correlated with the galaxy redshift.[46]

15. The angular size of visible nebulas surrounding some quasars does not diminish with increasing redshift. If anything, they might even increase with redshift.[47]

16. Absorption lines in the spectra of quasar light passing through hydrogen clouds are quite narrow, implying cloud temperatures of just 5,000 to 10,000 degrees: well below the 30,000 degrees expected for quasars.[48,v,49]

17. The so-called "iron quasars" contain extremely strong emission lines from ionized iron which defy explanation.[52]

18. The number of absorption clouds seen in Lyman alpha does not diminish as expected with smaller distance. The number of such inferred clouds between us and quasars at $z = 3$ is quite large. But between us and quasars at $z = 2$ there are about the same number of inferred clouds as between us and quasar 3C 273 at $z = 0.16$.[51] Other small-redshift quasars

---

[v]While reviewing problems with interpreting quasar redshifts as indicating great distances, we see that many of the same arguments apply to the so-called "active galactic nuclei" (AGNs). These lower redshift objects often have quasar-like behavior. One of them, Markarian 231, has now been shown to have three additional (lower) redshifts associated with it, seen as absorption lines in its spectrum. The newest and lowest of these absorption line sets has just recently been discovered because it wasn't present prior to 1984. The traditional interpretation is forced to conclude that intervening clouds between us and the AGN are causing the absorption. There must be one intervening cloud for every different set of absorption lines, or a total of three different intervening clouds at distances from each other so great that they cannot be physically associated. The sudden appearance of the previously invisible third cloud implies that it has just moved into the line of sight. All these improbable coincidences are avoided if it is assumed that the AGN is a gravitationally redshifted nearby object with absorption clouds in its own immediate environment, where they too will be gravitationally redshifted.

have similar anomalies. Moreover, the lack of metal lines indicates that the absorbing clouds are not generally galaxy halos.

19. Quasars with redshifts greater than 1.5 show no tendency toward clustering, and no evidence of voids.[52] Both clustering and voids are features of normal galaxies, which can be seen out to redshifts of about 1.

All these anomalies have explanations in conventional models. But most of these explanations were contrived after the properties were discovered, for the purpose of saving the hypothesis that quasar redshifts are distance indicators.[w] In several cases, argument centers on whether or not statistics have been properly calculated. At the very least, astronomers reviewing the preceding list ought to feel uncomfortable about the plausibility of the conventional model, even if they can still defend it in an ad hoc way.

In the Meta Model, we have already noted that there are no "black holes" in the traditional sense. But astrophysical theory predicts that stars more massive than about 10 times our Sun will eventually become supernovas and collapse, leaving behind a black hole. What does the Meta Model say about these cases? The collapse of a massive object would eventually cease, because internal gravitational shielding limits the strength of the gravitational field of the object. However, the gravitational field near its surface would indeed be intense. Light trying to escape from such an object would undergo a very large gravitational redshift.

Because of the high redshift, some infrared heat radiation from such collapsed objects would be shifted to radio wavelengths. These objects would then be radio sources. But the objects, being stellar remnants, would appear "quasi-stellar" telescopically. Since supernovas tend to acquire high velocities during their explosion, we would expect that such objects would often be found outside the galaxies they were created in. The same remark would apply to massive objects ejected from the central regions of galaxies.

---

[w]Explanations contrived purely to save a hypothesis are herein called "swidgets" (see Glossary). Many inferred quasar properties qualify for this label.

111

Of course, all these predicted features provide a very good description of quasars, whose name is a contraction of "quasi-stellar radio source." Note that their existence is predicted on a priori grounds by the Meta Model. The Big Bang theory may (with considerable difficulty, as just noted) be able to accommodate quasars, but it certainly never predicted them. The Meta Model, deductively, demands them! But they must be relatively nearby.

The Meta Model clearly implies that some quasars may be quite local objects, with some of them associated with our own galaxy. The clustered faint galaxies seen close to high-redshift quasars would then be background galaxies, magnified in brightness by the gravitational lens effect of the *foreground* quasar (the reverse of the way in which gravitational lenses are usually thought to act). In the Meta Model, every property of quasars in the list of puzzles for the conventional model has a simple, natural, uncontrived explanation. Other properties naturally fall into place as well. For example, low-luminosity quasars have wide jets, while high-luminosity quasars have narrow jets.[53] In the Meta Model, low- and high-luminosity quasars can be interpreted as nearby and far-away quasars, respectively. Naturally, the jets for the latter will be seen as narrower. Another anomaly: different emission lines in quasar spectra give systematically different redshifts by small amounts. These velocity shifts are not well understood in conventional models, but are believed to be due to outflowing or infalling gas.[54] In the Meta Model, where quasars are compact, high-mass stellar objects with gravitational redshifts, both the redshift anomalies for these emission lines, and the absorption line systems with completely different redshifts mentioned earlier, are simply chromosphere-like layers of different gravitational redshift in the "corona" of the quasar. There is no need for infalling matter or intervening clouds of hydrogen.

There are a few instances of double or multiple quasar images with nearly identical redshifts. These are usually taken to be gravitational lens images due to foreground galaxies. They may indeed be just that, even in the Meta Model, since distant quasars do exist and can be magnified by lensing. However, the existence of emission line companions (emission lines suggest that the light is passing through some sort of heated gas) to some high-redshift quasars[55,45] suggests another possibility. These secondary quasar images might be the natural result of refraction of quasar light passing through a gaseous medium, rather than gravitational lensing. Since the quasars are much closer to us than in conventional theory, not much refraction is needed to create a false image of a quasar. In particular, it would be logical to deduce that whenever we look at a quasar with one of its long jets directed toward us, we may see multiply refracted images of the quasar through the long jet's gas. In support of this idea, the quasar companions are bluer and more luminous than active galaxies should be, but just as refracted images might be. Moreover, in the case of high-redshift quasars, the light propagation delays are quite large, and the secondary image may simply be the quasar's location on the sky at some past epoch, seen through a gaseous nebula. Then the position will have since changed because of the quasar's proper motion.

In the real universe, many types of objects resemble quasars in certain particulars. Included with these are radio galaxies, Seyfert galaxies, and active galactic nuclei (AGNs). Recall that the Meta Model allows stars to contain more mass in their interiors than we can measure from the star's gravity. This has a profound effect on conventional ideas about stellar evolution, especially for the more massive end of the spectrum.

If the intrinsic brightness (luminosity) of ordinary stars is plotted against their temperature, most stars (which are dwarfs) fall along a curve called the "main sequence." But giant stars tend to fall into either the red branch or the blue branch, with a wide gap separating the two groupings. Upper limits to masses of stable stars are about 100 solar masses. But the Meta Model would expect that far greater masses would remain stable because of the gravitational shielding effects. So the red and the blue branches of giant stars should extend upward in luminosity into what I call the "supermassive" star domain.[x]

---

[x]Regarding the predicted evolution of "supermassive stars" and related ideas presented here, I am indebted to several dozen professional astronomers and astronomy graduate students who participated in a three-month-long debate on the relative merits of the Big Bang and the Meta Model, which took place during the summer of 1992 on the USENET computer network in the newsgroup "sci.astro."

The blue branch would contain the intrinsically brightest stars in the universe. Some of these would be individually as bright as entire dwarf galaxies. I would conjecture that the poorly understood "Wolf-Rayet stars," with their excess of ultraviolet light and emission lines, are a transition stage between the brightest ordinary stars (O-stars) and quasars. More generally, the so-called "blue stragglers" are an unexplained stage of stellar evolution found in all stellar populations, which may now be explainable as a supermassive star evolutionary stage.

Perhaps the most important feature of the brightest members of this expected new class of supermassive blue stars is their intense radiation in the ultraviolet part of the spectrum. Although intense, these radiations would have been unobservable through the Earth's atmosphere until recent spacecraft observations, which can view the sky from above the atmosphere. Indeed, excess ultraviolet radiation of unknown origin has been detected in the nearby Andromeda galaxy, and is apparently a common feature of certain galaxies. If such galaxies were viewed from a great distance with their light redshifted, they would appear to be quite blue relative to ordinary galaxies. There does exist a class of distant, blue galaxies. The Big Bang model has suggested that these are young galaxies, since they are more abundant the farther out and back in time we look. The Meta Model suggests these are ultraviolet-bright galaxies containing supermassive stars, whose ultraviolet excess has until recently been unobservable except at great distance where the ultraviolet light is redshifted into the blue part of the spectrum.

The red branch of supermassive stars would be physically quite large in diameter, with cool surface temperatures which would have little ionizing influence on their immediate environments. It would not be unusual for such stars to pulsate, but pulsation periods would be longer than for any ordinary stars, sometimes even several years long. In seems likely that the poorly understood P-Cygni class of stars is a transition type.[y] The light from ordinary galaxies would be dominated by red-branch supermassive stars, making the galaxies appear yellow nearby and red farther away.

---

[y] I am indebted to Damo Nair for this suggestion.

Some quasars may be close enough to the Sun in space to permit direct detection of a proper motion relative to the distant galaxies. In this connection, it is interesting to note that an attempt to identify quasars in fields of faint objects by their lack of proper motion failed when some known quasars seemed to show slight proper motions.[56] This was attributed to systematic errors. One possible source of systematic error would be real quasar proper motions.

In any case, the redshift of quasars would be virtually unrelated to distance, and related only to the degree of collapse. Because it is the brightest gamma-ray source, has short-period variability, and has apparent superluminal jet motions, 3C 279 may be an excellent candidate for being a nearby quasar with a detectable proper motion. The detection of a proper motion for any quasar would be a virtual proof that at least some quasars are nearby objects, and that their redshifts are not cosmological in origin. Are any astronomers looking?

Since writing the last sentence above, I have learned that very-long-baseline interferometry (VLBI) radio telescopes have been used to measure positions of about 20 quasars with unprecedented accuracy.[57] Most of these objects do show proper motions, and some of these measurements have statistical significance at the 4–6 sigma level (i.e., real beyond doubt). However, few of the astronomers take these potentially sensational results seriously. It is widely believed that small modeling errors are responsible, and that the apparent motions will vanish in a few years when the analysis improves. We shall see!

Conclusions

If the Meta Model does not seem probable to any reader, he should at least appreciate how amazingly fragile is all modern cosmological theory, based as it is on an assumption (that redshifts are due to velocities) whose rationale has since been severely undercut (some redshifts apparently are not due to velocities). Once again we see a phenomenon I believe pervades all fields of knowledge. While learned men and women are trying to advance the frontiers of knowledge in their fields, the fundamental assumptions underlying those fields are seldom re-examined, with the result that many times the scholars fail to see that they are in the wrong forest while making wondrous discoveries about the trees around them.

If we truly wish to make progress in science, we must continually reassess the most fundamental axioms. In addition to those we have just been examining, we must ask if the velocity of light is necessarily a limiting velocity. And is gravitation the principal force operative on a galactic distance scale? (In the chapter "On Gravity," we developed some reasons for concluding that neither is true.)

In this chapter, we have developed several hypotheses, one of which is a finite range for the force of gravitation. Some will call this an "extraordinary" hypothesis, because it proposes a change in one of the most fundamental, and most successful, laws of physics. But the existing law of gravitation simply assumes an infinite range for gravitation, without justification beyond no one having yet detected any limits observationally. The proposed finite range for gravity was derived deductively from a complete model of gravitation. And it happens to explain phenomena on the scale of galaxies which are otherwise poorly understood. The conventional view requires hypothesizing an ever-increasing amount of invisible matter in and between galaxies. By objective criteria, which is the "extraordinary" hypothesis? Surely it is gravity with unlimited range, combined with non-radiating, non-absorbing matter being the dominant constituent of the universe, which is extraordinary, unless our criterion is merely which hypothesis has been around longer!

In the preceding discussion, some readers may have considerable doubts that my conjectures about galaxies and the structure of the universe are correct in any detail. But surely I have at least made a point about the degree to which the accepted models in modern cosmology are uncertain, even unlikely! We must continue to re-examine the fundamental assumptions, and we must be willing to accept that there continually arise new observations which cannot be explained satisfactorily by any existing theory. When a correct explanation for the new observations eventually comes along, it will be easy to recognize. It will explain existing observations, provide insight and understanding, and predict new things not previously known. These are the trademarks of a correct theory—yet they are seldom present, and seldom requested by researchers. But we cannot make true progress without them.

5

· ·

On the Composition
of Substance

*Summary: Quantum mechanics differs from classical physics in three
main ways: 1. Quantum objects lack objectivity, seeming sometimes
to be particles, and under other circumstances to behave as waves.
2. The properties of quantum objects lack determinacy. The more
accurately any property (such as position) is measured, the more
uncertain its conjugate property (such as velocity) becomes. 3. Observations change reality. The actions of one observer can seemingly
instantly affect what another observer at a vast distance will see. To
account for these "weird" properties, the leading school of thought
in modern physics holds that "there is no deep reality." The only
apparent alternative is faster-than-light communication, as proved
by the Bell Inequality. But the Meta Model shows us a different picture. It suggests that electrons, light, and other quantum objects propagate as pure waves; but they may cause the emission of a short-lived
particle upon encountering matter. Properties that are split between
the particle and wave states of an object display the measurement
uncertainty phenomenon. And the reasoning behind the Bell Inequality may be seen as having a logical fallacy: if anti-correlations are
considered, the conclusion of instantaneous, remote influences is
invalidated. We conclude with a general discussion of the sort of
quantum world implied by the Meta Model, although we do not
develop these precepts into an alternative theory.*

Generalizations about Quantum Mechanics

Quantum Mechanics (QM) is the study of the nature and composition of the substance which comprises the smallest entities we are aware of. QM tries to extend our knowledge and understanding on the small-scale side, just as cosmology tries to extend them on the large-scale side. Not surprisingly, QM also believes it is dealing, at last, with the ultimate limits to the smallness of scale, just as the astronomers believe they are dealing now with questions of the size and age of the "whole" universe.

And just as there are severe conceptual and logical problems with the Big Bang theory, controversy over the nature of quasars, and questions about the speed and range of the principal operational force, gravity, so too there are severe conceptual and logical problems with present-day quantum theory, controversy over the nature of light and electrons, and questions about what generates the operative forces, especially the electromagnetic force.

With the Big Bang theory, there is no shortage of astronomers willing to criticize it, but a definite shortage of astronomers with alternative suggestions. It is the same with QM. Nobel laureate Richard Feynman, whose expositions of quantum mechanics have been as lucid as anyone's, has said: "I think it is safe to say that no one understands quantum mechanics. Do not keep saying to yourself, if you can possibly avoid it, 'But how can it be like that?' because you will go 'down the drain' into a blind alley from which nobody has yet escaped. Nobody knows how it can be like that."[58]

There are three main ways in which quantum physics and classical physics differ. These three are often referred to as "quantum weirdness," because they seem to defy common sense or perhaps even logic. These three points are:

1. Loss of Objectivity: quantum objects behave sometimes as particles and sometimes as waves. No one understands how one entity can behave like both particle and wave, depending only on how it is observed.

2. Indeterminacy: the Heisenberg Uncertainty Principle requires that the more accurately you know the position of a

quantum entity, the less accurately you know its velocity, and vice versa; and similarly for many other pairs of properties.

3. Observer-Created Reality: what one observer decides to do seemingly can instantly affect what another observer across the universe will see, though not in a way that can be used to send messages.

These three aspects of quantum weirdness are illustrated with a variety of famous examples, such as "Schroedinger's cat," various dual-slit experiments, and the "Bell Inequality." Collectively, they are considered so strange and inexplicable that the prevailing opinion in modern physics, called the Copenhagen interpretation, is that there is no true reality; that actions at a distance occur without intermediaries to carry the action; and that "God plays dice with the universe"—i.e., quantum events are truly and intrinsically random and unpredictable, and not just limited in their predictability by our lack of understanding of nature and the underlying physics. Another interpretation popularized by Heinz Pagels is that "God is in the details," meaning that quantum weirdness so defies human understanding that it virtually proves the intervention of a deity.

In his remarkable book, "Quantum Reality," Nick Herbert summarizes the experiments as requiring the existence of a real wave. "In order to match the quantum facts, this real wave must possess some quite remarkable properties: primarily it must connect with every particle in the universe, be entirely invisible, and travel faster than light." (Herbert, p. 121.)[59]

This situation first came about from the work of John von Neumann. "What von Neumann showed was that if you assume that electrons are ordinary objects or are constructed of ordinary objects—entities with innate dynamic attributes—then the behavior of these objects must contradict the predictions of quantum theory.... From its mathematical form alone, von Neumann proved that quantum theory is incompatible with the real existence of entities that possess attributes of their own." (See Herbert, p. 48.)[60]

Later, ... David Bohm showed how the wave-plus-particle concept could be made to work to produce a consistent picture of the quantum facts.... However, in order for [Bohm's model] to work, whenever something changes anywhere the pilot wave has to inform the electron instantly of this change, which necessitates faster-than-light signaling." (See Herbert, p. 50.)[59]

Then Bell's Theorem came along and reinforced this point by showing that the quantum facts alone (even without the theory) require "that any model of reality whatsoever—whether ordinary or contextual—must be non-local." (See Herbert, p. 51.)[59] "Non-local" basically means that faster-than-light communication must occur.

In dealing with these conclusions, there have arisen many schools of thought. But the dominant school in physics today, as we have noted, is the Copenhagen interpretation, *"There is no deep reality."* (I'm not making this up. Many physicists, faced with such impossible-to-comprehend experimental results, have basically given up on hard, objective, observer-independent reality.)

Not everyone has abandoned hope, however. Even Bell himself, the author of the theorem which has caused so much consternation, has said of successor theories to QM: "What is much more likely is that the new way of seeing things will involve an imaginative leap that will astonish us. In any case it seems that the quantum mechanical description will be superseded."[60]

Particle-Wave Duality

When photons and electrons are propagating through space, interacting with nothing but others of their kind, they behave like pure waves. They attenuate in an inverse square fashion, pass through each other without friction or collision, develop interference patterns, and experience diffraction and refraction. But when they interact with substance, they suddenly take on particle attributes.

One type of experiment which illustrates this effect is called a "two-slit experiment." For example, if we send electrons through two narrow, parallel slits, suitably spaced, they seem to strike particular spots on the phosphor screen on the other side, causing the emission of a photon wherever they strike. When both slits are open, interference bands are formed, creating some zones where no electron ever strikes. But if we cover one of the two slits, suddenly electrons strike everywhere, including in the band locations where they could not strike with both slits open. Such interference behavior is typical and well understood for waves. But the photon flashes are at discrete spots on the screen. This is one of the ways in which these entities display a dual character.

Electrons display other particle characteristics as well. We can measure their charge, mass, and spin; and they leave tracks in a Wilson cloud chamber. If we try to pin down whether an electron is a particle or a wave, it will change character before our eyes. For example, if we look at light scattered by electrons passing through a hole, the electrons behave like particles when the light is present, and like waves when it is not. And in scattering experiments electrons appear to have no structure, as if they were "point particles.".

There are related mysteries. If we pass light through a horizontal polarizing filter, only horizontally polarized light can get through. If we then pass the same light through a vertical polarizing filter, no light can get through both filters. But if we place a diagonal polarizing filter between the other two, some light now gets through all three filters in series.

Light, too, exhibits a particle phase. Light energy appears to be quantized into discrete energy packets, each with an energy of $h\nu$ (h = Planck's constant, ν = frequency of light). No light can exist with that frequency having an energy of, say, half that amount. Light also scatters when it encounters an electron in just the way that particles scatter, but not in the manner waves would behave.[a] Similarly, when an electron absorbs or emits a photon, the electron's energy is always increased or decreased by exactly $h\nu$, never more nor less.

The Meta Model in the Quantum World

The Meta Model began with an empty universe, then added substance one unit at a time, thereby deriving the universe's properties deductively. From that starting point we inferred that the scale dimension is infinite, which implies that there should be nothing truly special about entities the size of quantum particles. Moreover, it allows us to deduce some new properties of the quantum world

---

[a]This is called the "Compton Effect."

which permit an entirely different view of the puzzling experiments that have led to such drastic conclusions using standard models.

First, the Meta Model implies that the types of particles, waves, and forces found at any scale, though they may differ profoundly in detail (such as medium density), should be intrinsically the same as for any other scale. So entities such as photons or electrons should always be either particles or waves, but not simultaneously both. So the model implies that light and electricity propagate as pure waves only; there is no such thing as "photons" or "electrons" propagating through the universe. Then when these waves encounter matter (for example, a detector), the energy of the wave-matter interaction may cause the release of a pure particle (the thing we usually associate with a "photon" or an "electron").

In the case of an electron, the entity that may be generated when an electric wave encounters matter will then, and only then, have measurable mass, charge, and spin, and be able to leave a track in a Wilson cloud chamber. As a consequence, whenever we *observe* the effects of one of these entities, it always appears to have particle properties. But when it is propagating unencumbered by matter and therefore unobserved, it will have only wave properties. Since all the entities of quantum physics propagate with wave properties, the true quantum particles must be smaller in dimensions than the shortest wavelengths of light that we have been able to utilize in attempts to observe these particles directly.

When applying this idea to light, it also means something physical, not semantic. When light is emitted, it is a pure wave—no photons, and no particle properties. It propagates only at the velocity allowed by the "light-carrying medium," spreads in inverse square fashion, can refract, diffract, and interfere, and successive wavefronts remain coherent. It cannot collide with other waves, scatter, change velocity, or have any particle characteristics (mass, spin, or an exact place at each instant of time).

Now this wavefront collides with matter. Then and only then, the wavefront may stimulate the emission of a short-lived particle, the effects of which we call a "photon." If the wave is strong, a particle will always be emitted; if too weak, never emitted; and in between, there will be some probability of a particle emission. The "photon" produces the sensation of light in our eyes, can collide and scatter, has mass and spin, can change velocity, and is in an exact place at every instant of its short life until it decays. It has none of the properties of the preceding wave stage. The spherical wavefront which spawned it can stimulate the emission of many other particles coherently, even at great distances, wherever the wave encounters matter.

We say that when the wave encounters matter, it may trigger a detectable particle. Whether it does or not depends upon the extent of dilution of the wave, its phase, and the details of the encounter. So in any particular wave-matter encounter, there will be a certain probability of triggering a particle, and a complementary probability that none will be produced. To observers, this looks like the so-called "probability wave function," which has led to the description that quantum entities are "waves of probability" instead of physical waves, because they seem to be sometimes there and sometimes not with a predictable probability. We now see a way in which their behavior can have a good deal more definiteness.

The resolution of the "objectivity" dilemma implies the resolution of the "definiteness" dilemma as well. The properties which cannot be simultaneously measured with indefinite precision, such as position and velocity, are properties which are split between the particle and the wave states of the entity. Since the entity cannot be in both states simultaneously, both properties cannot be measured simultaneously with indefinite precision. When observations are multiplied over many entities, only some of them will materialize into detectable particles, and some will not. So there is an intrinsic limit on the accuracy with which properties spanning the particle-wave transition can be measured. If one could use entities such as C-gravitons to accomplish the measurements, no such dilemma would ensue. One could in principle measure all properties of quantum entities with indefinite precision, to the extent that they are defined. Note that it is ambiguous to speak of the "position" of a quantum entity in its wave phase—a wave does not have a single, well-defined, point-like position.

Since quantum entities always exist as either particles or waves, with a certain probability about which state the entity will be in after an encounter with matter, this resolves paradoxes such as "Schroedinger's cat." In the traditional quantum model, there is a cat in a box with a detector which either does or does not detect the decay of a single quantum particle, and which accordingly renders the cat either dead or alive. According to quantum physics rules, the cat is in neither state (dead or alive) until the box is opened and the results observed, since the single quantum particle's status (emitted or non-emitted) is not determined by

> "When the only tool you have is a hammer, all your problems start to look like nails."
> —from *Murphy's Laws and Other Reasons Why Things Go Wrong* (Arthur Bloch, 1977)

nature until the moment of observation. In the Meta Model, the cat's condition can in principle be uniquely determined moment-to-moment, though not by using light, which would itself influence the outcome. The moment of change of condition is knowable. The cat's condition is not just a "probability," even if information about it is not communicated to any conscious mind until much later.

The Bell Inequality

Quantum physicists are aware of a thought experiment called the "Einstein-Podolsky-Rosen paradox" (EPR paradox, for short), which purports to prove that quantum physics is not a complete description, and that there must be additional, undiscovered laws governing quantum events. The Meta Model is in full agreement with that conclusion and implies that the whole quantum world could be observed in as much detail as we please using suitably small sensors, such as C-gravitons, which will not themselves disturb or alter the entities we wish to observe. At the quantum level, using photons and electrons to make observations changes the results because these entities influence the observations.

Finally, we must consider "Bell's Inequality," which purports to show that reality is not local; that is, what an observer chooses to do locally can instantly influence what an observer at a vast distance will see or detect. The essence of the experiment which illustrates Bell's Inequality begins with a source of paired quantum entities—for example, two photons with identical polarization leaving the same source at the same time. We then need two observers, one local and one remote, with one of the paired photons headed toward each of the two observers. Since the photons have identical polarization, if the detectors for both of the observers are held at identical angles, there will be an identical pattern of detections and non-detections as successive paired photons are emitted.

In particular, if the detectors are oriented at 0 degrees to the polarization plane, all photons will be detected. If rotated to 90 degrees to the polarization plane, no photons will be detected. Such is the nature of polarization. At another angle in between, a pseudo-random pattern of detections and misses will occur: the closer to angle 90 degrees, the greater the relative number of misses. Now suppose the two observers place their detectors at angles which differ by x degrees. If x is small, then the detection-miss patterns, however random, will be highly correlated; but there will be some discrepancies. Now suppose the two observers place their detectors at angles which differ by 2x degrees. Approximately, the number of discrepancies will double. However, some of the cases which might be discrepancies will result from a change from detection to miss, or vice versa, at both detectors, resulting in an apparent correlation. So if x is very small, there will be almost no discrepancies; if x is somewhat greater, occasional discrepancies will arise, sometimes from one detector and sometimes from the other; and if x is greater still, there will be some occasional double discrepancies which will appear to be matches between the detectors, instead of discrepancies.

Now Bell's Inequality implies simply that because of the double discrepancies appearing to be matches, the number of discrepancies counted at angle 2x must average out to be less than twice the number of discrepancies at angle x (assuming a suitably large number of photons is examined). Certainly such an inequality would hold for ordinary particles behaving by the rules of classical physics. But experiments show that in fact, the number of discrepancies is greater, not less, at angle 2x. This appears to prove that the angle selected by one observer instantly influences what the other observer is going to detect, and hence that reality is non-local. (This means that either there is no absolute reality, or that influences far faster than the speed of light propagate out to cause the influence at the remote observer.)

But the Meta Model shows us that no such radical conclusions are called for. We must regard the polarized photons leaving the common source as pure waves, not as particles—at least until they actually hit the detectors. Now our reasoning changes fundamentally. Suppose that one detector is at an arbitrary angle, but the other detector is at exactly 90 degrees to the first. Then every detection in one detector will correspond with a miss at the other, and vice versa. This again is a property of polarization—nothing new yet. But even though all the events are discrepancies, we could not conclude that the selection of angle by one observer altered the pattern at the other observer. Instead we conclude that identically polarized lightwaves are certain, at the moment they leave the source, to be detected or missed oppositely by any two detectors at right angles to one another. There is no remote influence or "action at a distance."

By extension of this reasoning to smaller angles, we see the way out of the dilemma posed by Bell's Inequality. For pure waves, there is a certain probability that the detection-miss pattern will be correlated at two observers; and there is a complementary probability that it *will be anti-correlated* at the two observers. It is the anti-correlation probability that was omitted in the reasoning which led to Bell's Inequality. When we consider the probability of anti-correlated events, it correctly predicts the experimental results, quantitatively as well as qualitatively, that the number of discrepancies will be more than double at angle 2x over what it was at a small angle x. Specifically, the correlation/anti-correlation probability should follow a smooth cosine wave from 100% correlation to 100% anti-correlation as the angle between detectors goes from 0 to 90 degrees. And it does.

We have said nothing specific about why light has quantized energy and cannot have a fraction of that unit of energy for any given frequency. We have likewise said nothing about the meanings of "mass," "charge," and "spin" for quantum particles. Clearly they do not have the meanings we intuitively associate with those terms. The Meta Model, in predicting that sub-atomic matter would have the same variety of forms and properties as do astronomical bodies, would insist that no two "electrons" are exactly alike when in their particle phases. As to quantization, astronomer William

Tifft[61] originally argued that galaxy redshifts appeared to be quantized. But as discussed in the chapter "Stars, Galaxies, and the Universe," this redshift "quantization" may turn out to be a consequence of galaxies being organized into waves.

In an analogous way, wave properties of quantum particles may appear to have discrete, constant values, even though the particles themselves do not. It might be generalized that wherever properties appear only in discrete, exact values like quanta, those properties are attributes of a wave, not a particle.[b] Similarly, the properties of "antimatter" can be understood at some fundamental level. It is no mystery how identical, out-of-phase waves can annihilate one another when they come into proximity, as happens when matter and antimatter come into contact. When in a particle phase, the complementary (antimatter) counterpart of a particle is a hole of identical size in the underlying continuum.

I am not prepared in this book to elaborate a complete extension of the Meta Model into all areas of the quantum world. But I have shown how the model may interface with that world, and how it confronts and handles some of the most vexing problems therein. And the Meta Model clearly points the way toward how to develop an all-new quantum model.

We conclude then that the Meta Model provides new interpretations of the quantum world which enable us to dispense with the phenomena which have been described as "quantum weirdness." Although this by itself does not prove the model, it does show that classical, objective, definite, local physics with ordinary reality may be applied to the quantum world, if we so choose. And it suggests that we should not allow ourselves to be led into logical traps when investigating phenomena which we cannot observe directly and must learn about only through intermediaries. The means to avoid such traps is to reason deductively, not inductively, at every opportunity.

---

[b]As similar as grains of sand on a beach or molecules of air may be to one another, they are each different when measured and analyzed precisely enough. Waves, as ensembles of an indefinitely large number of individual entities, have vastly smoother measured properties.

The Forces of Nature

We might wonder if the agents acting in the quantum world must be of an entirely different type from those which produce gravitation. Because the force of gravitation is 10^{40} times weaker than the electromagnetic force at the same distance, it is easy to conclude that an entirely different sort of agent is required. However, the densities of atomic particles could be so great that few, if any, CGs could penetrate the particles. So it is not unimaginable that CGs might be involved in the electromagnetic force as well.

In this connection, it is interesting to do the following calculation. Consider the velocity of an electron in orbit about the nucleus of a Bohr hydrogen atom. Assume an inverse square force, and project what that velocity would become if the nucleus had only the mass of an electron. Then compute what the limiting velocity would be at the surface of the central body, assuming it has the "classical radius" of an electron. Finally, multiply by $\sqrt{2}$ to convert a circular velocity to an escape velocity. The result is quite close to the speed of light. So in some "classical" sense, the escape velocity from an electron is the speed of light. If this is not numerical coincidence, it may be telling us something fundamental about the nature of electrons.

Put a different way, the whole visible universe is about 10^{40} times less dense than an electron, and it also exerts a gravitational force which is about 10^{40} times weaker than the electron's at the same distance. This does imply the possibility that the same agents, CGs, may be partly responsible for the force in both cases. Presumably in the case of the electron, however, the involvement of the LCM is somewhat more critical in the process than it seems to be for the visible universe. In particular, when electrons propagate as waves at the speed of light, this is clearly happening in the light-carrying medium, not in the CG medium.

It is logical to ask if the electromagnetic and the two other fundamental forces in nature can be modeled in similar ways to gravity. Our knowledge about the structure of matter below the atomic level is evolving rapidly and in my opinion suffers from a lack of clear models with which to interpret new results. What is badly

128

needed is a collection of experimental results to which must we must adhere in forming new models. What is made available instead is the interpretation of those experimental results using the standard model. We are given measures of "spin," "mass," "charge," "color," etc., without any real understanding of what those properties mean.

I wondered for a long time how it might be possible for protons to repel protons, electrons to repel electrons, and yet protons and electrons to attract. Then one day it occurred to me that we can construct an analog in our familiar world of light and gravity. We can make a balloon satellite large enough that the repulsive force of light from the Sun would be greater than the gravitational force of attraction between Sun and balloon. Consider, then, a set of such balloon satellites and a set of Sun-like stars. All balloon satellites would gravitationally attract one another, because they emit no light. All stars gravitationally attract one another because light pressure is negligible in comparison with their gravitation. And yet all stars would repel all balloon satellites because light pressure on balloons exceeds gravitation from stars. Light, because it originates from within stars, produces repulsion; gravity is attractive because it results from the shadowing of external agents.

So in the case of protons and electrons, we must posit that each type of particle emits some sort of agent: an electron agent to cause electrons to repel each other, and a proton agent to do the same for protons. On a small enough scale, these entities must radiate agents the way a star radiates light. And we must also posit a sea of external agents to cause a force of attraction between protons and electrons (presumably, the LCM, since its natural wave velocity equals the speed of action for electromagnetic forces). Just as for the balloon satellites, this requires protons and electrons to be compositionally different in such a way that the internal agents dominate interactions between like entities, while the external agents dominate interactions between opposites.

In classical physics, one of the laws of thermodynamics is that the degree of disorder in the universe (its "entropy") must progressively increase with time. One criticism of infinite universes is that they must either conserve entropy, contrary to observations, or we must give up on the notion that the universe looks essentially

129

the same at any epoch, since its entropy is increasing. However, it is apparent upon reflection that systems with increasing entropy generally involve electromagnetic forces. By way of contrast, systems involving gravitational forces tend to do the opposite: large, disordered clouds of hydrogen gas tend to collect and condense into galaxies, stars, and planets; and stars tend to fuse hydrogen atoms into heavier elements.

Consider an example. If one has a certain gas contained by walls within half of a chamber, and a vacuum in the other half, then any action which allows the two halves to mix will allow the gas to spread throughout the chamber. This is what is described as increased disorder or entropy. To reverse the process, we must apply energy; for example, we could move a gas-tight wall from one side of the chamber to the middle, opposing the pressure of the gas, and restore the original state. But clearly the natural tendency of the gas is to increase its entropy to the maximum allowable amount. Again, gravity works in precisely the reverse manner. Its natural tendency is to collect matter together. Once a star or planet is formed, or heavy elements are created, it takes great energy (as in a supernova) to blow it back to its original state. Clearly, gravity obeys a "reverse entropy" law.

In the Meta Model, we might generalize these processes. Media such as the C-gravitons that operate from outside substance tend to increase the degree of order in that substance. Media that originate from within substance will tend to increase the degree of disorder. Averaged over all media at all scales, the entropy of the universe will then be conserved, hence removing the objection cited.

There is a lot of discussion in physics today about "unifying" the four recognized forces of nature, which generally means reducing them all to variants of a single force. But in the Meta Model we hypothesize that all forces, including gravitation, ultimately result from the collisional interactions of substance. This would seem to qualify as a unifying factor for all four known fundamental forces. We were already aware that many manifestations of those forces are collisional in nature; for example, sound is carried by the collisions of air molecules in wave form, and heat is due to the random collisional interactions among molecules. The electromagnetic force and the strong and weak nuclear forces are already known in quantum physics to be related, and due to collisional interactions among quantum entities. And we have seen here how such forces might arise within the framework of the Meta Model. By illustrating how gravity can also be the result of collisional actions, we have effectively shown the unifying factor underlying all forces in nature, including as-yet-undiscovered ones.

Niels Bohr is the author of the classical description of the structure of the atom, resembling a mini solar system, with electrons in orbit around a nucleus. Bohr also debated Einstein throughout his life about quantum reality issues. Einstein always maintained that there was more to quantum theory than presently understood, as he tried to demonstrate in the "EPR Paradox." Bohr could never accept Einstein's arguments and became the chief proponent of the Copenhagen interpretation, "There is no deep reality."

A visitor to Bohr's country cottage asked him about a horseshoe nailed above the front door. "Surely, Professor Bohr, you do not really believe that a horseshoe over the entrance to a home brings good luck?" "No," answered Bohr, "I certainly do not believe in this superstition. But you know," he added, "they say it brings luck even if you don't believe in it!" (See Herbert, p. 93.)

By no means has this chapter resolved all the dilemmas of quantum mechanics, or anything approaching that. I have merely hinted at how the Meta Model might be interfaced with existing experimental results. And we have seen faint glimpses of the sort of revised picture of the quantum world which the Meta Model would demand: drastically different from present viewpoints from the ground up, so to speak. This exposition needs a great deal of additional work by those more familiar with the details of experiments in modern physics. This chapter can at best merely point the way. But I know of no alternative for physicists but to undertake this task, unless they would prefer instead to hang a horseshoe over their entrance way and stay with the status quo, in which case I wish them "good luck"!

This completes the exposition of the Meta Model.

6

· ·

Orbits

Summary: Everything you need to know about orbits, but were afraid to learn, because all the books and classes are math-intensive. We begin with the basics, explaining the answer to the first question always asked about orbital motion: "Why doesn't everything just fall into the Sun?" We note that bodies in orbit have "potential" energy by virtue of their height, as well as "kinetic" energy by virtue of their motion. This leads to behavior which is counter-intuitive, because it doesn't happen that way on the Earth's surface. For example, to catch up with an orbiting body ahead of your spacecraft, you must "apply the brakes"! We then examine the concept of the sphere of influence of a body, within which it can hold smaller orbiting bodies ("satellites") indefinitely. We can then explain why our Moon remains a satellite of the Earth, despite the fact that the Sun's gravitational force on it is stronger than the Earth's. The conditions under which satellites can be captured, or can escape, are examined. The most common mechanisms are quite ineffective for this purpose. But we propose three new capture mechanisms which apparently have operated within the solar system. We conclude with a discussion of tides and tidal friction, showing their importance to the evolution of bodies. The relative importance of tides for solid, liquid, and gaseous bodies may be the opposite of what is usually assumed.

We turn our attention now to the solar system, where other puzzles await our interest. We will later see the possible link between the cosmological and solar system portions of this book, when we

133

develop the exploded-planet hypothesis. We discuss in the chapter "Stars, Galaxies, and the Universe" how that explosion might be the source of the microwave blackbody radiation.

The Importance of Motion

Orbiting: where one body circles another under the influence of the force of gravity between them. The whole concept is anti-intuitive, because nothing quite like it happens in our everyday experience here on the surface of the Earth. And indeed, there are many things about behavior in a gravitational field which must be deduced or observed, because the behavior of bodies in orbit acting under the influence of gravity is not like that of bodies on the Earth's surface. On Earth, inertial forces and friction are more important, and gravity is a one-directional force: down.

Why do planets orbit the Sun at all, instead of just succumbing to its gravitational pull and falling into the Sun? In fact, they would fall into the Sun if they had no angular motion around it. It is their angular motion (motion perpendicular to the direction of the Sun) that keeps them orbiting. This is because of the tendency of any body in motion to remain in motion in the same direction. It is true that the Sun's force continually changes the direction of the planet's motion. But if the planet begins to decrease its distance from the Sun, it must increase its speed as it "falls." The faster it moves, the more its tendency to keep moving in a fixed direction dominates the Sun's effort to change that direction. Eventually the planet's speed becomes great enough to permit it to maintain its distance from the Sun, and then begin increasing that distance again, starting to slow in the process.

If the planet's angular motion is just right, the planet keeps a uniform distance from the Sun as it orbits in a circle. If it does not have that much angular motion, it falls toward the Sun while moving forward too, until it gains enough speed that its angular motion prevents further falling. Its permanent orbit is then an ellipse with the Sun at one focus. If the planet started out with too much velocity for a circular orbit, it would move away from the Sun faster than the Sun can pull it back. This divides into two cases: 1. If the planet has less than escape velocity, the Sun eventually slows it, so that it orbits in an ellipse with the Sun at one focus. 2. If the object exceeds

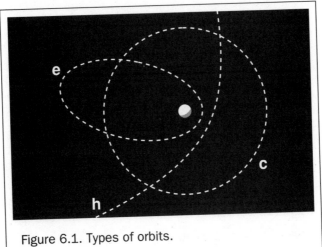

Figure 6.1. Types of orbits.

escape velocity, it keeps going away from the Sun forever. The planet's path in case 2 is the shape of a hyperbola. (See Figure 6.1.)

Given these basics, the next factor that one must get used to in understanding orbital behavior is that potential energy (energy that comes from height above a gravitating body) has a greater effect than kinetic energy (energy from the motion of a body in orbit). This also is the reverse of our experience on the ground, and it leads to some orbital behavior which, at first, seems pretty bizarre, as we shall see in a minute.

When I say that potential energy has a greater effect than kinetic energy, I mean that orbits with more total energy are higher, but bodies in them travel slower. Conversely, the objects which travel most rapidly are those in the lowest orbits, having the least total energy. Objects in lower orbits travel faster because they pick up speed falling in toward the central body. Higher orbits have a longer "period" (time to travel around the central body) for two reasons: they must travel a greater distance, and they move more slowly.

Now suppose you are piloting a rocket and trying to dock with a space station in orbit around the Earth. Let us assume that you start in the same orbit as the space station, but following some distance behind it. If you use your ground-based intuition, you will fire your rockets to propel yourself toward the space station in order to dock with it. This is what early astronauts and cosmonauts did,

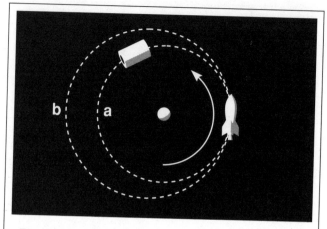

Figure 6.2. Increasing the speed of the rocket changes it from orbit A to orbit B, which has a longer period.

and they found docking almost impossible. Firing your rockets to propel yourself ahead adds energy to your orbit, increasing its average height and period, causing you to lose velocity as you climb in height, and putting you into an orbit which takes longer than the space station to get around the Earth. (See Figure 6.2.) The result: you fall further behind.

To catch up, you must fire retro-rockets. Although this slows you momentarily, you quickly regain that speed as you drop to a lower orbit which takes less time to get around the Earth, and you gain on the space station. Astronauts found that with the aid of computers to tell them how to fire their rockets to place themselves on an intercept orbit, docking was easy. It was only their intuitions which misled them.

We have been assuming that your rocket and the space station have negligible gravity themselves. Actually, once you get away from the Earth's surface, that is usually a bad assumption. We will see why in a moment.

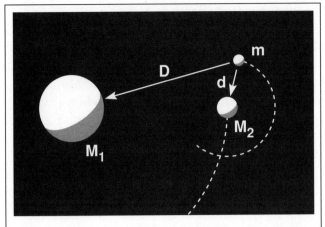

Figure 6.3. Two masses competing for control of a third.

Spheres of Influence

Suppose two gravitating bodies are competing for control over a third. Does the one with the greater mass always win? Not at all, because the distance of the third body from the other two is a more important factor than the masses. (Recall that gravity is proportional to mass, but inversely proportional to the square of distance.) Let us call our two competing gravitating bodies M1 and M2; and let us call the little mass they are competing for control over, m. Let the M1-m distance be D, and the M2-m distance be d. (See Figure 6.3.) Okay, then, is it safe to say that whichever body, M1 or M2, exerts the stronger gravitational force on m, wherever it may be, will control it? Again, not at all, because again, our intuitions fail.

It might seem that the body which exerts the greater force must control, and I am just being technical when I say that it often doesn't. But I am speaking about common, ordinary situations. Take the Earth's own Moon, for example. The Sun's mass is 330,000 times that of the Earth. To the accuracy we care about here, the Moon's distance from the Sun, D, is 400 times the Moon's distance from the. Earth, d. Let us calculate which exerts the stronger pull on the Moon: the Sun or the Earth.

Let the distance from Earth to Moon, d, be one unit of length, and the mass of the Earth, M_2, be one unit of mass. Then the gravitational force (M_2/d^2) is 1.0 for the Earth acting on the Moon. In these units, the Sun's mass, M_1, is 330,000, its distance, D, is 400, and we compute its gravitational force on the Moon as 2.1. This is the known result that the Sun acts on the Moon with a gravitational force that is always about twice as strong as the Earth's force on the Moon!

So why does the Moon stay a satellite of the Earth?

All the Earth's force on the Moon goes into attracting the Moon toward itself. The Sun's force on the Moon is almost exactly equal to the Sun's force on the Earth, so that both Earth and Moon are forced to accelerate or decelerate in nearly the same way by the Sun. The Sun's force, in other words, is not acting to tear the Moon away from the Earth, but mostly acts to keep both in the same orbit around the Sun. A very small part of the Sun's overall force does act differently on the Moon than it does on the Earth because the Earth and Moon are separated by $1/400$ of the Sun's distance. That small residual effect does disturb the Moon's orbit around the Earth, but by not nearly enough to pull the Moon away from the Earth. The Moon is a permanent satellite of the Earth, and no gravitational forces involving just Sun, Earth, and Moon could ever change that.

The amount of the Sun's force which does try to separate the Moon from the Earth is proportional to d/D. In the limiting case when d/D = 0, the Earth and Moon coincide, and all the Sun's force affects both bodies equally, none of it tearing them apart. If d/D = 1, then the Moon is equally distant from the Earth and Sun, and only the relative masses of Earth and Sun matter in the competition. At intermediate distances, to know which body dominates, it is not M/D^2 that we wish to compare to m/d^2; rather, because of the additional factor of d/D, we must compare M/D^3 to m/d^3 to see which body controls the Moon. Whereas M/D^2 is the total force, $d(M/D^3)$ is called the "tidal" or "disrupting" part of the force.

For any body in space, there exists another body which exerts the strongest gravitational force on it, even if that other body might be at a considerable distance. In the solar system, it is usually the Sun which exerts the strongest gravitational force, except for small volumes near the major planets where a planet's own force is greater

138

than the Sun's. We can now talk about a most important concept in dynamics: the "sphere of influence." This is the radius of a sphere within which a given body can hold smaller bodies ("satellites") in orbit, gravitationally bound to itself.[a] The sphere of influence would be infinite if there were no other matter in the universe. But since there is, there is always some other mass which sets the limit to a body's sphere of influence. All bodies have such a sphere of influence, regardless of their size.

If a body is too close to the Sun or a planet, its sphere of influence can be less than its own radius. That is the case for all objects on the Earth's surface, which is why we have no intuitive feel for this important dynamical concept. To calculate the radius of the sphere of influence, d, of a central body with mass m, in the gravitational field of another remote mass M at a distance D, then to good approximation, $M/D^3 = m/d^3$. That is, the sphere of influence extends out to the distance where the remote body's tidal disrupting influence becomes stronger than the central body's own tidal force.

In reality, the sphere of influence does not extend all the way to the distance d, since the possible dynamical behavior gets very complex near that distance and depends upon whether the satellite is moving direct or retrograde, among many other factors. The distance d simply represents the distance within which mass m's disrupting influence is greater than mass M's. The true sphere of influence for stable satellites is somewhat smaller, perhaps by a factor of two or so; but d always is a reasonable approximation of its size.

We can write this result in an even simpler form. Let r be the radius of the body with mass m, and let R be the radius of the body with mass M. The density ρ of any body is defined as the ratio of its mass to its volume: $\rho_m = m / (4/3 \, \pi \, r^3)$, and $\rho_M = M / (4/3 \, \pi \, R^3)$. Making these substitutions, we get:

$$r/d = (\rho_m / \rho_M)^{1/3} \, R/D.$$

---

[a]Of course, a potential satellite must not only be inside the sphere of influence, but also moving with a speed less than escape velocity. The velocity of escape gets smaller as the central mass gets smaller. (Interestingly, at any fixed number of diameters out, the period of a satellite is not changed as the central mass with fixed density gets smaller.)

For ordinary bodies, the term in parentheses on the right can be roughly approximated as unity, and ignored. Then d/2r = D/2R means that the radius of the sphere of influence of any body, measured in terms of its own diameter, is equal to the distance of that body from the limiting mass M, measured in terms of diameters of M. Since the Earth is about 100 solar diameters away from the Sun, we can make a sort of "rule of thumb": to a good approximation, bodies near the Earth's distance from the Sun will have spheres of influence of roughly 100 times their own diameters. Bodies elsewhere will have spheres of influence of 100 times their distance from the Sun measured in astronomical units (1 astronomical unit is the Earth's distance from the Sun). Amazingly, this is true regardless of the size of the body.

This is why we said earlier that one should not assume that small objects have negligible gravity once away from the immediate vicinity of the Earth. While the Earth's sphere of influence is about 100 Earth diameters (the Moon is only 30 Earth diameters away), the sphere of influence of a 1-km asteroid at the Earth's distance from the Sun is about 100 km; and the sphere of influence of a 1-meter meteoroid (or spacecraft) is about 100 meters. This is why astronauts on their way to the Moon found that materials dumped outside the spacecraft followed them all the way to the Moon, literally slowly orbiting the spacecraft as captive moons! Our intuitions gave us no clues that such small bodies would have such significant gravity fields, because they don't on the Earth's surface.

Of course, this does not continue to be true for *very* small masses, say the size of dust grains or gas molecules, because forces other than gravitation can affect them. Most notably, solar radiation pressure (the pressure of sunlight) and the solar wind will disrupt the orbits of extremely small objects or extremely low-density objects (such as balloon satellites).

So far, we have learned that when orbiting bodies are accelerated, they fall back; decelerated, they move ahead. And we have learned that all orbiting bodies have a sphere of influence within which they can hold smaller masses gravitationally captive as "satellites" of their own. Let us see what happens when we combine the two concepts.

General Capture and Escape

First, it is valuable to understand that if an object penetrates the sphere of influence of a body from the outside, it will not be permanently captured as a satellite, regardless of the mass of the body or size of its sphere of influence. Its velocity is always necessarily greater than the escape velocity from the sphere of influence. Even if the outside object started with a slower velocity, as it falls toward the body it picks up speed and always has more than escape velocity by the time it penetrates the sphere of influence. (This is why it is often said that when only gravity is acting, one of two bodies cannot permanently capture the other.) Conversely, if an object starts well inside the sphere of influence with less than escape velocity, it can never get out.

The only important exception to this rule is when forces other than gravity act. As a practical matter, the gravitational intervention of yet another body can also alter the stability of a parent body (i.e., cause moons to either escape or become captured). But to do this, the new body must temporarily reduce the size of the sphere of influence of the parent body well below its normal radius, then allow it to increase again as the new body goes away.

Now consider the case of an asteroid orbiting the Sun in or near Jupiter's orbit. Such asteroids actually exist: they are called "Trojan Asteroids." Why aren't they eventually swept up by Jupiter?

Let us assume that the asteroid is approaching Jupiter from behind. Jupiter's gravity begins pulling on the asteroid, which accelerates it toward Jupiter. This is just exactly analogous to a rocket firing to increase its velocity toward a space station ahead, as we have already discussed. The result of Jupiter's pull is that the asteroid must drop back in its orbit, away from Jupiter, because the asteroid is moved to an orbit with a longer period by the tug of Jupiter. Conversely, if the asteroid is ahead of Jupiter, Jupiter's tug slows it down, drops it into a shorter-period orbit, which causes it to move further ahead of Jupiter. Such an asteroid would "librate" back and forth in Jupiter's orbit relative to Jupiter (while always moving ahead relative to the Sun). Its orbit is stable, and it cannot ever be swept up by Jupiter.

In order to be able to penetrate Jupiter's sphere of influence, or to collide with Jupiter, an object's orbit must allow it to attain velocities relative to Jupiter which exceed Jupiter's own ability to cancel. Objects in orbits very similar to Jupiter's always have velocities similar to Jupiter's, so can never be swept up by Jupiter. (This is contrary to the often-invoked idea that planets all condensed from a collapsed cloud of material in orbit around the Sun. Planets cannot sweep up material moving in orbits similar to their own. This remains true even if the period of the planet were slowly changing, say, due to friction in a resisting medium ["drag"], or tides.)

Conversely, if an object's orbit is far enough away from Jupiter's that it can attain relative velocities large enough to penetrate Jupiter's sphere of influence, these relative velocities are too high for capture—not only gravitationally (which, as we have seen, can never happen), but also by tidal or gas drag forces. A gas cloud around a planet would have to remove more velocity in a single close approach to Jupiter than Jupiter's own gravitation could remove before the object reached the edge of Jupiter's sphere of influence. This would require a gas cloud so dense that captured objects would decay in it from drag and disappear into Jupiter's atmosphere. (This is also contrary to the theory still held to by a few astronomers that Earth's Moon and other planetary moons were captured in just such a way.) An object cannot reach the edge of a planet's sphere of influence from the outside without reaching a relative velocity which approximates escape velocity at that distance from the planet, and such an object cannot reasonably be captured.

The qualifier "reasonably" is to allow for the following situation. Suppose a moon of a planet in orbit around the Sun is in a stable, permanent satellite orbit around its parent. Now let that moon evolve outward very slowly—for example, by tidal forces. It must eventually reach the point where its orbit is on the threshold of stability: if the tidal force were turned off, it would still remain a moon forever, but if the tidal force is kept on for just a bit longer and then shut off, the moon would eventually be able to escape the planet. Integration (numerical calculation) of such orbits shows that such a moon, just past the threshold of escape, will continue to orbit for dozens, hundreds, perhaps thousands of revolutions, gradually increasing the greatest distance it reaches from its parent. Finally, it escapes and takes off on its own solar orbit, never to return. Subsequent close approaches to its parent planet are always outside the parent's sphere of influence. Usually the escape will occur on the Sunward side of the parent (through what is called the "inner Lagrangian point"), with the moon's solar orbit entirely inside its parent's solar orbit.

> "I do *not* believe I know everything! Of course, I could be wrong."
> —Leigh Palmer

Now an astute dynamicist will know that the escape path just followed is theoretically reversible. It is *possible,* although it has vanishingly small probability, that the moon could retrace its steps, approaching its parent through the inner Lagrangian point, spiraling around dozens, hundreds, or thousands of times until it once again reached the very threshold of stable capture. Then only a minute force could push it over that threshold and cause permanent capture. One's intuition is reliable in thinking that this is too improbable to occur in reality. It requires the approaching body to reach just the right position in three dimensions, traveling with just the right speed in just the right direction, to very high precision. We will next discuss some capture scenarios which have a realistic chance of occurring in the solar system.

In the solar system, a number of planets have moons which appear to be captured asteroids. Moreover, there is strong evidence that comets, minor planets,[b] and even meteoroids often have companions. How could this have come about if capture is so improbable?

We will discuss three capture mechanisms that apparently have operated in the solar system to bring about this situation: 1. changing the sphere of influence; 2. gravitational screen capture; 3. accretion capture. None of these rely on the small forces often invoked by astronomers who theorize about capture, such as tides or drag.

---

[b]See Glossary.

Changing the Sphere of Influence

Consider a comet at a great distance from the Sun: 42,000 astronomical units, the distance of the hypothetical reservoir of comets called the "Oort cloud." At that distance a comet 1 km in diameter would have a sphere of influence of about 4,200,000 km. (As great as this is, the average distance between comets in the hypothetical cloud is greater [2×10^9 km], even though there are imagined to be perhaps 10^{12} such comets.) Two corollaries of this large sphere of influence are: 1. Comets have no significant ability to capture new material from outside their spheres of influence, since both capture and collision of such material with the nucleus (to permit accretion) have negligible probability. 2. There is a huge volume within which comets could retain gravitationally bound material (gas, dust, and small masses of all sizes) if such material was already there at the time of the comet's formation.

Now suppose such a comet approaches the Sun. Let us assume it will reach a minimum distance of only 1 a.u. (the Earth's distance). The comet's sphere of influence steadily decreases from 4,200,000 km to 100 km. If there were orbiting material around the comet, it would escape once it found itself outside the comet's shrinking sphere of influence. Such a comet would appear to an Earth observer to "split" repeatedly as satellite material drifted off into independent solar orbit. (See Figure 6.4.)

This is an example of escape from a sphere of influence. Capture could occur under the reverse conditions: As the comet recedes from the Sun, its sphere of influence increases rapidly. Small bodies co-moving with the comet outside its sphere of influence could find themselves inside it as the sphere expands to encompass them. But this is quite improbable, since the object must have little velocity relative to the comet. Even objects which escaped on the inbound leg of the orbit would move away so quickly that they generally can't be recaptured on the outbound leg.

So how might plausible captures occur through this mechanism? Suppose a larger mass suddenly breaks up (collisionally or explosively). Numerous chunks leave the site of the breakup at high enough velocities to escape. Now follow the progress of one of the

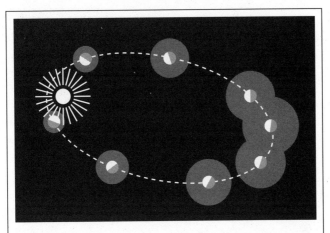

Figure 6.4. The sphere of influence shrinks as a body approaches the Sun, and expands as it recedes.

larger chunks. As it recedes, its sphere of influence expands. But there is plenty of other matter in its vicinity, moving away in the same general direction and with similar velocities. The large chunk will permanently trap these (capture!) when its sphere of influence enlarges to encompass them.

The small bodies in the solar system (comets, minor planets, meteoroids) seem to have companion bodies in numerous cases. Figuring out how such companions formed is such a vexing problem for dynamicists that some have preferred to question the extensive observations that such bodies exist at all. We now see a simple answer for the capture mechanism: capture through changes in the sphere of influence following the breakup of a parent body.

Gravitational Screen Capture

Imagine the same breakup event. Smaller chunks will tend to be propelled away with higher velocities, on average, than larger chunks because it takes more energy per unit area to propel a larger chunk.

Consider a distant planet with an atmosphere. The smaller chunks from the breakup will generally arrive before the larger ones because of that velocity difference. The spreads in arrival times will be weeks over the distances between major planets. Some of

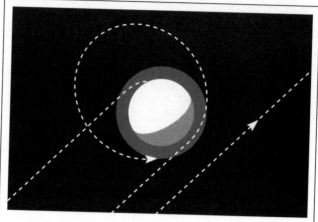

Figure 6.5. First stage of Gravitational Screen Capture: passage through a planet's atmosphere.

the early arriving small chunks will miss the planet and go on, and some will impact the surface. For the moment, let us ignore those and concentrate on the chunks which make a grazing pass through the atmosphere without impacting. If the atmosphere is dense enough and the chunk passes low enough, it will burn up or explode. If the atmosphere is too thin or the chunk passes too high, it will proceed on, just as chunks which miss the planet do. In between are chunks which survive the passage through the atmosphere, but lose enough velocity in the passage to become captured in an elliptical satellite orbit around the planet. (See Figure 6.5.)

Of course, such chunks will not last long. On each revolution they will again dip into the planet's atmosphere, losing still more velocity. Their orbits must soon decay, causing them to burn up in the atmosphere. But they will last hours, days, even weeks before that happens.

In the meantime, some of the larger chunks will be coming by. A new fate is possible for them: they can collide with the smaller chunks already in temporary orbits. The chunks large enough to survive such collisions have the possibility of being dropped into permanent satellite orbits around their new parent planet. This capture process I call "Gravitational Screen Capture": a breakup event creates a debris screen of material in temporary orbits which can collisionally capture objects into permanent orbits. The moons of Mars are likely examples of this process; but I suspect that all the inner asteroidal moons and rings of the outer planets may be the result of the same process.

To complete the scenario, the energy of continuous bombardment by small debris from the breakup can extend the lifetimes of some of the chunks in temporary orbits, so that they may last for months or years, not just weeks, before their orbits decay. In the process of decaying, orbits precess about the equator, and bits and chunks collide with one another. The average of a great many such mutual collisions is to cancel out all velocity components perpendicular to the planet's equator—i.e., drive all orbiting bodies toward equatorial orbits. Since the orbits are elliptical, objects have velocity components toward and away from the parent planet. Mutual collisions also tend to damp out these velocities, driving all surviving orbits toward circularity. This is why particles from fragmented bodies eventually flatten into circular, equatorial rings around a planet.

Accretion Capture

Another way that bodies can get temporarily captured is through the inner Lagrangian point, as already discussed. Although this is improbable, if one were to flood the vicinity of a planet with debris, as at the time of a major breakup event elsewhere in the solar system, a few of the chunks would have suitable velocities and orbits to approach a planet through the inner Lagrangian point and become temporary captives (to orbit tens, hundreds, or thousands of times, but eventually escape again).

A large planet such as Jupiter has a very large window within which matter could enter such temporary orbits. Jupiter also sweeps up a disproportionally great amount of the debris because of its mass, and because objects in Jupiter-crossing orbits are eventually either accreted by Jupiter or ejected from the solar system.

Now suppose that while a number of chunks are in these temporary satellite orbits just outside the sphere of influence, Jupiter accretes appreciable mass. Suddenly its sphere of influence is larger. Some chunks in temporary orbits will now be in deeper, longer-

147

lasting temporary orbits; and some may find themselves inside the new sphere of influence, and thus permanent captives. If Jupiter were to eventually accrete a major chunk of matter—say, the core of the planet which broke up—the sphere of influence might increase enough in one jump to permanently capture all bodies in temporary orbit into permanent satellite orbits. I call this "Accretion Capture," the most likely example being the outer, asteroidal moons of Jupiter.

Tides

We have seen how gravitation, collision, and even drag by an atmosphere can influence the orbits of solar system bodies. The remaining significant influence is the friction of tides. We will now examine what this force is, and how it acts.

Bodies are not perfectly rigid. So when one body is under the gravitational influence of another, it distorts, because its facing surface is attracted more strongly than its opposite surface. The body bulges in both directions along the line toward the attracting companion: the facing surface bulges toward the parent because it is attracted more strongly than the center, and the opposite surface bulges away because it is attracted less strongly than the center.

At the same time, the sides of the body feel compression because the force from the attracting companion tends to squeeze the body

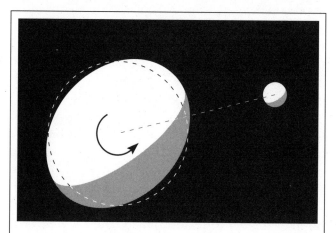

Figure 6.6. Tidal forces distort the shape of a body. Friction drags the bulge ahead as the body rotates.

as it pulls it toward a point (the center of the companion).

Solid bodies distort less than liquid bodies, which in turn are less responsive than gaseous bodies. Solid bodies simply flex and distort along the axis toward the attracting companion. As they spin, the tidal bulge gets dragged ahead of the axis line, because the body cannot reshape itself instantly. So the bulge is always displaced off the axis line in the direction of relative rotation—the faster the relative rotation, the greater the displacement. This delay in a body reshaping itself is referred to as "friction." (See Figure 6.6.)

For liquid bodies, the process of distortion has an additional aspect: the liquid can flow. Liquid on the front side of the body is pulled toward the center of the facing side and begins to flow in that direction. Liquid on the opposite side begins to flow toward the far apex of the bulging body. (See Figure 6.7.) If the body were non-rotating, flow would continue until the liquid piled up to the maximum height the gravity of the body would allow. But if it rotates, the liquid flows for a while first in one direction, then in the other, reversing every half rotation. (Actually, there is a time lag which depends on the amount of friction the liquid is subject to. Flow velocity builds up in one direction for half a revolution. Then, as the body rotates, tidal forces act to slow that flow, stop it, and reverse it. But the flow continues in the original direction for a time after the tidal forces have reversed, because of its momentum.)

Figure 6.7. Tidal forces (indicated by arrows) cause a fluid body to flow.

In the special case of the Earth, there are solid-body tides, ocean tides, and the friction which results from flowing ocean water running into land. It is especially acute when ocean tides are channeled into narrow inlets, such as the Bay of Fundy in Nova Scotia, Canada. Tides there can reach 50 feet because so much ocean water is forced into the wide mouth of the bay at the inlet, then squeezed down to a very narrow stream further inland. Much of the friction for the whole Earth is believed to occur in these special situations, and in general in the shallow seas.

For a gas giant planet, the solid-body distortion has extremely little lag as the planet rotates, because the gases are free to respond immediately to changes in tidal forces; so there is no opportunity for a lag or lead in the bulge to develop. However, the gases are free to flow. And they flow at different rates at every latitude, and different rates at every depth. So there is friction between adjacent layers of gas as the planet rotates differentially. In particular, if tides force a mass of gas to flow and change its latitude or depth, the mass of gas then acts as a brake or an accelerator on the other gases at that latitude or depth, because of their differing velocity. This is an aspect of tidal friction which has been much overlooked by planetary scientists.

Moreover, I have proposed that the giant spots on the gas giant planets are really floating masses, not storms. (See the chapter "Jupiter and Uranus.") If that is so, then there is also the friction of flowing gases running into the floating masses, analogous to oceans hitting land on Earth. There might even be "narrow channels" analogous to the shallow seas on Earth. There are clearly a number of tidal frictional mechanisms that may be active in any given body beyond the simple ones usually assumed, especially since we are often unaware of the presence of molten interiors, floating masses, and special frictional situations.

From the reasoning we have already discussed for the disruptive effect of one body on the moons of another, we can see that tidal forces are also proportional to mass over distance cubed, since a local region on the surface of a body may be thought of as a "moon" of the body for purposes of computing the forces. So with solid-body tides, the bulge raised on a body will be proportional to m/d^3. Rotation causes that bulge to *lead* the axis line to the companion if the body rotates faster than the companion revolves; or to *lag* if the body rotates slower than the companion revolves. Accordingly, tidal friction is either slowing the spin of the body (because the companion pulls on the leading bulge, slowing rotation), or speeding it up (because the companion is pulling on a lagging bulge).

For its part, the bulge's extra gravity operates on the companion as well, either accelerating its orbital velocity or decelerating it (for leads and lags, respectively). If the companion is accelerated, its orbit expands; and it could eventually escape. If the companion is decelerated, its orbit shrinks; and it could eventually end up on the body's surface, or burning up in its atmosphere. Note that this secondary action of the tidal bulge, back on the companion which creates it, is also inversely proportional to distance cubed. So the net effect of the companion on its own orbit through the bulge it produces on its primary is proportional to m/d^6. Sometimes the spin rate of the primary body is so affected by tides that one must also consider that the size of the lag or lead of the bulge is proportional to that spin rate, which may likewise be inversely proportional to $d^{1/2}$. So tidal friction may, in such cases, be proportional to $m/d^{13/2}$. It is safe to say that frictional effects are quite strongly distance-dependent.

The most familiar example of these effects is the Earth's Moon. Calculations indicate that the Earth's spin was at one time only about 2 hours long, at or near the fastest possible rate before spin would cause the Earth's surface to fly off. It is possible that the Moon fissioned from the Earth near that time, and went into a low Earth orbit. From that starting point, tides would have gradually slowed the Earth's rotation period from 2 to 24 hours, while the Moon's orbital period and distance increased. The Moon's period would have gone from a few hours to its present one-month value. Eventually in billions of years, the Earth's spin and the Moon's period will synchronize at about 60 days. When that finally happens, there will be no more lead to the tidal bulge (ignoring the Sun), and tidal evolution would halt.[c] Such a configuration, in which

---

[c]Actually, tidal evolution would not end because the Sun would continue to rob the Earth of some of its spin due to the tides raised by the Sun.

a satellite's orbital period and its parent's spin period are the same—so there can be no lag or lead of the tidal bulge—is called "synchronous" rotation.

Changes in spin, orbital period, and mean distance are the most visible effects of tidal friction from the perspective of the dynamicist. However, to inhabitants of the Earth, the most visible effects are the ebb and flow of the water on the surface of the planet. In general, one can appreciate from the foregoing discussion that tides produce shape changes, and therefore friction and stress. In solid bodies, this forced reshaping twice every spin causes strain in the interior of the Earth. This strain is undoubtedly in large measure responsible for most of the geologic activity of the planet. The stress manifests itself in occasional earthquakes, and the friction in heating, which is occasionally vented through volcanism.

Fortunately for us, the Moon is now at a considerable distance from the Earth. Billions of years ago, when the Moon was quite close, the solid-body tides which are now only a few feet might have been thousands of feet. Indeed, it is believed that the entire Earth melted from the heat and stress of those times. The closest analog we can see today is Jupiter's close satellite Io. Since tides raised by Jupiter are so enormous, that moon is today close to molten, with extensive volcanism going on right now. In general, when stable orbital situations are disturbed, great internal stresses can be set off inside other bodies, too. For example, the Moon's rotational lock with the Earth (keeping the same side toward the Earth) may have been disturbed in the past by the accretion of mass on one hemisphere. This would have caused the Moon to seek a new stable equilibrium, in which the hemisphere with the accreted mass would try to face the Earth permanently. The Moon's spin would librate until tides damped it out again. But in the meantime, the Moon would have been subjected to enormous internal stress and heat, possibly with active volcanism. This may have been the origin of the lunar "mare," or seas of solidified lava.[d]

---

[d]Twenty-five years ago astronomers debated whether the lunar mare were of volcanic or impact origin, since there was abundant evidence for both. We may now see a way in which both ideas were true. A number of nearly simultaneous large impacts selectively on one lunar hemisphere

To counter tidal stresses, orbits always try to circularize, and rotations try to synchronize. If an orbit around a primary is not circular, then tidal forces get larger and smaller as the distance changes. This application and release of pressure every revolution is called "tidal pumping" and creates internal heat. It may be seen that tides play an important role in the physical as well as orbital evolution of many solar system bodies.

We will encounter many applications of the concepts explained in this chapter throughout the remainder of this book.

from an explosion event would have formed large craters. The imbalance in mass distribution would have started the Moon librating with a large amplitude in the Earth's gravity field. This libration would have caused intense internal stress, partially melting the Moon's interior and triggering tectonic and volcanic activity, eventually spewing out lava to fill the low-lying lunar plains.

7

• •

Do Planets Explode?

Summary: A popularized brief history and overview of the evidence that a former major planet of the solar system exploded in the astronomically recent past,[a] leaving behind the thousands of fragments we call minor planets and comets. We deductively develop the consequences of such an event, and show that in every case, these agree with observations. Some characteristics implied by the planetary explosion scenario were not previously known to exist, but were nonetheless found to be true. And certain "explosion signatures," found among the orbits of fragments from man-made Earth satellites which have exploded, are also present in the asteroid belt. A synthesis of all the evidence is presented in another chapter; but here we discuss possible causes of the explosion. Then the recent timing of the event is used as a basis for the interesting speculation that the explosion may have been causally related to the origin of man on this planet.

Three Million Years of Solar System History

It is August 29, 1975. We think of the constellations as eternal and immutable. During our lifetimes we expect to see no change in

---

[a]For those seeking a less popularized, more technically precise discussion, see the reference to the author's published papers in this and later chapters. See also the chapter "A Synthesis of Recent Planetary Breakup Evidence."

155

Orion, Gemini, and Aquarius. But on this particular night, a change occurs. Cygnus, the swan or northern cross, acquires a new star. The reports begin to come in. It is seen first in Japan, then across Asia, Europe, and North America. Hundreds of sky-watchers send telegrams to the Central Bureau of the International Astronomical Union in Cambridge, Massachusetts, where all new astronomical discoveries are reported. The star brightens throughout the night, and eventually becomes the second brightest star in Cygnus. It remains visible for weeks, before finally fading back into oblivion. It becomes known in astronomical archives as "Nova Cygni 1975."

What was it? Nova means "new star," but astronomers now believe that "dying star" would be more accurate. At the end of their lives, when stars have burned up all their fuel, they are believed to explode violently. Our own Sun is destined for the same fate in perhaps another ten billion years, more or less. But there is one peculiar feature about novas: a great many of them are explosions of previously invisible stars in orbit around ordinary stars. We know this because the centers of the expanding gas shells from the explosion often show an appreciable velocity relative to the visible star. So we assume that invisible dwarf companion stars are the objects which exploded. But many astronomers now believe that many stars have planets in orbit around them, just as our Sun does. And these planets would also be invisible companions of ordinary stars.

Until recently there was very little reason to suspect that planets, even if common throughout the galaxy, would not survive as long as their parent stars. Now that picture has changed, because of events right in our own solar system. And we are led to ask, "Do planets explode?!"

Let us go back in time three million years. On Earth, the dinosaurs became extinct much earlier, land animals gave rise to the primates, and the very earliest ancestors of man have just appeared on the scene. Elsewhere in the solar system everything is as we know it in the twentieth century, with one major exception. There is one additional planet between Mars and Jupiter, larger than any of the others except Jupiter itself. From Earth the extra planet is bright enough to be seen in the daytime, and dominates the night sky with its brilliance.

156

Suddenly, it explodes! Like a nova in our own solar system, it brightens until it outshines the Sun itself. Solid, liquid, and gaseous debris is hurled into space at high velocities in all directions. Nonetheless, it takes months for the leading edge of the blast to reach the Earth. What a sight it would have been for early man to see! The sky ablaze with meteors night and day unceasingly for months. Great comets moving among the stars for years. Indeed, it would be many thousands of years before conditions returned to a more "normal" state. But even then the Earth would never again be exactly the same. Following an age of very warm climate which had continued uninterrupted for 100 million years, the Earth would now enter a series of ice ages alternating with mild climate, triggered by the cosmic influx.

Our story continues when man has advanced to the point where he begins to rediscover evidence of the explosion—the year 1772. If any record of the catastrophe had been preserved, it is still unknown to modern man, who is about to take his first step toward discovering for himself what happened. The astronomer Daniel Titius notices a curious fact about the spacing of the planets: each of the six known planets is roughly twice the distance of the previous one from the Sun, with only one exception, a gap between Mars and Jupiter. The gap is just the right size to hold exactly one additional planet. Astronomer Johann Bode publicizes the curious fact in 1778 as a "law." Not too much is thought of it until 1781, when William Herschel discovers the seventh planet, Uranus, and it is found to be in excellent agreement with Bode's law. This draws attention to the gap and the missing planet predicted by the law. Belief in its existence becomes high enough that searches are organized and prizes offered. None of these searchers is successful.

We move forward to the first day of the nineteenth century— January 1, 1801—when the story begins to unfold rapidly. The Italian astronomer Guiseppe Piazzi discovers the missing planet by accident while observing. The world is shocked and amazed. The new planet, given the name Ceres, orbits the Sun exactly where Bode's law said it should be. Yet it is so incredibly tiny compared to the other planets, not even big enough to make a good-sized moon. And its orbit is more egg-shaped and tilted than other planetary orbits. Whatever was to be made of this miniature wonder?

157

Before the year was over, the world received another shock from the astronomers. There were not one, but two, miniature planets orbiting at that distance from the Sun. The new one was given the name Pallas. And that is all the information Heinrich Olbers had when he announced a theory of what happened: a larger planet had exploded! He correctly predicted that many more pieces would be found, that they would all have similarly odd-shaped orbits, and that they would vary in brightness as they spun, because fragments should be irregular in shape. He also predicted the best places to search for more fragments, and himself discovered the fourth of the minor planets, Vesta. Olbers's theory seemed the only logical explanation of what had happened.

All was well until in 1814 the French astronomer Louis Lagrange extended Olbers's theory to explain the comets, pointing out that their extremely elongated orbits would also be a natural by-product of an explosion. But the better-known astronomer, Marquis de Laplace, whose nebular theory of the origin of the comets was very "in" at the time, attacked the ideas of both Lagrange and Olbers, making several telling arguments. The attack of this prestigious astronomer cast the planetary explosion theory into disfavor for most of the next 175 years. Various new evidence and argument, pro and con, appeared in the interim, but the astronomers as a whole were now committed to more conventional explanations. Even the appearance of a definitive treatise on meteorites by Brown and Patterson in 1948,[62] in which they concluded there was irrefutable evidence that meteorites were once an integral part of a larger planet, did not sway the bulk of the astronomers. By the 1960s, the exploding planet theory was still on the "outs" with the professional astronomers, who generally believed that the thousands of known minor planets orbiting between Mars and Jupiter were the remains of a planet which had never been formed, rather than one which had broken up.

Consequences of a Planetary Explosion

In 1972, the Canadian astronomer Michael Ovenden published a result that opened the way for reversing that opinion. Ovenden developed a "law" similar to Bode's, but much more elaborate, which predicted the spacing of planets as well as their major satellites. And he also came to the conclusion that a planet was missing from the area where the minor planets orbited. But Ovenden predicted that it must have been a giant planet the size of Saturn, and much larger than all the minor planets put together. This was an important possibility not previously considered. It meant that the event which destroyed the planet must have involved enormous energy. It also meant that much of the debris had been blasted out of the solar system completely. Once this was realized, other parts of the puzzle began to drop into place.

If a planet exploded between Mars and Jupiter with enormous energy, there would initially be debris all over the solar system. However, in just 100,000 years or so, Jupiter and the other planets swept up or ejected almost all the debris, except for the pieces between Mars and Jupiter which can never come close to any planet. This is where the surviving minor planets are found today.

The only other remaining debris we have any chance of discovering would be objects hurled to great distances from the Sun, with no opportunity to interact with the planets until eventually pulled back by the Sun's gravity. Some of these first-time returners have just come back within the last 100,000 years to the vicinity of the planets and the explosion. The planets have not yet had time to dispose of all these. The amazing thing is that comets match that description! Comets come from incredible distances from the Sun, trillions of miles away (though only one-fifth of the way to our nearest neighboring star). And a great many of them are known to be coming close to the planets for the first time since their birth. Perhaps most amazing of all, those that are visiting us for the first time since their births are traveling on orbits with periods of three million years. We therefore know that if comets did originate from the planetary breakup, they were born just that many years ago, which tells us when the planetary explosion took place. In the chapter "Where Do Comets Come From?" we explain this in more detail, including why these comets could not have been around their orbits more than once.

Is there other evidence that comets and minor planets originated in the "recent" explosion of a planet? Yes, a great deal. We can study the orbits of comets, and by using the laws of gravitation we can do what amounts to tracing these orbits back in time. We find a statistical tendency for the orbits to emanate from a common point between Mars and Jupiter about three million years ago, which we will describe in more detail in the next chapter.

> "There is no problem too big that can't be solved with high explosives."—Rush

Apparently the long and awe-inspiring tails of the comets are gas and dust from the parent planet loosed in the explosion. The minor planets don't have such a gaseous envelope only because the Sun's radiation has driven it away.

If and only if the orbits of all comets and minor planets originated at a common moment from a common place in a particular direction at a particular distance from the Sun and traveling near the plane of the planets with a particular velocity, there are a number of specific consequences. In my technical papers, I have derived these consequences and analyzed the orbits of comets to determine how well they meet these conditions.[63,64] *All* the consequent orbital characteristics are present in comet orbits to the degree which could have survived planetary and stellar perturbations after a few million years. These predictions are so specific, and so unlikely to arise in any other way, that the conclusion seems inescapable that comets did originate in the hypothesized manner. See the chapter "A Synthesis of Recent Planetary Breakup Evidence" for an overview of the breadth and depth of this evidence. The next three chapters elaborate specific lines of that evidence.

Analogous to comet orbits, the orbits of the minor planets also show imprints of an explosion event. We have learned what such imprints look like from studying man-made satellites of the Earth in a few cases where one of them has exploded. Other evidence comes from meteors from space which reach the ground without burning up and are recovered for study, where one can see first-hand what sort of material the planet was made of. From the tracks of cosmic rays in these meteorites, we have learned that they have been traveling in space only some millions of years, a small fraction of the age of the solar system. Some of them show evidence of rapid melting a long time ago, as if they were affected by an immense heat blast. A few show evidence of shock, others are badly charred. Some meteorites display evidence that they formed in a high-temperature or high-pressure environment, as in the interior of a large planet; for example, tiny diamonds have occasionally been reported in meteorites.[b,65,66,67,68,69,70] And there is specific evidence of exposure to an event of enormous energy, which conventional theory supposes to have been a nearby supernova.

Finally, there is evidence, particularly on Mars, for a recent influx of cratering. And *Viking*-orbiter photos show that vast quantities of water once flowed on Mars: fluid-cut channels, floodplains, river deltas, silt deposits and eroded shorelines, even though the Martian climate today is both too cold and too dry for flowing water to exist.[71] We infer from studies of comets and meteorites that water was an abundant ingredient on the missing planet. Did all that Martian water get dumped on Mars just after the explosion? Are sim-

---

[b]The presence of diamonds has led some experts to suggest that there must exist an unknown way to form diamonds by shock through collisions in space or during impact on Earth, without lengthy exposure to high temperature and pressure. This was the subject of a celebrated debate in the pages of the Journal of Geophysical Research in the mid-1960s (see next five references). (Note that scientific issues are rarely debated in the pages of scientific journals.) First, N.L. Carter and G.C. Kennedy concluded that "the diamonds probably precipitated ... under high gravitational pressures. The diamonds were subsequently shattered ... possibly from a pressure drop due to the disruption of the large parent planet. The physical evidence against the theory that the diamonds originated ... due to shock is convincing."

A detailed response was published by D. Heymann, M.E. Lipschutz, B. Nielsen and E. Anders, in which they present their case for a shock origin of the diamonds. It was followed immediately by Anders and Lipschutz's critique of Carter and Kennedy's paper. Included among the 19 listed conclusions of that paper are "There is no obvious way to break up and disperse moon-sized objects. There is no obvious way to make moon-sized objects vanish from the asteroid belt."

The debate continued with Carter and Kennedy's reply, and finally a brief reply to that by Anders and Lipschutz, dealing with more and more technical fine points of the debate. A decade later, Anders was one of the sharpest critics of my own presentation of new evidence for the planetary explosion scenario before an International Astronomical Union Colloquium in Lyon, France. A summary of that discussion appears in the last reference of the following set.

ilar features of the Moon's airless face which look water-carved of a similar origin? Perhaps we now have our first clues as to the origin of the magnetism in lunar rocks and of radioactivity in lunar soil brought back to the Earth by *Apollo* astronauts, neither of which can be native to the Moon.

On the Earth, it is a good guess that a particular and very special type of meteorite, called tektites, may be the surviving remains of the initial blast wave from the explosion. These glassy objects from space were also melted suddenly not long before reaching the Earth's atmosphere, and are found scattered in huge fields covering millions of square miles in certain parts of the world. It has been estimated that there may be more than 100,000,000 tons of tektites · in North America alone. If the estimated age of the main class of tektites, 700,000 years, is systematically biased on the low side, the planetary explosion provides a very natural source.

Other hints about the cataclysm are found throughout the solar system. For example, the only known body in the outer solar system to rotate more slowly than once per month is Saturn's outer satellite Iapetus, which requires nearly 80 days to complete one spin.[c] The significance of this is that at such a distance from the explosion, there would be a spread of several weeks in the arrival time of different parts of the blast wave. Only Iapetus would have encountered the blast on only one side of its surface; and true to that prediction, Iapetus is known today to be heavily blackened on one side only. Most other moons have extremely black material scattered all over their surfaces.

So it is just within the last few years that we have begun to find enough pieces of this puzzle to reconstruct the story of what really happened. Not all the pieces have been found yet; we have many more to discover. But we know enough now to want to ask two very important questions: What caused the explosion? And why did it happen only three million years ago?

---

[c]Neptune's outer satellite, Nereid, would take nearly a year to spin once if its rotation were synchronous with its orbital period. But neither its spin rate, nor a tentative observation that Nereid may be blackened on one face only, could be confirmed by the *Voyager 2* spacecraft as it flew by, leaving the status of Nereid unknown.

The Cause and Timing of the Explosion

It is intrinsically unsettling to conclude that planets can explode because, after all, we live on a planet ourselves and are totally dependent upon it for survival. Nonetheless, we wish to know the truth. Unfortunately, we have almost no evidence yet as to what the cause may have been, making it impossible for now to judge whether the missing planet was uniquely unstable, or whether our own Earth could one day share its fate. What we do know is that enormous energy was involved,[d,72] and that there was a dramatic increase in radiation from cosmic rays in the solar system at about that time, probably from the explosion. Other than that, we can do little more than observe that explosions seem to be a very real fact of life in the universe around us. Stars explode when they have exhausted their nuclear fuel, and evidence presented by the Dutch astronomer Oort indicates that entire galaxies, consisting of hundreds of billions of stars, may also explode. Perhaps, as suggested earlier, classical novas are actually planets exploding, rather than invisible companion stars, as usually assumed.

It is often objected that planets are unlikely to generate enough energy to explode through known processes. However, we have only recently learned that thermonuclear processes similar to those in a star may now be taking place in the core of the planet Jupiter, which emits more heat than it takes in from the Sun. Our sample of planets is just too small to generalize about possible processes in planetary cores.

But a specific speculation about the explosion energy source is perhaps possible. Gamma rays observed coming from roughly the galactic center have an energy of 511,000 electron volts (for comparison, visible light has about 2 ev), which is precisely the energy produced by the mutual annihilation of an electron and a positron, its antimatter twin. The observed intensity implies the annihilation

---

[d]Napier and Dodd (see next reference) showed that chemical and even thermonuclear energies are insufficient to blow apart so large a planet so violently.

163

of 10^{10} tons of positrons every second.[e] Gamma rays at 1.8×10^6 ev are also detected from near the galactic center, which implies the decay of the radioactive element Aluminum 26: several stellar masses' worth. The production of Al 26 is usually associated with supernovas. Taken together, these intriguing results may imply that antimatter plays a role both in the centers of galaxies and in major explosions throughout the galaxy. Al 26 is also found in carbonaceous meteorites on Earth in disproportionally large amounts, presumably arising from the planetary explosion event. But if Al 26 and electron-positron annihilation are associated elsewhere in the galaxy, the suggestion is clear that antimatter might have played a role in the explosion of the missing planet too. Although clearly no detailed mechanism can yet be proposed, the same lack of a detailed mechanism is true about the galactic center, where 511,000 ev gamma rays are a reality, not a theory.

This speculation is further supported by the characteristics of gamma-ray bursts. One of their two possible origins is that they are relatively local and symmetric about the solar system. Antimatter from the planetary explosion's blast wave encountering interstellar matter would be one way to nicely account for the seemingly inexplicable properties of gamma-ray bursts.

And what about the time of the event? Since the lesson taught us by Copernicus, we have been wary of thinking of the Earth as occupying a special place in the universe. We must likewise be wary of interpretations that seem to place man's presence on Earth at a special time in the life of the universe. Yet an event just three million years ago, from an astronomical perspective, is embarrassingly recent; indeed, human ancestors may already have appeared on Earth by then.

The first possible explanation of this mystery comes from our own changing perspective. We once thought that the solar system formed five billion years ago from a huge nebula, and that nothing much newsworthy has happened since. We now see the solar sys-

---

[e]The annihilation is not at a constant rate. The intensity decreased by a factor of at least four in 1977 (below the detectable limit), then later returned to full intensity.

tem as a place where a great many individually unique events have occurred. There is evidence to suggest that Mercury could be an escaped satellite of Venus; in any event, something robbed Venus of its rapid spin. The satellites of Mars and most of Jupiter's seem to have been captured. What caused Jupiter's "Great Red Spot"? A huge impact? When did Saturn's rings form, and how? By a satellite breaking up? And what of the rings of Uranus, which are entirely different from Saturn's in appearance and behavior? What event tilted the planet Uranus over on its side? What disrupted the existing satellites of Neptune? Is Pluto an escaped satellite of Neptune? How did Pluto get a satellite of its own? Where did the mini-planet Chiron come from? And why is the Sun tilted by 7 degrees to the mean plane of the planets? We are now beginning to see the solar system as a place of change, with a rich and varied history. Perhaps the breakup of a giant planet three million years ago is merely the most recent and most readily reconstructed of a long series of remarkable events in the solar system.

There is, of course, another possibility for explaining the coincidence of this explosion event with the beginnings of man on this planet, and that is to hypothesize that there was no coincidence, but instead a causal connection. We develop this interesting speculation in the chapter "The Origins of the Solar System and of Man."

8

• •

The Discovery
of Minor Satellites

Summary: In the late 1970s it was discovered that minor planets and other small solar system bodies apparently have satellites. This is so extraordinary and unexpected in conventional theories that the validity of the observational evidence is still debated. But we show that in certain cases, such as the photoelectrically confirmed 50-km satellite of minor planet Herculina, the evidence is beyond dispute. Then the frequency and generality of the phenomenon argue that such minor satellites must be numerous and commonplace. Although such a conclusion cannot be true for the conventional model of the origin of the solar system's small bodies—leading to opposition to the idea by many scientists—it is nonetheless exactly what the exploded planet hypothesis expects and requires. A spacecraft encounter with a minor planet, and images from the Hubble Space Telescope, will reveal the true situation within the coming two years. The crucial events in this discovery, and the credits due to the people responsible, are reviewed. We conclude with a brief analysis of the first spacecraft image of a minor planet.

The Discovery of Minor Satellites

"Minor satellite" is the term I have proposed to refer to satellites of the minor bodies in the solar system, principally the minor planets.[a]

---

[a]The terms "minor planet" and "asteroid" have identical meanings, and are used interchangeably.

Prior to 1978 it was generally believed that no such bodies existed. This impression was the result of an inappropriate application of intuition, since such small bodies could not possibly hold stable satellites in a gravitational field as strong as that at the Earth's surface. So astronomers generalized that small bodies, from hundreds of kilometers down to meter or millimeter size, could not possibly hold stable satellites while in solar orbit. That assumption turns out to be incorrect. Not only can such small bodies hold satellites of their own, but as long as they stay well away from the major planets, such satellites are strongly bound and can readily have stable orbits.

I first heard of the notion of a satellite of a minor planet from David Dunham, an astronomer colleague who was a fellow student at Yale University in the 1960s. On March 5, 1977, the minor planet Hebe passed in front of a bright star, blocking its light for tens of seconds for observers in Mexico. An experienced amateur observer, Paul Maley, saw the star disappear for half a second at about the same time from a location in Texas far enough away that that should not have been possible. Dunham interrogated Maley repeatedly about the circumstances of his observation, but was eventually forced to conclude that the sighting should be taken at face value, even though it seemed to imply the presence of a small body traveling near Hebe in space. At that time, Dunham believed that the small companion was outside the distance at which satellites could remain stably bound to Hebe. Nonetheless, he courageously reported the anomalous observation to the American Astronomical Society, despite the almost-unanimous disbelief that greeted him.

When Dunham first told me the story, I also concluded that some prosaic explanation was far more probable than an object associated with Hebe. Yet I was familiar enough with the observation of such events that the matter remained in my memory as an unresolved mystery. It was not until a later event involving another minor planet brought evidence too strong to ignore that I took the notion seriously. That evidence came on June 7, 1978, when another star disappeared behind the 250-km-diameter minor planet Herculina.

On that night, amateur astronomer J.H. McMahon successfully observed a 21-second disappearance event when Herculina passed in front of the star. But he also observed and timed six additional disappearance events with durations of one-half to four seconds occurring within the two minutes before and after the main event. No other similar events occurred over the rest of the 20-minute interval of observation then, or on many other occasions when the minor planet was not lined up with the star. Dunham once again thoroughly investigated the circumstances, concluding that there was no basis for dismissing McMahon's observations, which implied the existence of several additional small (5- to 50-km) bodies in the immediate vicinity of Herculina.

Due to Dunham's efforts in making the predictions and publicizing this event before it happened, there was also one major professional astronomical institution, Lowell Observatory, which observed and recorded the disappearance event. Dunham called the Lowell astronomers and asked if any other disappearances of shorter duration had been recorded, which would confirm McMahon's observations. Astronomers at Lowell answered in the negative. Dunham consulted with McMahon again, reviewing every reasonably possible way in which the observer might have been mistaken or fooled; but none seemed plausible. Dunham then calculated that only one of the secondary "bodies" causing the star to disappear at McMahon's location would have been large enough to be seen in the Lowell data as well, and that event occurred 91 seconds before the main event. Dunham called back the Lowell observers, who again assured him they had seen no shorter-duration events. Dunham asked them to check their recording specifically at 91 seconds before the main event. At precisely that location, the Lowell astronomers found a disappearance event in the record which had been previously overlooked. (Subsequent inspection showed that there was nothing subtle about the event in the record. It was merely that, if something is totally unexpected, it is easy to overlook it or quickly dismiss it as spurious.)

Dunham confronted me and other astronomers with confirmed evidence that at least one minor planet had at least one satellite. Nonetheless, I felt I had to put that idea into an acceptable theoretical framework for myself before even examining the calculations about whether or not such a satellite was dynamically possible (an attitude I would now sharply criticize). My publication of the "exploding planet" hypothesis as the origin of comets and minor planets was still fairly recent; and I suddenly realized how natural

169

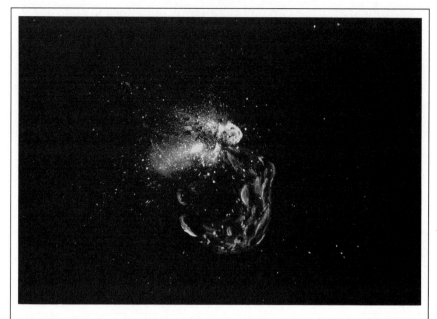

Figure 8.1. Artist's concept of the explosive impact of two bodies. Larger chunks will capture smaller ones as their spheres of influence expand. (Artist: Hartmann)

and inevitable would be the process of capturing satellites as large bits of matter flew away from the site of the explosion. The further away from their parent planet the chunks of matter flew, the larger would their gravitational "spheres of influence" become, as discussed in the chapter "Orbits." (See Figure 8.1.)

Thus armed with a theoretical framework for accepting the notion of minor satellites, I examined the calculations which seemed to show that minor planets could not hold stable satellites at such distances (1000 kilometers or so). I found the erroneous assumption and proved that small bodies at such distances could, after all, be very stably bound to a parent minor planet. I have since regretted that I was not open-minded enough to re-examine the calculations before figuring out a theory that would explain how such objects could come to be. When observational evidence is strong, that should be sufficient motivation, whether or not a theoretical basis for a conclusion exists!

During that summer of 1978, Richard Binzel did some work for me as a summer assistant at the U.S. Naval Observatory. He was interested in the notion of satellites of minor planets and managed to find numerous earlier instances of observations of such satellites that had been dismissed for lack of a plausible theoretical basis. He also turned up some revealing lightcurve evidence, showing features for certain minor planets which unmistakably resembled eclipses and transits of large satellites. We jointly published his evidence and my calculations in *Science* magazine the following March. By that time Binzel had amassed evidence for 23 candidate satellites of minor planets, and we had additional evidence added in proof from more observations made in December of 1978. We were able to draw the conclusion in this early publication that such satellites were "numerous and commonplace."

One additional case of a confirmed secondary occurred on October 10, 1980, when two visual observers each saw a short secondary occultation of consistent time and duration involving minor planet Kleopatra. Both observers also reported a sudden change from the bluish color of the star to the reddish tinge of the minor planet during the event, ruling out a near-Earth cause for the occultation (which would have occulted the asteroid also).

Since then, one additional type of observation has become possible: radar ranging to asteroids (see Glossary) passing close to the Earth. Even though there have been very few of these, evidence of the multiple-body nature of such objects has surfaced. The best evidence to date is from asteroid 1989 PB, reported to have returned at least a double radar reflection with a 4.1-hour periodicity.[73] Some of the same radar images hint at more complexity than a double object, possibly "a small cluster of bodies." More recently, some large main-belt asteroids have also been ranged by radar, and several of those have returned bi-modal reflections, suggesting that they are double or more complex objects.

Theoretical Considerations

Although the elimination of minor satellites by collisions among minor planets would take slightly longer than the age of the solar system, tidal forces would tend to evolve the orbits of minor satel-

171

lites much more rapidly. In fact, many minor satellites would either fall onto the surface of their parent or escape into their own solar orbit within 10,000 to 10,000,000 years or so. With such a short time scale for orbital evolution

> "Nothing exceeds like excess."
> —Anonymous

by tides, these satellites ought not to be as abundant as they seem to be unless they had a recent origin—for example, in the planetary explosion event three million years ago I discuss in the chapter "Do Planets Explode?" When the Hubble Space Telescope is repaired by 1994, it should be possible to observe many minor satellites directly, determine their orbits, and measure the rate of tidal evolution. In that way we should be able to soon prove whether these objects have been around for nearly the age of the solar system (billions of years), or whether they indeed originated merely a few million years ago, as implied by the planetary breakup theory.

There are some other fascinating implications of this discovery of minor satellites. The tendency for small bodies to hold other smaller bodies gravitationally captive as satellites would apply even down to bodies in the size range of meters, perhaps even millimeters. Recall the rule of thumb that at our distance from the Sun, a body with a density of a few grams per cubic centimeter would have a stable sphere of influence (within which it could hold satellites) of about 100 times its own diameter, regardless of size. (This is limited on the high end by the requirement that the body must be much smaller than the Sun, and on the low end by the requirement that the body must not be so small that it is more influenced by solar wind or radiation pressure than by solar gravitation. Otherwise, the result has full generality. This is developed in the chapter on "Orbits.")

Knowing this, it suddenly becomes possible to unravel some puzzles about other small bodies which have eluded explanation for quite some time. Comet puzzles are discussed in the chapter "Do Comets Have Satellites?" Among other puzzles, we can now easily see why meteor craters often occur in doublets.

Fireballs, which are meteors observed entering the Earth's atmosphere, have three puzzles about them that the discovery of minor satellites helps resolve: 1. Fireballs often "break up" at heights above 100 km in the Earth's atmosphere, where the shearing forces are too minute to cause fragmentation.[74] But we now realize that the "fragments" may have been separate bodies gravitationally bound, rather than a single mass. 2. The "brightness-to-mass" ratios of many fireballs are considerably higher than theory permits. But if a cloud of gravitationally bound debris, rather than a single body, is entering the atmosphere, then the mystery is resolved. 3. The radar cross-sections of many fireballs are greater than theory permits, with a likely similar explanation.

Note that the orbits of many of the small bodies around a parent tend to slowly decay toward the surface of the parent, because of the action of tidal forces. The largest satellites will feel the strongest tidal forces, and therefore tend to decay faster than the smaller satellites. Consider one large, close satellite. Eventually, its orbit will decay to the point where the large satellite makes grazing contact with the surface of the parent as it orbits. This is most likely to happen at the highest elevations of any surface features on the parent. As soon as the two bodies touch, friction will absorb the rest of the orbital energy of the satellite, and the two bodies will remain in contact. They form what is referred to, in the case of stars, as a "contact binary." The example of asteroid 624 Hektor provides a good model of what may occur: two or more bodies of comparable mass which have merged into a single, highly elongated body.[75] (See Figure 8.2.) We would expect to find many such contact binaries among the small bodies in the solar system, and indeed, there is considerable lightcurve evidence to support this conclusion.

This process would be similar for smaller satellites. They eventually make first contact with the highest elevations on the combined parent body. But their angular speed results in a brief contact, followed by bouncing and rolling until they come to rest in a niche or valley. We therefore expect to find that many small solar system bodies will be quite elongated and irregular (again, in agreement with observational evidence). And it follows that impacts of such bodies on moons or planets will often betray the multiple-body nature of the original asteroid or meteoroid.

Figure 8.2. Artist's concept of the double asteroid Hektor. (Artist: Hartmann)

Discovery Credits

Looking back over how this exciting discovery unfolded, several persons played key and indispensable roles. First was the observer Paul Maley in Texas, who saw a bright star disappear for half a second when it shouldn't have, reported it, and stuck to his guns when questioned closely by skeptics who believed the observation couldn't have happened as described. Although Maley's observation was dismissed by everyone except Dunham, it served to put the idea into several minds, including mine, enabling later developments to occur.

Similar praise is due to J.H. McMahon, who is credited with the first confirmed observation of a minor satellite. Again, no one except Dunham paid his observations any attention at the outset, and they, too, might have been ignored but for the Maley event and Dunham's persistent follow-up. Both Maley and McMahon took some abuse from some professional astronomers, and (despite years of experience and diligence) succeeded at first only in calling their

174

credibility as observers into question. But that is often a part of the story when a radical new discovery is made.

There is no doubt in my mind that the greatest credit for this discovery belongs to David W. Dunham. Without Dunham's calculations and advance publicity, neither of these nor numerous other like events would have been observed in the first place. Dunham was initially the only professional astronomer who took the observations seriously enough to follow them up. Dunham inspired numerous others, such as Binzel and myself, and many new observers, to turn their attentions to this interesting problem. And without his diligence, the confirmation of McMahon's observations would not have been discovered in the Lowell recordings. But it is no accident that Dunham was in the right place at the right time to play such a critical role in this important discovery. Dunham exemplifies the ideal all scientists should strive to achieve, of encouraging observations of an important new kind for their own sake, then following up on unexpected results despite no theoretical framework for understanding them at the time. I have little doubt that without Dunham, minor satellites would remain undiscovered at this writing. For even if the *Galileo* spacecraft shows pictures of them, that spacecraft would have been sent far closer to the minor planet it is encountering in 1991 and 1993 and would likely have been destroyed in the process!

Finally, I would add a word of praise for Richard Binzel, who so extensively researched the idea of minor satellites. Through his efforts the previously neglected observations of many earlier astronomers came to light and were given proper credit. Moreover, it became possible to see the phenomenon of minor satellites as having some generality, not merely as a few isolated and freakish cases.

Through the efforts of these individuals, an exciting discovery of some importance was made years ahead of its time. (Presumably the *Galileo* spacecraft and the Hubble Space Telescope will provide the first true images of double asteroids in the near future.) Through their efforts, an extraordinary hypothesis received extraordinary proof (which, even at that, is not widely accepted). Of course, the discovery might have been made up to half a century earlier if an extraordinary proof had not been required. We should all have been more open to the possibility of minor satellites exist-

175

ing when we first learned of Maley's observation, just as our predecessors should have been open-minded when certain minor satellites were suggested earlier in the century. If any of them had merely entertained the idea seriously, the proof would have been sought and obtained years earlier. This is an example of why I argue against the "extraordinary proofs" criterion in the chapter on "The Scientific Method"—it inhibits the discovery of some of the most interesting things yet to be learned.

First Asteroid Images: Satellite Analysis

Background. In view of the prediction that most minor planets will be found to have satellites, we will here briefly analyze preliminary results of the *Galileo* spacecraft flyby of minor planet 951 Gaspra on October 29, 1991. As of this writing, two images have been returned to Earth, giving us our first-ever close-up looks at a minor planet.

Motivations. The principal reason for predicting that most minor planets have abundant large satellites is observational. In two different stellar occultation cases, the presence of a large moon of a minor planet has been confirmed by a second, independent observer. In dozens of other unconfirmed cases, stellar occultations and radar reflections both strongly suggest the generality of the satellite phenomenon for minor planets.

Theory. The principal reason for doubting the generality of the phenomenon is theoretical. Stable satellites cannot be formed through known processes such as gravitational capture or collisions. Any satellites that might exist would tend to be removed by collisions. In particular, a major collision involving the nucleus would remove an entire pre-existing cloud of satellites from a minor planet. The satellites and collisional fragments would be sent into their own solar orbits with similar orbital elements, an arrangement closely resembling what are called "asteroid families."

Implications. If asteroid moons do exist in abundance, as the observations suggest, that condition could seemingly only have arisen at the time of asteroid formation. A finding that satellites are abundant would strongly favor the planetary breakup hypothesis of minor planet origin over the primeval solar nebula hypothesis, since the former predicts that all minor planets would be surrounded by a debris cloud immediately after the breakup. So the implications of the presence or absence of satellites are of considerable importance, as well as interest.

Caveats. Gaspra's spectrum is described as "peculiar S-type"; its small diameter is in the range where many objects of that size are collisional debris; and it is near the Flora asteroid family. Each of these factors increases the probability that Gaspra's present condition has been modified by a major collision. For example, it might itself be a former moon of the Flora family parent body. Nonetheless, I felt from the evidence that the chances were still about 80% that Gaspra would have moons. In any case, it was quite important that a prediction be made in advance of the encounter. I made such a prediction for the record at a meeting of asteroid experts in Flagstaff, Arizona in June, 1991.[76] At that time astronomer Don Yeomans, representing the majority viewpoint among the experts, publicly bet me that Gaspra would have no satellites. By the time this book is published the results are likely to be known.

Encounter. On October 29, 1991 the *Galileo* spacecraft took 150 pictures in the close vicinity of minor planet 953 Gaspra. Two of those pictures have now been received on Earth. The rest are stored on a tape recorder, awaiting either a resolution of the spacecraft's antenna problem or its return to the Earth's vicinity in December 1992.

Gaspra Images. A glance at the pictures reveals an elongated, highly irregular shape. The scarcity of large craters suggests that Gaspra may itself be a relatively young fragment of a larger minor planet. Gaspra has a mean diameter of about 12 km, and the picture frame extends out to about 70 km from Gaspra. No satellites are in evidence.

Satellite Analysis. The synchronous rotation orbit about Gaspra is about 22 km from its center (mean radius = 6 km). At the synchronous orbit, a satellite would revolve in the same time, 7.03 hours, that it takes Gaspra to rotate. Inside the synchronous orbit, satellites are unstable against tidal forces. Outside, the stable region extends to about 800 km. Volume-wise, the downloaded image frames reveal only 0.001 of the space within which Gaspra might have stable moons. Images still on board the spacecraft will tell us more about the remaining space. However, the synchronous orbit is the most stable one; and the absence of large moons in the por-

177

tion of it which can be seen does significantly lower the probability of finding moons in the rest of the volume.

Image Processing. The available images were processed to maximize the contrast in the image of Gaspra itself, which tends to suppress stars and small satellite images that might be present. Later processing will do a better job of checking for small moons which might already be in the images we now have.

Detection? In the paper I presented to the Asteroid specialists' meeting the summer of '91 in Flagstaff, Arizona, I remarked about the possibility that Gaspra might have no moons because of a collision event. I then said, "Even so, tidal forces prior to the collision would have operated to bring down minor satellites orbiting inside the synchronous orbit, which for Gaspra is about two mean diameters out. They should end up lying on the surface of the nucleus." In the upper portion of the images we have, there is a large object about 5 km long which appears to be a physically distinct piece lying on the surface of an otherwise contiguous object. This is just the sort of object I anticipated with my remark. The proof of its origin as a moon of Gaspra could come in later photos if tracks caused by the object rolling on the surface after decaying from orbit can still be seen.

Future. Since no obvious, presently orbiting satellites were seen yet, we must await the following developments: 1. Better processing of the images we have, to bring up possible faint background satellites. 2. Downloading of many additional images of Gaspra and the space near it from the *Galileo* spacecraft, sometime in 1992. 3. *Galileo's* probable encounter with minor planet Ida in 1993. (But Ida is an asteroid family member and a probable collisional fragment.) 4. Hubble Space Telescope observations of many minor planets, when its priorities permit such observations to be made.

Falsifiability. To be useful, a hypothesis must be falsifiable. I accept that if the first three minor planets examined with sufficient resolution (including a least one C-type asteroid over 50 km diameter, but excluding the four largest asteroids) have no moons, then the hypothesis of abundant asteroid satellites may be considered falsified, with corresponding implications for theories of asteroid origin. It would be in accord with the best scientific methodology if my colleagues were to be equally forthcoming about the implications for asteroid origins if abundant satellites *are* found.

9

•••••••••••••••••••••••••••••••

Where Do Comets
Come From?

Summary: Three different theories of the origin of comets have been proposed from the conventional viewpoint: formation in place, interstellar formation, or formation within the planetary region of the solar system. All three theories accept the existence of a so-called "Oort cloud" of comets at 1000 times Pluto's distance from the Sun, which the observations seem to require. We construct a scale model to contrast these conventional theories with the new theory for the origin of comets proposed here. The new theory was arrived at deductively from the exploded planet hypothesis, and points out a way to avoid the unlikely Oort cloud hypothesis which had never before been considered. This scale model also emphasizes certain implausible aspects of the conventional theories. And it illustrates how a modified Scientific Method can be helpful in finding and disposing of fundamentally incorrect ideas that have taken root within a discipline of science. We explore the considerable problems with the Oort cloud concept and examine how the only dynamically viable alternative, the exploded planet hypothesis, eliminates those problems. We conclude with some predictions.

A Scale Model of the Oort Cloud

I introduce this subject here with three motivations in mind: 1. to illustrate by example how difficult it is for fundamentally new scientific hypotheses to gain the attention of the scientific community;

2. to use this forum to promote some ideas of my own about the nature of comets; 3. to discuss a subject of some intrinsic interest, which may have implications for our understanding of the origin and evolution of the solar system.

Comets are unquestionably remarkable objects. But are they leftover remnants of the original solar nebula from which the planets in our solar system are thought to have condensed? Or could they have their origins somewhere in interstellar space? Were they perhaps ejected by one or more of the known planets or satellites? We will here summarize evidence for a new theory suggesting that none of these three standard ideas may be the answer; instead, comets may have originated from the breakup of a former solar system body.

To place our current knowledge about cometary origins in perspective, let us construct in our imaginations a scale model of the solar system. We do this to help us appreciate some of the properties of the so-called "Oort cloud," which in the currently popular theory is the supposed reservoir from which all comets come. We must reduce the real scale of the solar system by a factor of 10^{15} (one thousand trillion) to reach visualizable dimensions. In our scale model, we identify a central point to represent the Sun, and we can then barely perceive the Earth's orbit—a circle with a radius of 0.15 millimeters (1/150 of an inch). The orbit of Pluto has a diameter of just over one centimeter (about the size of a U.S. dime), roughly marking the limits of the planetary part of the solar system. The nearest star is 41 meters away (about 135 feet), a lightyear on this scale being 9.5 meters, and a parsec 31 meters.

We are now ready to add the description of the Oort cloud to our model. In the usual theory, it is deduced from various observations that "new" comets—those which haven't been inside the planetary part of the solar system before—come from a cloud of at least a trillion comets[a,77] with a mean distance of 43,000 astronomical units (au; see Glossary). In our scale model, we would construct a sphere 6 meters from the Sun to represent the mean distance of the comets in the cloud, where the model will have about one

---

[a]P.R. Weissman now estimates there are about 7×10^{12} comets totaling 50 Earth masses (see next reference).

comet every cubic millimeter. These comets are essentially stationary with respect to the Sun, having mean velocities in the scale model of just 3 millimeters per 1000 years. Passing stars, on the other hand, move relatively rapidly, with typical speeds of a meter or so per 1000 years, and stir up the comets they come very close to. It is deduced that in this way, an occasional comet will by chance have its motion redirected toward the Sun in such a way that it will manage to pass within the 1mm-diameter sphere centered on the Sun, within which we on Earth can discover and observe it. We can calculate that fewer than one in 10,000 comets will ever come this close.

This scale model brings the comet cloud down to visualizable dimensions, while making the Earth's orbit and most of the domain of planetary space around us a mere speck. The reality is just the converse of this. The volume of planetary space around us is almost unimaginably large. For example, it is possible to fit the 200 billion stars in our galaxy entirely within the volume enclosed by the orbit of Pluto, yet have no stars touching! But the volume enclosed by the comet cloud is a billion times greater yet. It truly is unimaginably large, surviving as a plausible idea in large part because our intuitions fail so miserably to comprehend the vastness of this volume.

The scale model accurately reflects current theories about comets. They travel through space with the Sun and are clearly gravitational captives of the Sun, though at distances so great that other stars occasionally pass through the comet cloud. They exhibit no tendencies to favor the ecliptic (the plane of the Earth's orbit around the Sun) or any other plane. The number of comets within the cloud is believed to be immense in order to provide the few comets we observe, because the chances are so small of any one comet being perturbed into the observable range. And the absence of certain planetary perturbations in their motion proves that a large number of new comets arriving from distant parts of the cloud could never have passed so close to the Sun before, even though they complete a revolution around their elliptical orbits every few million years. How could these curious objects evolve into such a seemingly improbable situation?

Theories of Cometary Origins

As we have mentioned, theories of cometary beginnings may be separated into three categories: origins in interstellar space, origins near the present location of the Oort cloud, or origins in the solar/planetary environment. Strong arguments have been made over the years to support each of these suggestions. There are several characteristics of cometary orbits—particularly the tendency of the directions of approach to the Sun to cluster toward the direction of the Sun's motion through space—that suggest an interstellar origin. The difficulty with such an idea, and it is a substantial one, is that the Sun moves far too rapidly with respect to its stellar neighbors for a gravitational capture to be possible. One must therefore invoke an exotic capture mechanism; but none of the theories advanced to date do a satisfactory job of predicting the observed characteristics of cometary orbits.

Theories of origin from condensation of an extended solar nebula have fewer objections, since many comets could have remained in orbits similar to their present ones over the lifetime of the solar system, as long as they didn't come too close to the Sun. Even if they had originally condensed in a plane, perturbations by passing stars would have stirred them up into a spherical distribution in a few billion years. But such theories fail to provide a priori explanations for many non-random features of cometary orbits, such as the preferred direction of approach to the Sun; and it is certainly not well understood how comets could wind up at such huge distances from the Sun, 1000 times farther out than Pluto. It is also becoming increasingly difficult to account for the absence of any comets approaching on hyperbolic trajectories, which should arrive at the rate of at least a few per century if comets have been interacting with passing stars for billions of years.

But the most difficult objection for the condensation theory to overcome is how such objects could form in the first place. The sphere of influence of a typical 1-km comet nucleus in the Oort cloud is about 4,000,000 km. That's a lot of empty space, within which gravitational capture is impossible, as already discussed in the chapter on "Orbits." And the mean distance between comets is 1,000,000,000 km, so collision and accretion have negligible probability also. Forming anything in this vacuum, more perfect than any on Earth, would be quite a trick.

Origins within the planetary regions are easiest to invent (ejection from Jupiter or Io are popular versions), but have one major difficulty they must address. New comets arriving near the Earth's orbit reach infalling velocities with respect to the Sun which exceed 40,000 meters per second, so that the ejection of such comets from the planetary regions to their present orbits would have to be at similar velocities. Yet if these new comets were given just 0.5 meters/second more velocity than they already have near the Sun, they would exceed the velocity of escape from the solar system, and never return. Mechanisms that can pump up comet velocities so close to the critical velocity in such great numbers have been difficult to imagine. In particular, S. Yabushita[78] showed in 1979 that the initial minimum distances of the comets from the Sun must have exceeded about 1500 au to have any chance of evolving into an Oort cloud.

To minimize these difficulties it is now imagined that the Oort cloud comets come from a hypothetical "inner core" between the planetary region and the Oort cloud. There is no observational evidence for such a region—it is simply a theoretical construct. Then the inner core is fed by a hypothesized "Kuiper belt" of comets in nearly circular orbits near the plane of the other planets, beginning just outside the orbit of Neptune, which is supposed to have been left over from the primeval solar nebula.[79,80] Again, there is no observational evidence for this region either, despite many intensive searches leading one expert to make this comment: "We're disappointed because we thought it [observing a Kuiper belt comet] would be much more straightforward. But there's no reason to say there's something madly wrong with [comet] theory; with a little fine-tuning, our work fits with current models." (R. Webster, U. of Toronto.[82])

But the number of comets required by the theory is enormous, since this belt must constantly resupply the inner core, which in turn must resupply the Oort cloud's trillion or so comets.[b,81] Yet the

---

[b]The proposed Kuiper belt of comets was an effort to show where short-period comets came from. However, the calculations are based on

entire Oort cloud gets eliminated several times during the solar system's history by passing giant molecular clouds, galactic tides, and passing stars, and it must then be regenerated.[82] Another problem mentioned earlier is the complete absence of observed comets on hyperbolic orbits. Stirring of the Oort cloud by passing stars must occasionally send some of them toward us at speeds faster than escape velocity from the solar system; but such comets have never yet been observed. Their continued absence is becoming another embarrassment to the whole Oort cloud theory. Hence we have the situation that the description of the Oort cloud and theories of its origin, both of which are intrinsically extraordinary, have come to be widely accepted as necessary to explain what is observed about comets, despite numerous theoretical and observational inconsistencies.

---

an incorrect assumption: that capture by Jupiter is equally probable at all inclinations. Duncan, Quinn, and Tremaine, in computations which disagree with their predecessors, show that inclinations of Jupiter-captured short-period comets are approximately preserved. They conclude that an isotropic distribution of starting inclinations cannot lead to the observed dominance of low inclinations among the short-period comets. But this reasoning ignores that comets with low starting inclinations are far more likely to be converted by Jupiter into short-period comets.

We may reason as follows: At any given distance from the Sun, only the comet's velocity, but not its direction of motion, determines its period. As long-period comets come into the planetary region of the solar system, impulses by Jupiter to their velocities are quite efficient at inclinations near 0 degrees or 180 degrees, where such impulses essentially add or subtract from the comet's velocity. But at inclinations near 90 degrees, the impulses from Jupiter are nearly perpendicular to the comet's orbit, and have little effect on the comet's orbital velocity. So Jupiter more readily converts comets with orbits close to the ecliptic plane into short-period comets.

Similarly, perturbations on direct comets (inclinations near 0 degrees) last longer and are therefore larger on average than perturbations on retrograde comets (inclinations near 180 degrees). So it follows that low-inclination comets should indeed dominate the observed short-period comets if they all came from long-period comets, contrary to the reasoning that revived interest in the Kuiper belt of comets.

Full technical details of these arguments are presented in the next reference.

184

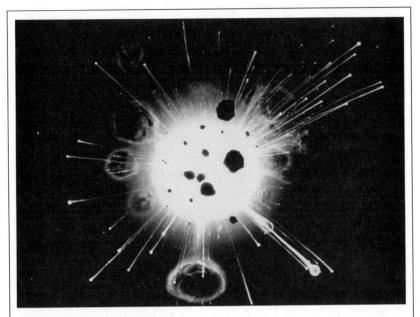

Figure 9.1. Cataclysmic breakup of a solar system body could lead to the formation of comets, minor planets, and meteors. Smaller fragments may become gravitational captives (satellites) of nearby large fragments. (Artist: Bensusen)

The Planetary Breakup as the Origin of Comets

In 1978, I proposed a new theory[83] which helps explain the major characteristics of observed cometary orbits in an a priori way and meets some other important criteria: it is consistent with the observations, adds new insight and understanding, and makes predictions which can be tested.

This new theory proposes that comets originated in the energetic breakup of a body orbiting the Sun in or near the present location of the asteroid belt in the relatively recent past. (See Figure 9.1.) Various lines of evidence have suggested the possibility of such an event.[83] This theory, though simply stated, has a great many consequences owing to the position and motion of the source body within the solar system and the implied existence of a common point of origin of comets in both space and time; and all these consequences turn out to be descriptions of the observed characteristics of cometary orbits!

To understand how this is so, let us first consider the fate of the debris ejected in all directions from such a

> "Where there is no solution, there is no problem."
> —John G. Price

breakup. Some fragments will enter elliptical orbits about the Sun with a great variety of speeds and directions. Almost all these fragments are eventually eliminated by the effects of the planets acting on their orbits. Only two types of orbits can survive the gravitational effects of the planets (their perturbations of the fragments' orbits) after a few million years: 1. roughly circular orbits which generally do not come close to the orbits of other planets (e.g. asteroid orbits); and 2. ellipses of such great distance and long period that the first return, and the consequent effects of planetary perturbations, have not yet occurred (e.g. comet orbits).

With respect to asteroid orbits, it is known that such orbits fill the entire volume of space which is stable against planetary perturbations over millions of years at that distance from the Sun. Moreover, the orbits exhibit "explosion signatures," which are a set of characteristics in the distribution of orbits that imply origin in an explosion.[84] For example, since all the fragments originated at one point at one moment, all the original orbits must have passed through that point. Precession of the orbits would have long since eliminated the "common point" for all orbits. But there would still remain several patterns; for example, a minimum eccentricity (ellipticity) for every mean distance from the Sun. Orbits at the mean distance of the explosion could have zero eccentricity. But orbits with a smaller or greater mean distance must have at least enough eccentricity at some time that they can reach the mean distance of the explosion. The asteroids do indeed have this characteristic: with the exception of some S-class asteroids (which may be collisionally evolved), the farther their solar mean distance is from 2.8 au, the greater is the minimum eccentricity of all the orbits found at that mean distance.

One very puzzling characteristic of the distribution of asteroid orbits is the so-called "Kirkwood gaps" in their mean distances. It is known that perturbations by Jupiter cause the asteroids to spend less time at these special mean distances than at other mean distances. But it is not known how asteroids could have originated in conventional theories without populating these empty zones with the same densities as the adjacent zones, if they formed over any period of time. All suggestions to date have been remarkably ad hoc. But if the asteroids originated all at once in an explosion, then the distribution of orbits in mean distance would be smooth at the outset, but would soon thin out in the regions where perturbations cause asteroids to spend less time. Hence the long-term average mean distances (one of the so-called "proper elements") would show gaps at those special distances, resolving the puzzle in an a priori way.

Let us consider the second type of orbit that can survive over millions of years. In particular, at an epoch x years after the breakup, fragments on orbits with periods of revolution less than x years will already have returned and suffered perturbations by the planets; all fragments with periods of exactly x years would be just returning for the first time; and all fragments with periods greater than x years will make their first return in the future. In that case, the periods of the orbits of the returning fragments at any epoch then tell how long ago the breakup occurred. And since period and mean distance of a fragment from the Sun are proportional, near any one epoch they will all seem to arrive from roughly the same distance from the Sun, even though fragments were ejected to all distances.

What we have just described is a characteristic of new comets. To within the limits of observational uncertainty and stirring by stellar perturbations, it is perfectly possible that all the observed new comets have almost exactly the same average period, and come from almost exactly the same mean distance, 43,000 au. (See Figure 9.2.) According to one very significant study,[85] after allowance for certain non-gravitational forces affecting the new comets, the reconstructed original mean periods are close to 3.2 million years,[c]

---

[c]The formal uncertainty of this estimate is only ±100,000 years. Changes by somewhat more than the formal error might occur if significant additional mass were discovered in the planetary region of the solar system; e.g. the hypothetical "Planet X" (see chapter of that name). But there seems to be very little possibility of changing the estimated time of the breakup event appreciably.

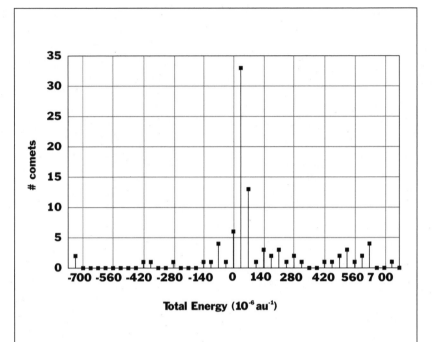

Figure 9.2. Number of comets (vertical axis) versus total energy (horizontal axis), which is closely related to both period and mean distance for each comet.

indicating that the hypothesized breakup event would have occurred that recently. Such a recent origin for the current observed comets is also supported by the calculations of S. Yabushita,[78] who argued that if the comet population is not in a steady state, then it must be only three to nine million years old.

Another important prediction of the breakup model is that since the event occurs relatively close to the Sun, the nearly parabolic orbits that are to become today's new comets are not sent off in equal numbers in all directions, even for symmetric breakup. This is called the "Sun-selecting influence," and when the orbital mechanics are worked out, it means that somewhere between 71% and 82% of all comets are ejected by the Sun toward one hemisphere of the sky centered on the ecliptic. The lower figure applies to the breakup of an object stationary with respect to the Sun, and the latter to an object with a circular orbit around the Sun.

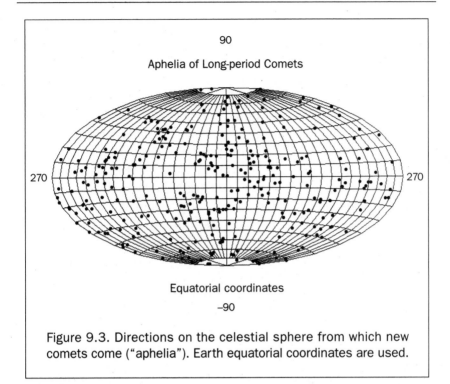

Figure 9.3. Directions on the celestial sphere from which new comets come ("aphelia"). Earth equatorial coordinates are used.

The observed figure for the actual new comets is 70% (see Figure 9.3.), but it turns out to be more like 84% when allowance is made for observational selection effects. (For example, more comets are discovered in the northern hemisphere because there are more observers; and there are more observers active in summer than in winter. Methods are available in the literature to calculate how much bias these effects introduce.) Not only are the observed and predicted distributions of directions of new comets on the sky in excellent agreement with the breakup model, but the figures even suggest support for the idea that the parent body was in a roughly circular orbit around the Sun. No other cometary origin theory has made such a specific quantitative prediction of this directional bias.

If comets did originate in a breakup event in the inner solar system, then the original distances of closest approach to the Sun (perihelion distances) for their orbits must all have been less than or equal to the distance at which the breakup occurred. Although this distribution of perihelion distances gets smeared out by stellar perturbations while the comets are far from the Sun, we can still predict that there will be fewer comets with perihelion points inside the Earth's orbit than for a comparable range outside the Earth's orbit. All competing theories, however, require that an essentially equal number of comets will be found within any given interval of perihelion distance, because of the much greater randomizing effect of stellar perturbations in these other models. Observations of how close new comets come to the Sun again favor the prediction of the breakup model: significantly fewer comets have perihelion distances inside the Earth's orbit. It has been argued ad hoc, however, that the bias in this distribution may be an observational selection effect for new comets, and due to the evaporation of part of their material by the Sun for old comets (although no such effect has yet been detected). But because of these loopholes, we can only say that the perihelion distance distribution favors the breakup hypothesis because of its a priori prediction of the effect.

For many years the Russian astronomer V. Tomanov[86] has argued for the interstellar origin of comets based on correlations of both orbital characteristics and physical properties (brightness, tail formation) with the solar apex (the Sun's direction of motion through the stellar neighborhood). It turns out that the breakup model even expects these characteristics when we examine the details of how the fragments become distributed in a breakup and how passing stars may later perturb them. However, there is one prediction of a breakup event which would be particularly convincing proof of our model—the intersection of all cometary orbital planes at a point (the point of breakup). This prediction cannot yet be verified directly because stellar perturbations, even if acting for only a few million years, are of sufficient size to have randomized this characteristic so that it can no longer be detected.

Summary and Predictions

One interesting possibility to study this point further is to turn things around and use the observed orientations of known comet orbits, in combination with the assumption that they all once intersected at a point. From these we could in principle reconstruct the masses, distances, and directions of the two or three most significant stellar encounters with our solar system during the last few million years. Of course, such a project cannot hope to succeed unless the underlying breakup hypothesis is correct.[d] Unfortunately it requires a great deal of calculation to test this, and the project has yet to be undertaken. But it offers the possibility of a decisive test of the validity of the breakup theory.

In summary, the hypothesis that comets originated in a breakup event only a few million years ago in the inner solar system makes a number of very specific predictions: that there will exist a category of first return ("new") comets; that these will have huge aphelion distances with intrinsically very little scatter; that they will come from preferred directions on the celestial sphere with a specific percentage bias; that the number of orbits will diminish as one looks closer to the Sun; that the distances and directions of approach will be correlated; and several other characteristics. And despite the fact that these predictions seem intrinsically improbable, they are a quite accurate description of the principal observed characteristics of actual comet orbits. Efforts to explain these characteristics with alternative theories inevitably must invoke an "Oort cloud" type of explanation, with its highly remarkable and, some would say, a priori implausible description. In the breakup model, comets are debris raining back on the site of their origin; and since a significant percentage of all comets return, instead of only the few specially selected by passing stars, the predicted space density of comets at 43,000 au from the Sun is a factor of ten thousand less than in the Oort model.[e]

Despite the arguments summarized here, many astronomers have rejected the breakup hypothesis, arguing that such an event

[d]It is understood that a nearly perfect match could be obtained by reconstructing a large number of such hypothetical encounters—say, one for every comet. But two or three such bodies could not hope to produce consistent perturbations over a sample of 100 or so comets by chance alone.

[e]Although this chapter criticizes the Oort cloud model extensively, such criticism should not in any case, but especially in this case, reflect on the person behind the idea. Astronomer Oort always maintained that an origin of comets from within the solar system, perhaps in connection with the event which gave rise to the asteroid belt, was the most probable.

in the recent history of the solar system is even less probable than the mysteries it explains. To compound the non-palatability of the new idea, I originally proposed it as supporting Ovenden's[87] arguments for the breakup of a 90-Earth-mass planet in the asteroid belt. Ovenden, however, felt that his event must have happened much more than several million years ago. If one assumes 10^{16} grams as a typical comet mass, the parent of this recent breakup event might have had only the dimensions of a typical planetary moon, although a planet-sized body seems altogether more likely.

What would it take for more astronomers to accept this model? The breakup hypothesis for the origin of comets may yet become the theory of choice if future verification of some of the following predictions is added to the existing evidence:

1. An adequate modeling of stellar perturbations will show that all new comet orbits intersected at a common point in the inner solar system 3 million years ago.

2. The Hubble Space Telescope will reveal that comets, like asteroids, have multiple nuclei as a result of many fragments in a breakup event remaining gravitationally bound to each other.

3. A comet fly-by mission will reveal that densities of cometary nuclei are consistent with rock, showing that comets are not exclusively frozen volatiles.

4. When a spacecraft returns a comet sample, it will show cosmic-ray exposure ages of only a few million years, even for "new" comets.

10

· ·

Do Comets Have Satellites?

Summary: This chapter deals with the nature of comets. We first review the traditional models, including the currently accepted "dirty-snowball" model. But after reviewing new data that does not fit that picture, and pointing out the similarities between comets and minor planets, we introduce the "satellite model" for the physical nature of comets. The satellite model follows directly from the exploded planet hypothesis and requires that comets, like minor planets, be small debris clouds of a multiple-body nature. Unlike minor planets, comets have still retained much of their original gas and dust, since they have spent relatively little time near the Sun. We develop again the sphere-of-influence concept to show both the stability of cometary satellite bodies and how they originated. We then review evidence from all aspects of observed cometary behavior. Especially definitive is evidence from the observed splitting of comets. The velocities of such splits provide a clear test of comet models, which is resolved unambiguously in favor of the satellite model. The implications of an intense meteor hazard for comet-approaching spacecraft are emphasized, along with other consequences implied by the new model.

Previous and Current Comet Models

Recent extensive evidence that many minor planets may have satellites, together with recently discovered physical, chemical, and lightcurve similarities between minor planets and comets, lead naturally to the question, "Might comets have satellites also?" This chapter explores several puzzling features of comets that do not fit easily into conventional cometary models, but which can be satisfactorily explained if it is assumed that comets have a full range of gravitationally bound masses ("satellites"), from dust size to the size of the nucleus, in orbit around a primary nucleus. This new model for what a comet is challenges the widely held "dirty-snowball" model for comets and fully supports the idea that comets originated in the explosive breakup of a large solar system body within the last few million years.

Despite much attention to the study of comets by astronomers, they remain among the least understood of solar system members. The currently dominant model to explain the principal behavior of comets is the so-called "dirty-snowball" model, which is an evolution of the "icy-conglomerate" model due to Whipple.[88,89,90] This model envisions comets as low-density, loosely packed frozen volatiles with embedded dust, coated with a thin crust of dust and debris. As they approach the Sun, the comets are heated by solar radiation, vaporizing the volatiles to form the gaseous or dusty comas around the nucleus. As they approach closer to the Sun, solar radiation pressure and solar wind interactions drive away some of the coma material, forming the long, streaming tails which make comets so unique in appearance.

While this model was derived to explain several important aspects of the behavior of comets, it has also left numerous unanswered questions and has had the awkward characteristic of requiring patchwork and a little "magic" to accommodate much recently discovered information about comets. Deficiencies in the model have been very much in evidence at recent colloquia on comets.[91] The basic idea behind the model has frequently been challenged, for example by Lyttleton, who questioned the existence of a nucleus at all and proposed instead that comets consist of swarms of high-velocity dust particles which become luminous through mutual collisions. Although Lyttleton has made an interesting case for his model based on the problems not solved by the dirty-snowball model, his dust-swarm model has the severe difficulty that such high-velocity particles could not remain gravitationally bound and would quickly dissipate, especially in the case of Sun-grazing comets.[a]

Similarities Between Minor Planets and Comets

We will next review the observational evidence suggesting that comets and asteroids are the same basic type of rocky bodies, despite the prevalent belief that comets are more ice than rock.

The similarities between minor planets and comets have frequently been noted, despite their obvious differences. It has even been suggested that at least some minor planets may be extinct comet nuclei. Eighty per cent of minor planets show spectra broadly consistent with those of carbonaceous meteorites (the most common type), leading to the identification of most of these as type C (for carbonaceous) minor planets. But dust samples from the upper atmosphere collected during meteor showers that are associated with disintegrated comets are also primarily of the carbonaceous type,[92] suggesting that the parent comets are, too. Most fireballs have orbits which go out beyond Jupiter,[93] associating them with comets rather than minor planets; yet most fireballs must be made of carbonaceous, not fluffy, materials, as evidenced by their ability to survive to such low altitudes while burning up in the Earth's atmosphere.

Measurements show that the reflectivity of light from comets is less than 10%,[94] and typically just a few percent, as is characteristic of carbonaceous minor planets, but rather unexpected for icy bodies. The similarity in reflectivity of cometary nuclei and minor planets has long been known,[95] although this is quite unexpected if the compositions are as different as the models imply. Additionally, radar echoes returned from Comet Encke yield a radar reflectivity of about 10%, again similar to minor planets and implying a non-porous (probably rock) surface material.[96]

---

[a]In my opinion, although Lyttleton's own model was too inductive and failed, nonetheless Lyttleton's clear thinking and maximum use of observations unconstrained by pre-conceptions should earn him significant credit whenever the history of comet models is written. Certainly his ideas have been influential to me in developing the satellite model for comets.

Such similarities between comets and minor planets lead naturally to the suggestion that minor planets are basically identical to comets except for having lost all their volatiles and dust by virtue of their prolonged proximity to the Sun. However, there are numerous objections to such a model, chiefly because of evidence that comets must be quite low-density objects to behave as they do—for example, the splitting of their nuclei. In this paper it will be shown that such objections all disappear if one takes into account that minor planets are not the simple, isolated, single-body systems they were thought to be.

The Satellite Model for Comets

This section outlines the proposed new model for what a comet really is, together with the observational evidence supporting this model.[b,97]

Evidence has surfaced over the past 10 to 15 years that minor planets have satellites,[98,99,100] a view which has been defended against challenges.[101] The tentative conclusion from observations to date is that such satellites and other orbiting debris must be both numerous and commonplace, and are likely to be present for most, perhaps all, minor planets.

We are therefore led to ask if comets might have satellites also. By the term "satellites," we contemplate a full range of masses from dust-size particles to objects of the dimensions of the primary nucleus. Comets would differ from minor planets in that small particles down to dust size could remain in orbit around the primary nucleus indefinitely, until the comet had been in close proximity to the Sun for hundreds or thousands of years. They could also have a full complement of frozen volatiles which would likewise be consumed by solar heating only quite gradually. Such a model can readily explain the gross properties of comets as easily as the dirty-snowball model. We will now investigate how well it fares with the puzzling and poorly understood aspects of cometary behavior.

---

[b]In addition to technical details in references already cited, a model update and critical discussion may be found in the next reference.

We will first consider direct observational evidence for the "satellite" model. To begin with, the literature is full of reports of suspected and confirmed secondary, multiple, or "granulated" nuclei of comets. Sekanina points out that these usually do not pass his test for being comet nuclei which split,[102] and he concludes they must be largely artifacts of observation. Sekanina speaks of ghost images, plate flaws, guiding problems, star images in the coma, and blurred stars near the horizon. For present purposes, it suffices to note that many of these observations do not need to pass Sekanina's splitting test if they refer to satellite bodies still under the gravitational influence of the nucleus, and therefore there is no problem with accepting the observations as correct.

The best observed lightcurve for a comet is that for D'Arrest,[103] which is of a distinctive triple-maximum, triple-minimum type. Among the minor planets there are similar lightcurves, such as for Betulia (same reference), for which an explanation invoking satellites has now been proposed. Each of these similarities leads us to ask whether the idea of orbiting satellites or debris, apparently valid for minor planets, has any applicability to comets. Similar ideas about the multiple-body nature of comet nuclei were earlier suggested by Öpik,[104] who should perhaps be credited as the first to propose this idea.

In the satellite model, comet comas consist of dust and debris which are orbiting the nucleus inside the comet's sphere of influence, even in deep space. Solar heating may still vaporize material, adding unbound gases to the coma at smaller heliocentric distances, and there are still plenty of volatiles—especially in the form of interstitial water-ice as found in meteorites—but the basic coma material would be orbiting and gravitationally bound to the nucleus. (See Figure 10.1.)

The Sphere-of-Influence Concept

For densities near unity and near the Earth's distance from the Sun, the sphere of influence within which permanent, stable satellites may reside is approximately 100 times the diameter of the principal nucleus (see the chapter "Orbits"). This remains true for bodies of all dimensions, bounded on the high side only by masses which

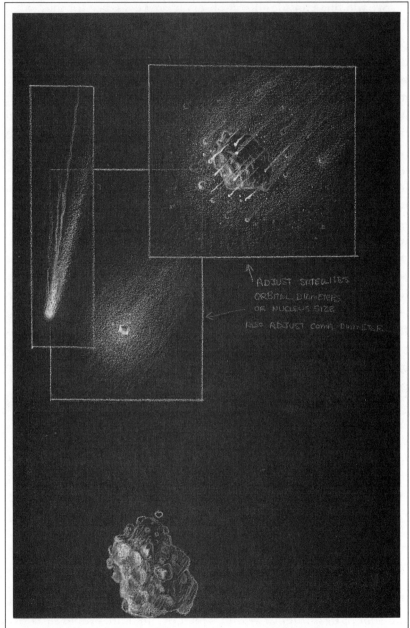

Figure 10.1. The satellite model for a comet, showing the orbiting debris cloud. (Artist: Bensusen)

approach the Sun's, and on the low side by masses so small that forces other than gravitation become dominant. Even a body one meter in diameter could hold stable satellites out to 100 meters' distance. This remarkable fact defies our intuition because it is of course untrue of bodies on the Earth, which are in a gravitational field 1700 times stronger than the Sun's at one astronomical unit. Similarly, a smaller sphere of influence may be set by the close approach of a body to Jupiter or another planet. At a distance of 0.5 au from Jupiter, the sphere of influence of a body is limited equally by the Sun and by Jupiter. It might also be noted that the sphere of influence of the satellite of a small body is very roughly its distance from its parent multiplied by the ratio of diameters, satellite to parent.

We can also calculate that the sphere of influence will extend only out as far as the surface of the body at a solar distance of about 0.005 au. For ordinary bodies bound together by cohesive forces rather than gravitation, this so-called "Roche limit" is irrelevant. However, for loosely-bound bodies, such as tidally decayed satellites of comets, such a limit is relevant. For such close approaches to the Sun, we may expect physical breakup of the major masses comprising the nucleus to set in at solar distances of about 0.01 au. A few comets do reach such small distances—most notably, members of the Kreutz Sun-grazing family of comets, members of which show up from time to time. It would be natural to conclude that this unusual family of comets was once a single typical comet whose satellites escaped and whose nucleus then re-fragmented. Each such satellite or fragment would then become an individual comet in a very similar orbit on subsequent returns to the vicinity of the Sun.[c]

---

[c]We might note in passing that close to the Sun's hot corona, the temperatures of these "Sun-grazing" comets must exceed 1,000 degrees. Such temperatures are one argument invoked for comets being primarily water-ice, since ice is such a poor conductor of heat that it would allow Sun-grazing comets to survive. But the basically rocky nature of comets in the satellite model also consists of plenty of interstitial water-ice which serves the same purpose.

Comet Coma Problems

Now let's examine problems not explained well or at all by the dirty-snowball model, but which are easy to understand in the satellite model of a comet.

Why do comets display large comas at very great distances from the Sun, where the solar vaporization of cometary materials is expected to be small?[105] Why do the linear dimensions of comas decrease, rather than increase as expected, when the comet approaches the Sun?[106] New comets are on rare occasions discovered at nearly Saturn's distance from the Sun, and always with comas which must be quite extensive to be seen at all at such distances. Both of these characteristics may be seen as evidence favoring the satellite model for comets over the dirty-snowball model. The second point, that comas decrease in linear dimensions (though not necessarily angular) as they approach, is particularly telling. It is exactly the behavior predicted by the satellite model as the sphere of influence shrinks during the approach. On the inbound trajectory, orbiting material which was previously bound indefinitely to the comet nucleus can escape.

Evidently most of the dust pushed into the tail by solar radiation pressure comes from weakly bound material in the outermost part of the coma, if this model is correct. Of course, the visible comas are larger than the stable sphere of influence, due to escaping gas and dust.

Comet Brightness Anomalies

Next we will look at additional problems with the physical appearance of comets where the dirty-snowball model had to be patched up to keep it viable, but where the satellite model provides a natural, unforced explanation.

Why do new comets (those approaching the Sun for the first time) lose two or three magnitudes in average brightness,[107] while old comets show little evidence for further brightness decreases?[108] Why do new comets follow a different brightening law as they approach the Sun than as they recede, or on subsequent revolu-

200

tions?[107] If the answer is that comets change physically upon their first approach to the Sun, why do they still have large comas and tails? And why isn't the occurrence of this physical change influenced by how close the comet gets to the Sun?

There was no decrease in brightness (to less than 0.1 magnitude) for 11 periodic comets studied over many revolutions (an average of 10 each). Yet new comets making their first approach to the Sun lose two or three magnitudes in brightness, primarily on the inbound leg (to judge from the magnitude behavior). The dirty-snowball model has been amended with the idea that a highly volatile surface frosting must evaporate on the comet's first approach to the Sun, leaving behind a hard crust. The difficulties with this suggestion are that the comet continues to have a substantial coma and tail, despite no detectable further magnitude loss; and that the frosting loss needs to be essentially the same for all different comet orbits, regardless of how close they get to the Sun. Moreover, the argument implies that comets must be quite young; for otherwise, nova and supernova explosions near the solar system over its four-billion-year history would have already had the crust-forming effect of an approach to the Sun, even if such events had not vaporized all comets outright.

By contrast, the satellite model predicts all this behavior without need for amendment to the theory. Far from the Sun a comet's gravitational sphere of influence is very large. On its first approach to the Sun, the sphere of influence shrinks to some minimum value at perihelion (the point of closest approach to the Sun), and a large part of the coma is able to undergo gravitational escape from the nucleus. On subsequent revolutions, as long as the comet's perihelion distance is nearly the same, the sphere of influence will reach the same minimum; hence new losses from the coma are limited to those caused by radiation pressure and solar wind. Further substantial losses by gravitational escape could occur only if perturbations reduced the comet's perihelion distance to a new minimum, thereby shrinking its sphere of influence further than it had ever shrunk before.

New comets tend to be relatively bright far from the Sun and brighten very slowly on their first approach, but behave pretty much as periodic comets do following their first perihelion passage, in conformity with the satellite model. To the problems already cited with the "surface frosting" explanation, we could add the prediction that cometary reflectivities, which generally are only a few percent for the nucleus, will be found to be essentially identical before and after the first perihelion passage if the satellite model is correct. The dirty-snowball model would clearly expect different albedos[d] before and after loss of the surface frosting.

The Mysteries of Split Comets

This section contains a discussion of the important phenomenon of cometary "splitting": when it can occur, and what it means in each of the two models—actual splitting of the nucleus in the dirty-snowball model, and escape of satellites in the satellite model.

When a comet splits, the separation velocities are amazingly small—generally less than 1 meter per second, even though orbital velocities around the Sun are typically 50,000 m/s. What causes such splits, and why are the velocities generated so small? Why do comets split preferentially before perihelion, even at Saturn's distance from the Sun, or else at perihelion, sometimes within hours of perihelion passage, but not in general afterwards?[109] Why did 4 of 5 new comets observed to split do so at distances greater than 2 au from the Sun? Why is it that only 4 of 21 split comets are periodic, and all those had recently interacted with Jupiter?

In the usual models, it is inferred that the nuclei of comets must be small and very low-density to permit such gentle splitting and to ensure that the escape velocity from the nucleus is smaller than the observed separation velocities. By contrast, in the satellite model, no such restrictions apply. The "splitting" is really the wandering off of one or more of the larger orbiting satellites which has found itself outside the sphere of influence of the nucleus for the first time as the comet approaches the Sun. The velocity of separation is then the orbital velocity of the satellite around the nucleus before escape. Separation velocities of 1 m/s and densities of 3 g/cm imply nucleus diameters of a few kilometers to produce the right amount of gravitation—a size estimate well in accord with direct observations.

---

[d]See Glossary for unfamiliar terms.

Comets can "split" by escape of satellites at any distance from the Sun, but only on the inbound leg or near perihelion, while the sphere of influence is shrinking. Once the sphere of influence begins enlarging again after perihelion, the probability of an escape considerably diminishes. The theoretical limit to the time after perihelion for gravitational escape of a satellite from a comet whose solar orbit is parabolic would be given approximately by $68\,q^{1.5}$ days, where q is the comet's perihelion distance. This reflects the tendency of low-perihelion comets to move away from the Sun immediately, and high-perihelion comets to remain close to their perihelion distance for prolonged periods of time. This time interval varies from just one hour in the case of a Sun-grazing comet $(q = 0.007\text{ au})$, to 68 days for a perihelion distance of 1 au, to 11 months for perihelion at 2.8 au.

The only exception would be the case of a close approach to a planet. Any example of a comet clearly splitting well after perihelion without a planetary cause would contradict the satellite model. It is therefore all the more remarkable that of 32 components resulting from 21 observed cases of split comets,[110] none of them provides the counter-example to the model. In all 14 cases with enough observations to determine estimates of the separation velocities, the computed epochs of splitting ranged from three years before perihelion to ten days afterwards. For the remaining 18 cases where too few observations exist to ensure a unique solution for splitting epoch, 8 of them seem to fall in the range from 12 to 125 days after perihelion.[e] However, the correlation between lateness of split and

---

[e]When the satellite model for comets was first submitted for publication in an astronomical journal, a referee correctly pointed out that if one can find an unambiguous example of the split of a comet as it moves rapidly away from the Sun, this would contradict the satellite model. Sekanina is of the opinion that at least comet 1899I, component B, is such a case. But there are insufficient observations to distinguish between two possible cases: that the comet did indeed split while moving rapidly away from the Sun, contradicting the satellite model; or that the "split" actually occurred while the comet was still approaching the Sun, but was hidden from view on Earth. In this second case, by the time the comet and its separated companion came into view again on the other side of the Sun, the companion would actually have been quite far from the comet,

increasing uncertainty in the solution is readily apparent; for example, the three latest solutions are based on only two observations each.

> "There's no limit to what can be done if it doesn't matter who gets the credit."
> —Anonymous

The satellite model predicts that usually only new comets can divide long before perihelion passage. Comets that have been close to the Sun before can split only if perturbations have lowered the perihelion distance, so that the comet comes closer to the Sun than ever before; or if a satellite had started to escape at the previous apparition but did not complete the process. Perturbations of the perihelion distance are usually small, so that old comets will spend perhaps only a few hours or days at distances closer to the Sun than they have been before. These are the most likely times for splits to occur, just as observed. In the conventional models, the excess number of old comets splitting so very close to perihelion would not be expected, since the differential changes in perihelion distance for any one comet are usually inconsequential for changing the thermal or radiation impact on a comet. As it happens, all four of the "old" periodic comets in Sekanina's table which split had at least a mild encounter with Jupiter on the preceding revolution, resulting in larger than normal changes in their orbits. As already explained, this can induce splitting at the next perihelion passage when the comet's sphere of influence becomes smaller than ever before.

Sekanina has undoubtedly done more research on the cause of comet splitting than any other investigator. As he says,[110] "The breakup of Comet 1957 VI on its first approach to the Sun at a distance comparable with that of Saturn ... has far-reaching implications for theories of the structure of cometary nuclei." This is surely true, and it is interesting to note how well the satellite model explains such an event in comparison with other models.

---

but nearly "behind" it as seen from Earth. The "split" event would then have been simply the appearance of the distant companion from behind the comet as both moved along in their solar orbits.

The Split Distance-Velocity Relationship

Next we describe the results of an observational test that unambiguously tells us which is the more nearly correct model.

Sekanina has made the important discovery[110] that the velocity of separation of split components is correlated with the distance from the Sun at which the split occurs. In the conventional models, we would expect either little or no correlation between velocity and distance from the Sun at splitting ("power law" correlation parameter b = 0.0) if splits are due to internal processes, or that b = 1.0 if the process is related to solar radiation or heating, which are inverse square forces.[f] In the satellite model, the prediction is simple and unambiguous. Separation velocity must be equal to escape velocity from the sphere of influence, whose radius depends on distance from the Sun. The satellite model predicts b = 0.5 exactly. Sekanina finds from observations that b = 0.57 ± 0.10. This result essentially proves that the satellite model is more nearly correct than any of the other models.

Physical Properties of Comets

We continue with a variety of miscellaneous other properties of comets which seem in some way diagnostic between the two mod-

---

[f]For those interested, I will explain the power law parameter "b" in more detail. If R is the distance of comets from the Sun at the time of a split, then b is defined as the negative power of the R (i.e., R^{-b}) which best matches the behavior of the separation velocities of the split components. If splits are due to entirely internal cometary processes not influenced by the Sun, then there should be no connection between split velocity and solar distance (i.e., b = 0). If splits are affected by solar light, heat, or tidal forces, then the available energy will be proportional to R^{-2}, which implies split velocities proportional to R^{-1} (i.e., b = 1). If splits are gravitational escapes of orbiting material, then split velocities will be proportional to the square root of component distance from the nucleus at the time of split. Because the size of the comet's sphere of influence (which determines maximum component distance from the nucleus to remain in orbit) is directly proportional to comet distance from the Sun, this case implies b = 0.5.

els. We will also mention the meteor hazard implications of the satellite model for spacecraft approaching comets and minor planets.

According to the exploded planet hypothesis, comets originated at a distance of 2.8 au from the Sun (the distance of the missing planet, and the center of the asteroid belt). This solar distance then determined the initial size of their spheres of influence. On subsequent returns to the vicinity of the Sun, it is observed that comet tails tend to "turn on" at a solar distance of about 2.8 au, when the sphere of influence is first forced to a smaller size than it had at formation. Once inside that distance, gravitational escape of orbiting material will be added to the escape of gas and dust through solar radiation pressure and the solar wind. The dirty-snowball model accommodates this behavior by assuming that comet volatiles begin to vaporize at that distance. The exploded planet theory has a priori reason for expecting a change in behavior at just that precise distance.

In the satellite model, I would expect each and every body in orbit around the nucleus to be a separate source of material for the tail. In general, gas would be from heated, vaporized volatiles; and dust would be from material trapped in orbit around the nucleus, or around one of the numerous satellite bodies of the nucleus. Escape of dust would never be from the surface of any of these bodies, but only from the sphere of influence of one of them. In effect, each mass would produce its own tail, just as is seen when comets split.[g] But only the largest orbiting masses would produce tails with enough contrast to be observable within the coma around the comet's nucleus.

Sekanina uses the conventional model and the strength of the operative tidal forces on two cases of apparent Roche limit breakups to estimate an upper limit for the tensile strength of cometary material, which is an extremely low value, comparable to the gravitational binding forces alone. As already discussed, after all orbiting material is stripped away, the satellite model contemplates the breakup of tidally coalesced satellites that have merged with the nucleus, for which low tensile strengths are appropriate (since the

---

[g]Multi-tail single comets are also observed on rare occasions.

fragments were never physically part of the nucleus, but only lying on it). From the relative accelerations and brightnesses of fragments, Sekanina also concludes (using the dirty-snowball model) that fragments must be relatively flat, pancake-like sections of cometary surface crusts with volatiles preserved intact. Other investigators have reasoned in a similar way to the conclusion that comets must be fluffy dustballs,[111] despite their being made of primarily carbonaceous materials. Neither of these odd deductions is necessary when using the satellite model.

Another problem for the dirty-snowball model is the absence of ices in the reflection spectra of comets at any reasonably expected level.[112] This is another problem which does not occur in the satellite model, where comet ices are interstitial (within the rock), not on the surface of the nucleus and its satellites.

What about non-gravitational forces and eruptive phenomena? Comets are observed to be gently propelled away from the Sun by something called a "non-gravitational force." In the dirty-snowball model, it was originally inferred that comets had densities perhaps as low as 0.01 to 0.001 that of water, so that they would be able to yield to solar radiation pressure by the observed amount. When such low densities became untenable, it was hypothesized that the Sun triggered massive "jets" on the sunward side of their nuclei that propel comets away.

In the satellite model, the radial force comets experience away from the Sun must be entirely due to radiation pressure, rather than reactive outgassing or jets. Solar radiation pressure is a considerably larger force than would otherwise be calculated because there is a large cross-section of orbiting material which experiences the pressure, not just the nucleus. This large surface area gets around the dilemma experienced by Sekanina, that differential non-gravitational forces in split comets imply fragment diameters of at most a few meters, which would certainly be unobservable. Much larger fragments can experience the same forces because their debris clouds also intercept solar radiation.

Transverse (along the velocity vector) and normal (perpendicular to the orbit) components of non-gravitational forces would be due to the transfer of orbital angular momentum to the nucleus from material which gravitationally escapes the sphere of influence, rather than due to rotation of the nucleus. Since most such escapes occur in the comet's orbital plane, transverse non-gravitational forces would be far larger than normal ones. Precession phenomena, such as exhibited by Comet Encke,[113] would represent precession of an equatorial plane of the larger satellites, rather than precession of the nucleus. Even for material which does not escape, solar radiation pressure would produce a small transverse component of force—just as it does for balloon satellites of the Earth—by systematically altering the orbital eccentricities of the comet satellites and orbiting debris.

The sudden brightenings of comets might then be associated with collisions and the tidal decay onto the nuclei of the larger satellite bodies, with the consequent release of clouds of dust and debris. Both collisions and tidal decay can be exacerbated by solar radiation pressure forces. The frequency with which such outbursts occur at or beyond Jupiter's orbit suggests the existence of a vast field of meteoroids captured by Jupiter, in the same manner that short-period comets are captured by it.

In considering the physical nature of comets, it should not be forgotten that the surfaces of comets undergo extreme variations in temperature whenever a comet approaches the Sun.[h] The accompanying expansion and contraction of the nucleus from the extremes of heating and cooling are surely not without their consequences. A spacecraft probe landing on a comet would seem likely to discover those consequences early in its visit.

The Meteor Hazard

A further important implication of the satellite model is that the material escaping from comets is not just fine dust blown off the nucleus, but may be dense clouds of dust and debris of a range of sizes undergoing gravitational escape. What happens when we enter the "wake" of such escaping material may be most dramatically demonstrated by the well-known Leonid meteor showers of 1833 and 1866 (the skies were filled with thousands of meteors). Yeomans has shown that whenever the Earth passes through a certain

---

[h] I am indebted to my wife Barbara for pointing out this consideration.

position close to the orbit of the parent comet near the time when the comet is there also,[114] these intense showers occur. There is no basis for concluding that the parent comet of the Leonids is exceptional in this regard, especially since its intense displays can be traced back in historical records for at least seven centuries.[i]

However, it is unlikely that the Earth approached closer than half a million kilometers to the densest part of the accompanying cometary debris! There is therefore a clear implication of this model regarding the hazard of flying spacecraft in the vicinity of comets, or for that matter, minor planets as well. It is further implied that certain directions of approach will be safer than others. Spacecraft should avoid flying through the orbital plane of a comet close to the nucleus, especially near the in-track part of the orbit. High-speed travel well inside the sphere of influence may be expected to be fatal to spacecraft.

Note 1: Five spacecraft were sent to the vicinity of Halley's Comet in 1986. The spacecraft all approached the comet from directions well out of the comet's orbital plane. All spacecraft survived intact except the one which mildly penetrated the comet's sphere of influence (to about 500 km distance). That spacecraft hit two particles about 1–2 millimeters in diameter, causing a temporary loss of communications and other damage (because of the high relative speeds).

Note 2: Why weren't satellites seen when spacecraft flew by Halley's Comet? Because the comet coma was a bright continuum of light, making it very difficult to see anything inside it. The published photos are a bit deceptive, since the background light levels were adjusted to black by computer enhancement; whereas in fact, they were relatively bright. Contrast was so poor that light and dark areas on the surface of the nucleus made it look at first as if there were separate bodies present. Satellites, which were necessarily much fainter than the nucleus, had no chance to be seen. Moreover, the most probable locations for satellites are from five diameters

---

[i]According to advanced estimates, and bearing in mind that the prediction of such "meteor storms" is still a haphazard process with many uncertainties, nonetheless it appears that conditions may well be favorable for a repeat performance in November, 1999.

of the nucleus out to 20 diameters for Comet Halley (because closer satellites would have tidally decayed from orbit). None of the spacecraft had the capability to scan such regions for possible satellites. They simply searched for the region of maximum light, and photographed that. However, two different and inconsistent rotation periods were observed for this comet. One way to resolve that inconsistency is to postulate an orbiting satellite to account for the longer (7-day) period.[j]

Some of the photos showed what were described as "jets" emanating from the nucleus. In the best composite picture available, these do not look so much like jets to me, because they are relatively diffuse and unfocused. The overall appearance is consistent with spots so relatively bright that the reflected sunlight from them scatters and preferentially illuminates the coma material immediately above them.[k] The fact that the Comet Halley lightcurves were so similar between 1910 and 1986 suggests that the "jets" were the same each time, as if from fixed spots. And measurements show no accelerations or pressures in the so-called jets above the ambient pressures. However, there clearly is removal by solar radiation of the lighter volatiles from both the primary nucleus and from every secondary body of every size in the whole complex. Some of this removal might be via weak jets.

The Hubble Space Telescope will have the same difficulty seeing satellites of comets, because the problem is one of contrast, not brightness or resolution. Nonetheless eventually a comet will come along with one or more satellites so relatively large that the Hubble Telescope should be able to see them distinctly, although they will look very much like "condensations" in the coma. Their satel-

---

[j]A debate still rages in the literature over the "correct" spin period of Comet Halley. No single value seems to fit all the observations. Various bizarre spin states and mass distributions have been considered. But none of the models have considered the tidal influence of a large satellite, which might potentially resolve all the apparent conflicts of data.

[k]It is normal behavior for comets and asteroids to preferentially backscatter light along the incoming direction. This is known in astronomy as the "opposition effect" in the magnitude or brightness of these objects.

lite nature will be betrayed by orbital motion around the nucleus over a period of days or weeks.

Note 3: The *Galileo* mission to Jupiter scheduled two approaches to minor planets along the way. There should be minimal hazard from debris escaping the minor planets, since the debris satellite orbits have remained similar for millennia. The main added risk would come from deep penetration into the sphere of influence. For the Gaspra approach, October 29, 1991, anything closer than about 1000 km would start to get hazardous. For the Ida approach around August 28, 1993, the equivalent distance would be 3000 km or so. Since survival of the spacecraft is important, such close approaches should be avoided until more is known. The spacecraft actually flew by Gaspra at a distance of about 1600 km from Gaspra. Although this is within the theoretical sphere of influence, fortunately the outer portions of the sphere of influence for a minor planet should be fairly well depopulated due to tidal forces. In any event, when additional photographs from the approach become available after December 8, 1992, they may reveal satellites of Gaspra (see the chapter "The Discovery of Minor Satellites").

Conclusions

From the preceding discussion it may be concluded that the satellite model is in better agreement with the observed characteristics of comets than is the dirty-snowball model or any of its current variations. In addition, the satellite model provides new insights into the nature of comets, with important implications for their origins and for the hazard of spacecraft missions to comets. Indeed, it would be fair to conclude that the satellite model is able to explain or shed new light on every puzzling aspect of comet behavior considered here, even in cases where the conventional models offer no explanation or lead to otherwise absurd deductions about the nature of comets. We can therefore feel fairly safe in concluding that comets and minor planets are indeed similar structures dynamically, physically, and chemically (since such similarities are what suggested the model in the first place).

The model of a comet that emerges from this discussion is a primary nucleus consisting of a chondritic mass a few kilometers in diameter, with a large number of tidally coalesced masses of a range of sizes on its surface. In orbit around this nucleus will be other masses covering the full range of sizes from dust to nearly nucleus-sized dimensions, out to distances of perhaps 100 times the diameter of the nucleus. The coma is the extension of this stable inner sphere of orbiting material, and represents gaseous emissions and other chondritic material in transition to gravitational escape of the nucleus. The tail, which only turns on inside about 2.8 au from the Sun, is coma material, especially gas and dust, pushed away from the Sun by solar radiation pressure. As comets approach the Sun, the radius of their stable sphere of influence shrinks, permitting the escape of orbiting material. Comet splits are the escape of relatively large satellites. The abundance of escaped material of dust and small meteoritic dimensions would make approaching a comet a hazardous undertaking, unless the spacecraft were adjusted to the comet's velocity, since the velocities of this material relative to the comet are quite small. A minor planet would then be the same sort of structure, with the exception that all volatiles and dust would have been removed by solar radiation pressure.

Finally, we should comment on the origin of the sort of structures implied by the satellite model. The very stability of the systems dynamically precludes an origin by gravitational capture of the ordinary two-body sort; nor can tidal forces enhance the capture probability above an insignificant level. The chief alternative explanation usually proposed is origin through collisional breakup. Even if a case could be made for minor planets, it would be especially difficult to apply to comets, for which collision probabilities must surely always have been negligible. But in addition, collisionally ejected material leaves the collision site on trajectories which, if it does not escape immediately, must return to intersect the surface from which it originated after one orbit. Even if multiple collisions or solar perturbations raised the pericenter distance somewhat, so that a fragment's satellite orbit was temporarily stable, tidal forces would cause its decay back onto the surface of the primary nucleus in short order. Therefore, collisional processes cannot produce satellites other than in rare and highly unusual circumstances.

One mode of origin which works well for both comets and minor planets and produces just the sort of satellite structures suggested by observations is the explosive breakup of a large mass. As fragments of a wide range of dimensions and velocities flee the breakup site, their individual spheres of influence begin to enlarge. The limit on the size of the sphere of influence of each fragment is set only by its nearest neighbor of comparable or larger mass, until all recede to such distances that the Sun sets the ultimate limit. As the sphere of influence enlarges in this non-reversible way, all material traveling with similar velocities which finds itself within that sphere of influence will be captured into stable orbits. It is therefore inevitable that all fragments will capture abundant debris into satellite orbits as they take up independent solar orbits of their own. A verification of the satellite model would therefore be an additional argument in favor of the "exploded planet" hypothesis.

By no means have we now covered all the evidence for the planetary breakup model. In fact, it would be fair to say that, in the manner of a deductive hypothesis with a correct starting point, almost any bit of related observational data fits well into this framework, without need for "patches" to the theory. The chapter "A Synthesis of Recent Planetary Breakup Evidence" provides an indication of the length and breadth of that evidence, which is pervasive. A pattern is clearly visible: the planetary breakup hypothesis explains the observations easily and well. Conventional models require the invention of numerous new explanations for numerous new observations.[1]

Although it changes the way we view the solar system and our current understanding of the nature and origin of the solar system's small bodies, and despite its unsettling implications, we conclude that the planetary breakup hypothesis accounts for the observational data, provides better understanding, and makes many testable predictions. By the criteria we have discussed, this should entitle it to acceptance *as a hypothesis* in good standing in mainstream astronomy.

---

[1]My wife Barbara compared the situation to the proverbial blind men trying to describe an elephant after each touching one part of it. Each scientist sees his own part of the picture, interprets his own experiments or data in terms of the conventional models as best he can, and fails to see how it all fits into the bigger picture.

Combining these new results for the solar system with the earlier results for cosmology, we begin to see that a generalization can be made—a generalization which seems to be true in all authoritarian bodies, not just in astronomy: when new data become available, the existing models are patched instead of being re-examined from first principles. As a consequence, everything appears to be in order at the working levels in all fields, even when it is not. And challenges to the fundamental underlying assumptions are not generally encouraged, since such challenges adversely impact the greatest number of people.

This need to re-examine the fundamentals as new data become available is one of the themes which unifies the diverse topics of this book. But there may be another, physical connection as well. The planetary breakup hypothesis implies that a fireball originated in the solar system a few million years ago, expanding in all directions. Although the flux from it would remain uniform as seen from the inside, it should eventually cool to the limiting temperature set by interstellar radiation: about 3 degrees Kelvin. Radiation from this fireball, just as for the hypothetical Big Bang fireball, should be of the blackbody type. In other words, the planetary breakup hypothesis seems to predict a uniform microwave blackbody radiation just like the one which is observed, but of relatively local origin. But the existence of the cosmic microwave radiation, presumed to come from beyond the farthest galaxies, is the strongest remaining argument supporting the Big Bang theory of the origin of the universe. So if it can be shown that the exploded planet event did produce a local fireball which is now the source of the 3-degree microwave radiation, these solar system results will require a revolution in cosmology as well.

11

• •

A Synthesis
of Recent Planetary
Breakup Evidence

Summary: A recent major planetary breakup event should have left evidence all over the solar system. This summary is organized into evidence from asteroids, comets, planets and their moons, and meteoroids, leaving little doubt that such an explosion did happen.[115] We also cite miscellaneous evidence, and evidence which does not fit the hypothesis. (References not shown here may usually be found in the author's technical papers.)[116]

I. Evidence related to asteroids

A. The gap between Mars and Jupiter is filled with tens of thousands of irregular-shaped, fragment-like bodies, the asteroids. Their orbits have a much higher range of tilts and ellipticity than if they had condensed as the other planets did. Their small size and these orbital characteristics led Olbers to first formulate the planetary breakup theory in 1802.

B. The orbits of the asteroids are distributed throughout the entire volume of space at their distance from the Sun which is stable against planetary perturbations. They are therefore clearly just the remnants of a much larger original population from which the escaping and unstable orbits have been eliminated.

C. The mean relative velocities between asteroids are 5 km/s. This is easy to understand as the result of a breakup, and difficult to explain if the asteroids condensed from a solar nebula, especially since mutual collisions tend to damp out rather than enhance the mean relative velocities.

D. The predicted mean time between major asteroid collisions is about 5% of the age of the solar system. All asteroids should already be highly fragmented unless their origin is relatively recent, as in the exploded planet theory.

E. Asteroids exhibit "explosion signatures" in the distribution of their orbital elements. These relationships between the orbital elements a (semi-major axis), e (eccentricity), and i (inclination) were first found among fragments from artificial satellites of the Earth which exploded in orbit, and then were found to hold for the asteroid belt as well.

F. One of the "explosion signatures" in the asteroid belt, the "Kirkwood gaps," cannot be explained without the introduction of special, ad hoc conditions in the conventional theories of origin of asteroids. But they are apparently a natural consequence of an explosion origin for asteroids.

G. Satellites of asteroids appear to be numerous and common-place. Although that is disputed, it is clear that they are not rare, since they have turned up in several of the relatively few occasions when occultation observations could show them. Their existence is a natural and inevitable by-product of the expanding spheres of influence of the parent bodies as they flee from a breakup of a larger mass. Satellites are troublesome to explain in other models because gravitational and collisional origins for them can be virtually ruled out by the laws of dynamics.

H. Tidal forces and collisions should have eliminated most minor planet satellites in far less than the age of the solar system, but not in a time as short as a few million years.

I. There are still approximately 1000 asteroids bigger than 1 km in Earth-crossing orbits, despite the inevitable elimination of such objects by the Earth, mostly by collision, within about 30,000,000 years. Dynamicists have shown that either a recent source or a continuous production of these objects is required. Proposed models for a continuous production have so far all been criticized as untenable.

J. The four known meteor streams associated with asteroids instead of comets all apparently "broke apart" near their perihelion. The satellite model (from the exploding planet hypothesis) predicts that when any asteroid's orbit has its perihelion lowered by planetary perturbations, some satellites will escape into its solar orbit, because its sphere of influence gets smaller. The conventional model expects these breakups only from infrequent collisions, so they can occur near perihelion only by coincidence.

K. The three principal bands of zodiacal dust detected by the IRAS satellite are associated with the three principal asteroid families: Themis, Kronos, and Eos. Apparently the collision event which broke up the parent asteroids and created these three families dumped many fragments and enormous amounts of dust into the same regions. In the breakup model, the fragments are former satellites, and there was far more room for dust to have been stored inside the sphere of influence of the parent asteroid than there was on its surface.

II. Evidence related to comets

A. In 1814 Lagrange pointed out that the extremely elongated orbits of comets would be a natural by-product of an explosion in the solar system (fragments raining back on the site of the breakup), but was not expected to occur through condensation from a nebula.

B. The exploded planet theory is the only dynamically viable alternative to the Oort cloud. The latter requires the existence of an implausible cloud of more than a trillion comets orbiting the Sun at distances 1000 times that of Pluto, so remote that passing stars would frequently pass through it.

C. The failure to detect a source of re-supply of comets in the Oort cloud from a hypothetical inner "Kuiper Belt" means that Oort cloud comets should have long since been depleted by passing stars, galactic tides, and passage of the Sun through giant molecular clouds, unless comets originated quite recently.

D. The absence of observed comets on hyperbolic orbits, which encounters with passing stars over billions of years must produce in abundance, requires a much more recent origin for all comets.

E. Many "new" comets coming directly from the "Oort cloud" for the first time develop tails when they reach 2.8 au from the Sun. In the breakup model, all comets originated at 2.8 au from the Sun. Those that headed away from the Sun and are returning for the first time have never been closer. When they first get closer than 2.8 au, some orbiting material will be able to escape the comet's gravitation for the first time, forming the tail.

F. The chemical abundance ratio N2 / NH3 in comets should be 100–200 from conventional models in which comets originate in the outer solar system or farther out—essentially any cold environment. But the observed ratio is 1/10 in Comet Halley, suggesting origin much closer to the Sun, as in the exploded planet hypothesis.[117]

G. After correction for selection effects, 84% of comets arrive from one hemisphere of the sky, 16% from the other. This is required by the exploded planet hypothesis, provided that the exploded object was orbiting the Sun as would be expected, not stationary relative to the Sun. The Oort cloud hypothesis offers no explanation for this asymmetry.

H. Significantly fewer comets have perihelia inside the Earth's orbit than in an equal interval outside. This bias is predicted and required by the exploded planet theory and is assumed by the Oort cloud theory to be a bias in the observations.

I. Correlations are observed of both orbital characteristics and physical properties (such as brightness and tail formation) with direction of arrival, as predicted by the exploded planet theory. The coincidence of the direction of symmetry lying in the broad, general direction of the solar apex was previously taken as support for an interstellar origin of comets. But interstellar origins are not dynamically viable, since capture cannot occur by gravitation alone.

J. Spectra and albedos of most minor planets, comets, and meteorites are all closely similar, although distinctively different from all other solar system bodies (except planetary moons that appear to be captured asteroids), strongly suggesting a common origin in time and place.

K. The optical reflectivity of minor planets and comets is extremely low, as expected from the charred residue of an explosion. The dirty-snowball model predicts ices, which are conspicuously absent from the reflection spectra of comets. Radar reflectivities also imply comets are rocky, not porous or icy.

L. Some comet lightcurves and some observations of multiple nuclei suggest that comets, like minor planets, have a multiple-body nature, as would result naturally from an explosion.

M. The satellite model for comets, implied by the exploded planet theory, would explain the formation of the Kreutz Sun-grazing family of comets from a single parent comet from which all satellites were stripped, including those lying on the surface of the nucleus. The dirty-snowball model is vague on the details of the formation of this family, since it does not imply any particular splitting mechanism.

N. Sun-grazing comets come so close to the Sun's hot corona that their temperatures must exceed 1000 degrees. This is not a problem for rocky bodies with interstitial water/ice, as in the satellite model. But in the dirty-snowball model, comets are highly volatile snowballs that might completely vaporize under these conditions, but do not obviously show any ill effects.[a]

---

[a]This argument is sometimes seen in reverse. Water droplets in a newly heated frying pan will vaporize quickly. But at higher temperatures, a vapor layer forms which insulates the water droplets, and they can survive far longer. It is concluded that icy comets will survive longer than rocky ones through this mechanism. But the fallacy with this argument is that the comets must constantly go through the temperature range where vaporization occurs quickly as they rotate in hours to days. So icy comets will repeatedly pass through the quick evaporation stage. Rocky comets with interstitial water would survive longer because the vapor layer protects the rock from melting at high temperatures, and the rock prevents dissipation of the vapor layer at lower temperatures.

O. The comas of comets are large at great solar distances, and decrease in size as they approach the Sun. This is the opposite of the behavior predicted by the dirty-snowball model, but exactly the behavior predicted by the satellite model through the sphere-of-influence concept.

P. New comets lose an order of magnitude in brightness on their first approach to the Sun, whereas old comets show no further detectable losses, even after ten revolutions. This latter behavior is opposite to specific predictions of the original dirty-snowball model (which has since been amended), but exactly what the sphere-of-influence concept would require. For new comets, the brightening power law changes character near perihelion, exactly as the satellite model says it must.

Q. In all 14 cases of split comets where the date of splitting is well determined, all splits occurred before or near perihelion, as required by the satellite model. This is not only unexpected by the dirty-snowball model, but was a completely unknown fact (because of many split companions seen only after perihelion, but where the date of split was unknown) before the satellite model predicted that it must be so.

R. Relative velocities of split-comet components are quite small, consistent with gravitational escape of satellites, but not with collisional or eruptive processes. This also supports the satellite model, as derived from the exploded planet hypothesis.

S. Variations in relative split velocities with solar distance are accurately in agreement with the satellite model, and strongly inconsistent with models in which splits are due to either internal comet processes or to solar light, heat, or gravity. This data alone effectively disproves all existing competitors to the satellite model.

T. If comets are not gravitationally bound multiple-body systems, as implied by the exploded planet theory, then their implied tensile strengths in certain breakup cases are very low. Taken together with the relative accelerations of fragments, it is implied that fragment comets are quite flat and have the densities of fluffy dustballs. These absurd but apparently necessary conclusions of the dirty-snowball model are inconsistent with much other data.

U. Differential non-gravitational forces in split comets imply fragment diameters of at most a few meters in the dirty-snowball model, which would certainly be unobservable. In the satellite model, the area subject to solar radiation pressure is the entire sphere of influence, often 10,000 times larger, which would imply larger fragments having brightnesses about as observed.

V. Blobs of OH emissions in Comet Wilson, seen with the VLA radio telescopes, persist at distances up to 10^6 km from the nucleus,[118] suggesting non-dispersing streams of meteoroids accompanying the comet. The satellite model easily explains these as under the control of an escaped asteroidal satellite of the comet. This behavior is not understood in the dirty-snowball model.

W. Bursts of dust particles in Comet Halley seem to come from parts of the coma other than the nucleus.[119] This is easily understood if the sources are satellites of the nucleus, but poorly understood if all the coma was itself ejected from the nucleus.

X. Spacecraft measurements of Comet Halley showed that a large fraction of gases in the coma were not evaporated from the nucleus, but rather were released from grains in the coma at large distances from the nucleus. This again is in perfect accord with the satellite model, and unexpected in the dirty-snowball model.

Y. When a European spacecraft approached Comet Halley to within about 500 km, it was struck by a particle with a size of about 2 mm. This is larger than can be lifted off the nucleus by solar radiation and implies that the particle had been orbiting prior to impact, as the satellite model would predict. The dirty-snowball model now suggests that such particles are lifted by the action of geyser-like jets on the nucleus.

Z. The IRAS satellite has discovered infrared trails in the orbits of comets, typically 10,000 km wide. These must consist of dust and larger particles with very low relative velocities, as would be expected if they gravitationally escaped the comet's sphere of influence. Dust ejected in geyser-like jets should have been dispersed over far wider areas.

AA. In the dirty-snowball model, the observed "jets" in Comet Halley are actively transferring material away from the nucleus. Calculations show that these should produce torques that affect the rotation of the nucleus in a short time. But long-term observations clearly show that the rotation of the nucleus has not been affected significantly by torques. In the satellite model, the streamers called jets are actually coma dust made visible in columns over bright surface features by the tendency of sunlight to reflect preferentially back on itself, rather than to scatter. Such dust columns would produce no torques.

AB. Long, narrow, dark streaks are sometimes seen within the tails of comets. These very much look like the shadows of small bodies near the comet, in accord with the satellite model.

AC. Tail disconnection events in comets seem to occur at regular intervals, typically about a week apart, preceded and followed by long periods without such events. The cause of this behavior is unknown in the dirty-snowball model. It may be readily visualized as caused by large satellites of comets, which would produce eclipses of active regions on the nucleus at regular intervals, until precession caused their shadows to miss the nucleus altogether.

III. Evidence related to planets and their moons

A. Although Mercury's location in the inner solar system causes it to be coated all over by debris from the breakup, much of which orbits the Sun, its slow rotation would cause the initial blast wave to crater it more heavily on one hemisphere, as observed.

B. The abundance of deuterium on Venus relative to hydrogen indicates the presence of abundant water on Venus in the past, far more than can be accounted for by cometary influx alone. But its source and quantity are still unknown (ignoring the planetary breakup as an origin).[120]

C. The thick atmosphere and high surface pressure and temperature of Venus heavily erode craters within a few hundred million years. But the surface shows an abundance of craters in the 5- to 50-km range which appear in pristine condition, as if formed quite recently (i.e., in the last few million years). Almost no craters show signs of erosion or degradation. The conventional explanation is that a global episode of volcanism wiped the surface clean of craters, then ceased operating quite suddenly. But a recent episode of cratering from a breakup event elsewhere in the solar system can more easily explain this anomaly, provided there was no significant number of objects in Venus-crossing orbits immediately prior to the breakup.

D. Venus should also show a hemispheric asymmetry in its cratering because of its relatively slow rotation. At this writing (11/92), the situation is complicated by large gaps in the crater distribution apparently caused by huge lava flows. So this prediction must be modified to expecting a major asymmetry in the ratio of the number of small versus large craters in the two hemispheres, which has not yet been determined.[b]

E. A particular and very special type of meteorite found on Earth, called tektites, may be the surviving remains of the initial blast wave from the explosion. These glassy objects from space were pre-melted suddenly not long before reaching the Earth, where they were again partially melted during atmospheric entry. They are found scattered in huge fields covering millions of square miles in various parts of the world. The planetary explosion provides a very natural source for at least some classes of these unusual meteorites, whose origin is the subject of much debate.[121] It also explains the premelting.

F. Around the same epoch as the hypothesized planetary breakup, the Earth's climate changed from warm, equatorial-like global conditions, uninterrupted for at least 50,000,000 years, to a succession of ice ages over the past 3,000,000 years or so. The rea-

---

[b]More large asteroids would have less than solar system escape velocity, and would remain in Venus-crossing orbits to strike it at random. More small asteroids would hit Venus along with the initial blast wave, with those that missed then escaping from the solar system so that they don't get a later chance to hit the planet.

sons for the discontinuous climate change are not known in conventional theories. A massive influx of water vapor from the planetary explosion may have been responsible.

G. Certain regions of the Earth's surface retain evidence for a unique, massive flood several million years ago. For example, the Spokane Flood evidence indicates a short-lived event involving not less than 2000 cubic kilometers of water discharged per day.[122] This singular event might have been caused by a major impact event in the Pacific Ocean; or it might be the direct result of a massive influx of water from the planetary breakup, as suggested by evidence on other planetary surfaces.

H. The frequency of doublet craters on Earth implies that many of the impactors must have been at least binary objects separated by at least four times their mean diameter.[123] This condition is a natural by-product of a planetary breakup and can scarcely arise in any other uncontrived way.

I. The calculated cratering rate on the Earth and Moon from the present populations of Earth-crossing comets and asteroids exceeds the total observed cratering by a factor of eight.[124] This discrepancy would not need special explanation if the impactor population has been this high for only the last few million years.

J. The Moon's hemispheric asymmetry could have been caused by the blast. It would then be no coincidence that the hemisphere with all the dark "seas" faces the Earth, since the extra mass accreted by the Moon (which shows up as "mascons"—mass concentrations under the lunar "seas", which are actually lava flows) would have caused the Moon to change its orientation until its "heavy side" faced "down."

K. A large lunar libration induced by this re-orientation would have lasted tens to hundreds of thousands of years. This would have caused enormous internal upheaval and internal heating on the Moon through "tidal pumping" (similar to actions on Io by Jupiter). This in turn would produce lava flows to fill the great lunar basins and form the mass concentrations therein. A recent origin for these "mascons" is implied and would thereby explain why they are still

"Murphy's Law of Research: Enough research will tend to support your theory."
—from *Murphy's Laws and Other Reasons Why Things Go Wrong* (Arthur Bloch, 1977)

near the lunar surface, instead of sinking toward the lunar center. The strength of lunar rocks is such that the mascons should have lasted less than a billion years and should have sunk to their present depth within a few million years.

L. Perhaps the breakup event provides our first clues as to the origin of the magnetism in lunar rocks, as well as radioactivity in lunar soil, neither of which can be native to the Moon.

M. Areas of 100% radar reflectivity are found under the lunar surface. These ordinarily indicate the presence of water ice, but that is considered impossible in the case of the Moon. We now see a possible external source for lunar water allowing the high-reflectivity patches to indeed be water ice, instead of some other exotic substance.

N. The existence of rims of numerous large lunar craters with elevations of 1000 meters or so implies that lunar rock is perhaps 1000 times stiffer (less viscous) than typical Earth basalts, or the crater rims would collapse in about 10^8 years. Because some of these structures show so little degradation, the only alternative is that they are very young.[125]

O. Mars shows direct evidence for a recent influx of cratering in the form of a number of small, fresh craters. In conventional theory, the larger, older craters are assumed to have been obliterated suddenly by some unknown past event.

P. Martian winds and sand should erode older craters at the rate of 200 meters per million years. Certainly any crater older than, say, 100 million years should be long since gone, but Mars is covered with craters.

Q. Mars displays evidence that there was enough water for a brief period to produce flowing rivers and channels, although that would be impossible today. Sinuous rilles on the Moon and Mars are almost certainly water-carved features, and relatively recent as well, judging from the lack of overlying craters.[c] The assumption that they must be from lava flows is inconsistent in some cases, since the rilles don't slope away from potential lava sources, and neither lava nor any other candidate substance is not known to carve sinuous features. Comets and asteroids appear to be about 20% water by bulk, suggesting that the breakup event could have been the source of a sudden, short-lived, massive influx of water. We now know that prolonged water flow on an airless world is possible, since laboratory tests show that ice forms immediately over the surface, preventing evaporation of the flowing water beneath.

R. The ratio of deuterium to hydrogen on Mars implies that almost all its formerly abundant flowing water has been lost in just the last 10^5 to 10^7 years. Such remarkably recent changes are just what the exploding planet hypothesis predicts, but are quite unexpected in conventional models.

S. The Martian moons Phobos and Deimos appear to be captured asteroids. The breakup provides a natural origin and capture mechanism ("Gravitational Screen Capture"), whereas traditional capture mechanisms are strained at best, especially since Phobos is inside the synchronous orbit and Deimos outside. This capture mechanism is further supported by the presence of stress cracks and the huge crater "Stickney," which nearly shattered Phobos.

T. The capture process from the breakup event is further supported by the large number of low-angle impacts on the Martian surface—suggesting a former large population of temporary

---

[c]The Magellan spacecraft has seen sinuous rilles on Venus, too. The pressures there are so high (nearly 100 atmospheres) that many substances will behave in atypical fashion. But even on Venus, the idea of flowing liquid water is not as unlikely as it might seem, since the boiling point of water at 100 atm pressure is nearly 600°K, as compared to the 735°K surface temperature of the planet. Water temporarily shielded from the atmosphere, for example by ice (since the melting point of water is also quite high), might indeed be able to flow long enough to carve sinuous rilles before evaporating.

moons—and by the "grooves" on Phobos, likely caused by the collision which captured Phobos into its Martian orbit.

U. Phobos will tidally decay into the Martian atmosphere in about 30–40 million years (1% of the age of the solar system), which is less coincidental if it originated 3,200,000 years ago.

V. A gap in the spacing of the planets large enough to accommodate a missing planet exists between Mars and Jupiter. Jupiter's mass is insufficient to have interfered with the formation of a normal planet at that location.

W. Ovenden's dynamical calculations indicate that a massive planet, perhaps Saturn-sized, is missing from the gap between Mars and Jupiter, where the main belt of asteroids is found.

X. Jupiter will have swept up almost all the mass from the exploded planet that did not escape the solar system. Jupiter's excess heat flux over what it receives from the Sun may be an indication of relatively recent mass accretion by the planet.

Y. The "Great Red Spot" on Jupiter (as well as other similar spots on the gaseous giant planets) may be the site of an unusually large "impact," perhaps from one of the largest fragments surviving the breakup.[d] The debris from such an event may now be held together by gravitation and cohesion, and remain floating in the planet's atmosphere.

Z. Jupiter's apparently-captured asteroidal satellites can neither be captured nor escape, given Jupiter's present mass. Their origin by capture would be explained if Jupiter accreted substantial additional mass from the planetary breakup event.

AA. The rings and close asteroidal moons of Jupiter, Saturn, Uranus, and Neptune are natural by-products of the breakup of a massive planet, which would have sent considerable debris past these planets with atmospheres. The process is called "Gravitational Screen Capture." (See the chapter "Orbits.")

---

[d]This idea is developed into a model in the chapter "Jupiter and Uranus." The "impact" is into the planet's denser atmosphere, since gas-giant Jupiter has no surface.

AB. Saturn's moon Enceladus must have been disrupted within the last 15 million years to produce the moon's observed resurfacing, and to cause it to emit Saturn's E-ring material.[126]

AC. All atmosphere-less bodies in the outer solar system are coated with an extremely dark material. This may be the carbonaceous residue from the blast. Those which rotate more slowly than one month (Iapetus and possibly Nereid) are coated *on only one side*. Pluto, which can rotate pole-on at times, is coated on only one hemisphere. Triton, whose orbital tilt hides one polar region from view for years at a time, is coated everywhere except its south polar regions, which are icy bright.

AD. Spectrally, the dark material on outer solar system satellites is the same as Type C and D asteroids, both of which are associated with carbonaceous chondrite meteorites.[127]

AE. A cohesive floating surface resulting from the entry of huge breakup fragments provides a natural explanation for the unmoving "lenticular" cirrus-like clouds that remain near Neptune's "Great Dark Spot." Such a surface would allow the clouds to cast visible shadows. These conditions are easier to imagine than the "haze layer" whose existence has been conjectured in order to make the shadows visible, or the "permanent hurricane" explanation for the spot itself.

AF. Some of Neptune's inner, asteroid-like moons are inside the Roche limit where tidal stresses would tear apart a forming body.[128] So these moons could not have formed near their present orbits. As with all the solar system's other asteroid-like moons, the exploded planet provides a natural origin.

IV. Evidence related to meteoroids

A. Brown & Patterson reviewed all meteoritic evidence available to them in 1948.[129] They wrote: "The conclusion appears irrefutable that meteorites at one time were an integral part of a planet." The new evidence since then has done nothing to weaken that conclusion.

B. Glassy tektite meteorites found all over the Earth have numerous characteristics which are implied by origin in an exploded planet. One of these is strong evidence for melting shortly *prior* to entry into the Earth's atmosphere. Another is their implied high pre-entry velocities.[121]

C. Cosmic ray exposure ages of carbonaceous meteorites are generally measured in millions of years, not billions. The conventional explanation—that they keep fragmenting and exposing new surfaces—is quite strained, since important collisions occur only at intervals of hundreds of millions to billions of years. In the exploded planet model, the exposures are really 3.2 million years, plus some additional (original-location-dependent) radiation exposure from the breakup event itself, which agrees well with the data.

D. The average amount of exposure to cosmic rays varies from one type of meteorite to another, with iron meteorites having the most exposure, and the most "primitive" carbonaceous stony meteorites having the least. These mean exposure ages are arranged in the same way such types of objects would be arranged within a planet. For example, iron would be near the core, and lighter elements near the surface. Cosmic rays can penetrate rock only about a meter and would not affect objects in a planet; but a central explosion could produce just the observed irradiation during breakup.

E. Most meteorites show evidence of having been affected by the separation of heavy and light chemical elements, a process (called "chemical differentiation") that can only occur in large bodies with a lot of gravity to produce the separation as heavier elements sink toward the center.

F. Some meteorites show physical and chemical evidence of rapid melting prior to arrival at Earth. Some were heated to the point where material would boil away. Many are badly charred. This suggests that they were affected by an immense heat blast long before entering the Earth's atmosphere.

G. L-type chondrites specifically are quite blackened, show evidence of shock, and have been subjected to pressures of at least 0.1 atmospheres, consistent with having been subject to a blast wave.

H. Condensates found in carbonaceous meteorites seem to imply that they formed in a high-temperature and/or high-pressure environment, such as in a major planet. The material is clearly non-homogeneous, likewise implying a complex formation environment.

I. Isotopic anomalies in carbonaceous meteorites imply the action of nuclear processes, not just chemical ones. Chondrule evidence strongly suggests origin in an unspecified high-energy event, definitely not pre-solar system. To account for these anomalies, meteorite experts have now concluded that preserved interstellar materials exposed to supernovas have been incorporated into meteorites.[130]

J. It is known that carbonaceous chondrites and ureilites must have had surprisingly large ancient magnetic field intensities. This, too, suggests origin in a major planet.

K. Tiny diamonds found in some meteorites suggest formation in a high-temperature, high-pressure environment, as in the interior of a planet. This anomaly has led some experts to suggest instead that there must exist an unknown way to form diamonds in space collisions or during atmospheric entry or by Earth-impact shock, without need for lengthy exposure to high temperature and pressure. But new findings show that in at least one unshocked meteorite (named Abee), none of these ad hoc suggestions can be operative.[131] And diamonds found at the K/T geologic boundary are confirmed to be of extraterrestrial origin, not shock-generated or terrestrial, based on delta C-13 measures.[132]

L. Carbon-12 and carbon-13 isotopes found in graphite grains in meteorites are believed to have been formed in a "nova" explosion. In traditional theory, the nova products mixed with the solar nebula, and later condensed into meteorites. But it then remains unclear why graphite is much less abundant than diamond, since the latter should be less stable, even in the same meteorite. Formation of the carbon isotopes in the nova-like explosion of a planet fully explains the observed meteorite abundances.[133]

M. Meteorites are deficient in krypton and overabundant in xenon relative to solar system abundances. This implies modification by a heavy neutron flux. Conventional theory suggests this occurred from a nearby Type II supernova.

N. When fireballs break up, it is sometimes at altitudes greater than 100 km above the Earth prior to atmospheric entry. The shearing forces are too minute to cause fragmentation at that height. This implies the meteoroids were already gravitationally bound multiple bodies before they became fireballs, as would result if they originated from the explosive breakup of a larger body.

O. Most fireballs survive to such low altitudes that they must be made of solid, carbonaceous materials, not at all fluffy ones. Yet their large aphelion distances (generally far beyond Jupiter) associate them with comets, not minor planets. This is further evidence that comets are carbonaceous bodies, as predicted by the exploded planet theory but contrary to the dirty-snowball model. Conventional theory has no explanation for the high frequency of meteorite orbits with such large aphelia.

P. An am/pm asymmetry in chondrite falls on Earth implies either a very short destruction lifetime or a source younger than 10,000,000 years.

Q. The "brightness-to-mass" ratios of many fireballs are considerably higher than theory permits. But if a cloud of gravitationally bound debris, rather than a single body, is entering the atmosphere, then the mystery is resolved.

R. The radar cross-sections of many fireballs are greater than theory permits, with a likely similar explanation.

S. The existence of so many elongated small asteroids and meteoroids, and of crater chains, again implies an origin through the tidal decay of orbiting satellites, which likely originated in an explosion.

T. The Leonid meteor stream occasionally has produced intense meteor showers, when it "rained meteors." In conventional models it is not understood how these meteors can stay together in clumps to produce these showers, instead of dispersing. But debris clouds that have gravitationally escaped from comets have such similar initial velocities that they can stay together indefinitely.

U. The Cyrillid meteor shower on February 9, 1913 was a cluster of at least 32 separate, low, bright meteoroids which moved from horizon to horizon, spread out over a time span of about six minutes, and visible along a ground path from northwest Canada all the way down to Bermuda. The origin of this anomaly is officially unexplained. But if individual asteroids and comets are actually clouds of debris, then the mystery is explained. The debris cloud made a grazing passage through the Earth's atmosphere, which reduced it to a low Earth orbit with a period of about five hours. Then on the next revolution, which occurred after dark, the debris cloud completed its decay into the Earth's atmosphere, much the way an artificial satellite decays.

V. Other miscellaneous evidence

A. Small holes are seen to form in the Earth's atmosphere at ultraviolet wavelengths, which seem to suggest frequent impacts by mini-comets with dimensions of 10 meters or so.[134] Such a high frequency of impact would be expected only for objects 100 times smaller. But if the spheres of influence of even very small objects are filled with debris, including volatiles, ultraviolet holes of the observed size would be expected to form with the observed frequency.

B. Recent examination of the global distribution of interstellar hydrogen "clouds" by G. Verschuur[135] suggests that the majority of the observed ones actually are parts of filaments (as would result from a supernova explosion), are quite young, and lie within 100 parsecs of the Sun. This surprising result suggests a linkage with the planetary breakup event in the solar system.

C. At the present time our Sun is imbedded in a uniform, X-ray absorption-free emitting region of variable extent. Evidence indicates that the X-rays originate within a few hundred parsecs and may be associated with gamma-ray bursts. The observed background soft X-ray and extreme ultraviolet spectra seem to suggest that an energetic explosion of possibly supernova proportions occurred within the last four million years, affecting the interstellar medium surrounding the Sun.[136] It would be surprising if this event turned out to be unrelated to our planetary explosion event, since a supernova that close that recently is rather improbable.

D. Radio scintillation maps suggest that the solar neighborhood is encapsulated in an envelope of plasma turbulence, most probably "the relic of a supernova explosion of a nearby massive star."[137]

E. Additional evidence for a recent and nearby nova or supernova (or planetary explosion) event exists in the form of excess Aluminum-26 in the local interstellar medium. The half-life of this radioactive isotope is only about a million years, requiring a recent source to inject the abundant quantities we observe today.

F. Unless the exploded planet was a lot less massive than the evidence suggests, chemical or collisional processes do not generate enough energy to blow it apart. Nuclear processes are indicated by the meteoritic evidence. It has been objected that planets are not hot enough even in their cores for nuclear reactions. Yet natural fission reactors have been known to operate even on the Earth's surface in the geologic past, suggesting related possibilities.[138] But the most natural way to produce the isotopic anomalies observed in meteorites, and supply abundant energy, is by a matter-antimatter explosion. This speculative possibility might result from a magnetic separation and storage of the antimatter in a planet over billions of years before the explosion; or from some sort of chain-reaction high-energy antimatter generation process; or from the intervention of intelligent beings. In my opinion, the last possibility should not be dismissed out of hand.

G. The primary source of gamma-ray bursts must be within about 500 parsecs, because of their uniformity over the sky, and the lack of indicators of cosmological distances. Fainter bursts do concentrate toward the galactic plane, but must still lie within a few kiloparsecs of the Sun, and cannot be spread uniformly throughout space or within our galaxy.[139] There is a great variety of observed bursts with unknown sources, which fail to match up with known astronomical objects at any other wavelengths. There are abundant bright bursts, but a deficit of faint bursts. Some spikes have durations as short as 0.2ms, requiring either relativistic beaming or small source bodies, probably only kilometers across.[140] This puzzling picture would be neatly explained by an expanding shock wave from the planetary explosion event, producing such bursts whenever it ran into matter in any form. Specifically, the high energy of gamma-ray bursts would be a natural consequence of antimatter from the explosion encountering interstellar matter.

H. Evidence for the local bubble in the interstellar medium exists in observations at all wavelengths from gamma-ray through radio. There also appears to be a trough in the nearby interstellar dust which is roughly Sun-centered. All this evidence supports the planetary explosion hypothesis.

VI. Evidence that does not fit the hypothesis

A. The main asteroid belt between Mars and Jupiter drops off steeply as it approaches the orbit of Mars, as if Mars had eliminated most of the Mars-crossing asteroids further in. But dynamical calculations show that it would take about a billion years for Mars to have the observed effect because of its weak gravity. That is inconsistent with the timing of the planetary explosion event. One conjecture to account for this is breakup of asteroids through collisional processes, which should happen with ever greater frequency at smaller distances from the Sun. This is both because the volume of space decreases rapidly (with solar distance cubed), and because the angular speed of asteroid motions increases rapidly (with solar distance to the minus 1.5 power). Changes in spectral properties of asteroids in the inner belt are consistent with this hypothesis.[e]

---

[e]Another conjecture is that a single large fragment many Earth masses in size survived the explosion in a highly elliptical orbit. The fragment would have been eliminated by Jupiter within about 100,000 years. But in the meantime it would have removed many asteroids and changed the orbits of many others. Most of the effect of such a fragment would necessarily have occurred in the inner belt for the same reasons that collisions are more frequent there. And because of its larger mass, the time scale for its effects would be far shorter than for Mars.

B. Such a major explosion should leave evidence all over the solar system, and apparently has. Yet in the geological record on Earth, there is little to support the hypothesis of a major explosion specifically at 3.2 million years ago. There is evidence for the onset of a series of ice ages about then, after a long span of tropical climate. And the origin of man dates to around then. But one would have expected a global layer of carbon deposits, enrichment in the element iridium, shocked quartz from impacts, multiple impact craters,[141] micro-tektites and micro-diamond formation, enhanced volcanism, atmospheric and ocean changes, a single global fire,[142] mass extinction of species, and many other dramatic changes. Such things are seen in several places in the geological record, but not near 3 million years ago according to the presently adopted geochronology. Strikingly, all those features are seen together at the Cretaceous-Tertiary (K/T) boundary, dated at 65 million years ago, when the dinosaurs and many other species became extinct. The expectations from the astronomical evidence and the realization in the geophysical evidence appear to be identical except for dating. I have searched carefully for any possibility of error in the astronomical dating of the event, but can find none. The Oort argument that new comets with orbital periods of about 3 million years could not have made more than one revolution seems invincible; and many of the other arguments, such as cosmic ray exposure ages of meteorites, likewise could not stand such a drastic upward correction. Yet Occam's Razor virtually demands that the astronomical and geological events be reconciled. This leads naturally to the conjecture that the geological time scale (based as it is on radiometric dating, stratigraphy, magnetic reversals, sea-floor spreading, and a few other techniques) may not be interpreted correctly. For example, among the possibilities for such a drastic rewriting of the geological record, the rocks that are radiometrically dated to 65 million years ago may indeed have formed at that epoch, but were perhaps only deposited into the geological layers where we find them about 3 million years ago. Or radiation from the explosion may have falsified the radiometric ages. To pursue these conjectures, a geologist would have to consider what effect an energetic, irradiating event like the planetary explosion would have had on each type of geological clock, and then determine if there is an alternative way of synchronizing the various geological clocks. Certain existing clues, such as the mystery of the polonium halos in granitic rocks[143] (which shouldn't exist if the accepted chronology is correct), may be indicating that the accepted chronology does indeed need extensive modification.

12

• •

Sunspots and Eclipses

Summary: We discuss how tidal forces can become appreciable in gaseous bodies, having even greater impact than solid-body tides throughout the solar system. We then discuss a possible planet-sunspot causal link. Some little-known phenomena associated with lunar and solar eclipses are also explained, including the advantages of observing total solar eclipses from near the path edges.

Sunspots

Can sunspots be influenced by the planets? At first the question may seem more astrological than astronomical, but we are considering whether the gravitational forces exerted by the planets on the Sun, although quite small, can possibly affect solar activity. There are many conjectures in the literature concerning a causal connection between the Sun's planets and the solar sunspot cycle. One of the most notorious in recent times was "The Jupiter Effect,"[144] which suggested a series of causal links between planets and sunspots culminating in increased earthquake activity in California at the time of the "planetary alignment" in 1982.[a]

---

[a]The increased earthquake activity did not occur. But the motivation for suggesting it was not clear either. Two planets can never lie exactly on a line from the Sun since their orbital planes are slightly different. They can only approach alignment to some given precision. When many planets are considered, it is customary to speak of the angle at the Sun which

237

I would here like to propose my own conjecture for a causal connection between planets and sunspots. While the implications are not nearly so ominous for life on Earth as in "The Jupiter Effect," the conjecture holds the potential, if correct in its essentials, for a greater understanding of the mechanics of the entire sunspot phenomenon.

The problem with accepting the proposition that planets can gravitationally influence sunspots is that the forces seem far too small to be significant. The relevant forces are tidal forces. The direct gravitational force of a planet on the Sun causes the entire Sun to accelerate (free-fall) toward the planet. However, such a free-fall causes the Sun no stress, since it is free to yield completely to the force. Instead we must consider the consequences of the direct gravitational force of the planet being slightly different in strength and direction at different points on the Sun's surface. For example, the planet pulls more strongly on the Sun's front face than on its back (as seen from the planet) simply because the front side is closer. (This is elaborated in the chapter "Orbits.")

The Earth's Moon exerts only a minute tidal force, sufficient to distort the Earth's figure by a few feet at most. Yet tides may reach 15 meters in special places, such as the Bay of Fundy in Canada. The reason is that the Moon's lifting force is not the cause of tides, since land and water are raised an equal amount by such vertical forces. Instead, it is the component of the Moon's force that pulls horizontally, and to which the water yields and flows, whereas the land does not, that causes Earth tides. Water is pulled alternately one direction, and then the other, every twelve and a half hours or so. When great masses of ocean water all begin to flow, however slowly, in the same direction, the result is a "piling-up" of water at land-water boundaries, and the phenomenon of ocean tides. If there is a narrow inlet on a shoreline, the effect may be greatly magnified by channeling a large volume of water into a small place. The point is that the "longitudinal" component of the tidal force is what matters, not the vertical component. Moreover, if the longitudinal

contains all nine planets. In 1982, that angle briefly reached 98 degrees, an unusually low value. Obviously the use of the word "alignment" for such an arrangement is misleading.

component could act in one direction for much longer than twelve hours at a time, tides raised by it might be much larger than they are. Yet the Moon's tidal force would remain minute.

In the case of the Sun, the situation is similar, yet different in several critical ways. The 1,400,000-km-diameter Sun bulges only about a millimeter due to the stress it feels from planetary gravity. There is no unyielding "land" on the Sun, so the longitudinal component of the tidal forces of the planets has no analogous effect to that produced on Earth by the Moon. But the Sun is tilted seven degrees to the mean plane of the planets, so there is a "latitudinal" component to planetary tidal action which needs to be examined. Moreover, the Sun's rotation period of a month allows plenty of time for the "small" effects to build up into considerable volumes and masses of solar material transported by tidal action.

The second factor to be appreciated about the solar case is that the Sun does not rotate the way a solid body rotates. The solar equator rotates faster than mid-latitudes, which in turn rotate faster than near the Sun's poles. This "differential rotation" would cause a large flat object placed on the Sun's surface (assuming it could survive there) to spin slowly, since the solar material to its north would pass by at a different rate than the material to its south. It can also greatly magnify the effects of any north-south movement of solar material, since the displaced material will be forced to speed up or slow down in longitude as it changes latitude. An analogous situation occurs with depth, since rotation speeds at different depths are also different.

The third factor to consider is that if we make any displacement of solar material away from a perfect equilibrium figure for the Sun, even in the absence of external forces, that material will try to flow back toward the equilibrium figure position and will oscillate back and forth about equilibrium until friction damps out the oscillation. The period of this oscillation will be a function of the size and mass of the Sun and the density of the solar material. Hence this "free" oscillation will be superimposed on the various "forced" oscillations of solar material caused by planetary tidal action.

So the new picture that emerges from these considerations is that planetary tides cause bulk flow of solar material in latitude, which operates in one direction for two weeks at a time before reversing as the Sun rotates. As solar material is forced to change latitude, it enters streams of other solar material traveling at different rotational speeds, and so is forced to accelerate or decelerate and to rotate. These motions interact with the natural periodicity of displaced solar material, which would tend to oscillate back and forth with some viscosity-dependent frequency even in the absence of external forces.

Although Bob Harrington and I did some brief experiments at the Naval Observatory to develop these ideas into a model for the formation of sunspots, we were unsuccessful; but time and priorities did not permit adequate research on this subject. Nonetheless, I believe there surely is a connection of the type postulated, because it has the potential to explain in a very natural way the various puzzling properties of the sunspot cycle, including the 11-year reversal of polarity (the magnetism changes from "north" to "south" about every 11.1 years), latitude drift and the "butterfly" pattern for sunspots (the mean latitude of sunspots changes during the 11-year cycle), and long-period variations in sunspot maximum amplitude. It even explains why no spots ever form near the Sun's equator or poles, where there is no differential rotation. It is not easy to understand how all these features might arise purely from processes internal to the Sun.

Although solar tides are too small today to have a significant effect on the planetary orbits in the way that Earth tides affect the Moon's orbit, this surely was not the case in the early solar system, when the contracting Sun was much larger in diameter than it is at present. The effect of solar tides on planetary orbits increases by two orders of magnitude with each doubling of the Sun's diameter. Indeed, solar tides and drag in an extended solar atmosphere may have caused substantial evolution of the inner planet orbits since their formation. This seems a viable explanation for why most of the angular momentum (a particular form of energy—see Glossary) in the solar system is in the planets instead of the Sun; and why the planets are proportionally much further away from the Sun than most other known orbiting systems are from their primaries.

The astronomical literature has many papers that assume tidal friction is most effective in the case of solid bodies, less effective for liquid bodies, and extremely inefficient in the case of giant gaseous bodies. This is because there did not seem to be an adequate source of friction to maintain a significant lag or lead for the tidal bulge produced on the gaseous body. The new mechanism described in this chapter has some generality, however, and would seem to reverse our thinking about the efficiency of tidal friction: least efficient for solid bodies, more efficient for bodies with extensive fluids (as for the Earth's oceans), and most efficient for differentially rotating gaseous bodies, where differential rotation drives tidal bulges to large displacements from their formation point. Applicability to the evolution of the satellite orbits of the outer planets comes immediately to mind. And we should not ignore the additional factor of tidal friction from floating masses in their atmospheres.

Lunar Eclipses

Here are two related multiple-choice questions:

Q1. What is the source of the light the Moon reflects during a total lunar eclipse?
   a. direct sunlight, bent by refraction while passing through the Earth's atmosphere;
   b. diffuse sunlight scattered by its passage through the Earth's atmosphere;
   c. Earthshine (sunlight reflected off the Earth, which sometimes makes the dark side of the Moon visible);
   d. primarily other light (none of the above).

Q2. What would an observer on the Moon during a total lunar eclipse be able to see?
   a. all parts of the Sun's disc at once;
   b. only the outer portion of the Sun's disc;
   c. only the Sun's corona (atmosphere), but not the Sun's disc;
   d. nothing at all of the Sun.

Take your best guess, but be forewarned—most astronomy textbooks don't have the correct answer. Then read on.

The transparency of the Earth's atmosphere is good enough under ordinary circumstances to let sunlight pass through it, even at sea level. For example, the rising Sun can be quite bright if the air is clear. It generally suffers only a few magnitudes of extinction (loss of light). But such sunlight (just grazing the Earth's surface) is bent by slightly more than one degree toward the Earth by atmospheric refraction (half a degree coming into the atmosphere, another half a degree leaving it).

In the astronomy textbooks, the Earth's shadow is drawn as if the Earth had no atmosphere—as the apex of a cone just touching the Earth's disc and the Sun's disc. Such a "shadow" would extend well beyond the Moon. In reality, however, sunlight is bent as it passes the Earth; and direct sunlight enters the zone the textbooks call the Earth's "shadow." The Earth's real shadow, the region where no direct sunlight can enter, is much shorter and in fact does not reach as far out as the Moon. (See Figure 12.1.) So, in a highly technical sense, a "total eclipse" is impossible for the Moon (although it certainly is possible for most of Earth's artificial satellites).

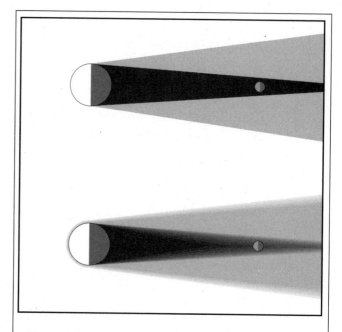

Figure 12.1. The shadow the Earth would cast if it had no atmosphere, and the Earth's real shadow.

The answer to Q1 is a.: "direct sunlight, bent by refraction" illuminates the Moon during total lunar eclipses. The eclipsed Moon is darker than a Full Moon for two reasons: 1. Refractive defocusing—sunlight is spread over a much wider

> "For every rule, there is an exception. There is no exception to this rule."—Ron Baalke

area by refraction (very much like the spreading of light by a prism). 2. Extinction—global clouds, haze, and particles in the Earth's atmosphere which affect its transparency. Just after a major volcanic eruption, when the upper atmosphere around the globe is filled with dust and ash, the Moon has been known to disappear to the naked eye during eclipse.

The answer to Q2 is also a., as follows from the discussion in answer to Q1. To an observer standing on the Moon, the Sun's disc would seem to spread out into a flattened glowing bulge on one side of the Earth, continuing to spread more and more as the eclipse progressed. If the observer on the Moon were at the middle of the eclipse (on the line joining the centers of the Sun and Earth, extended), the Sun's disc would be spread out into a glowing ring completely surrounding the Earth. The image of a sunspot anywhere on the Sun's disc would also spread out into an extremely thin ring encircling the Earth. That is because light from the sunspot can pass through the Earth's atmosphere at just the right height to be refracted to the lunar observer from anywhere around the Earth's apparent disc.

Although no observer on the Moon has ever witnessed this impressive spectacle, Earth observers have witnessed such phenomena while viewing other events. An occultation of the bright star Epsilon Geminorum by Mars 10-15 years ago showed the predicted refractive defocusing and image spreading of the starlight as the atmosphere of Mars moved in front of the star.[145] During the event the Kuiper Airborne Observatory flew to the center line of the occultation (where the star passes directly behind the center of Mars). At mid-occultation there was a sudden brightening of the combined light of Mars and star, the so-called "central flash," as the starlight briefly became visible all around Mars's atmosphere as a complete ring of light around the planet.

Theoretically, a brighter region corresponding to the "central flash" should be visible on the totally eclipsed Moon whenever part of the Moon passes right through the center of the Earth's "shadow" during a suitable eclipse. To the best of my knowledge, this has never been observed (nor, for that matter, looked for). Now there's a challenge for the observers!

Solar Eclipses

Total eclipses of the Sun are one of nature's greatest spectacles, but are rather rare from any one location, occurring only about once every 400 years. However, if one is willing to travel, total solar eclipses may be seen frequently in a lifetime, because there are at least two every year from somewhere on the Earth.

The duration of the total part of solar eclipses is usually only a few minutes, the maximum possible for an observer on the ground being under eight minutes. During that total phase, light from the Sun's disc is completely blocked by the Moon (which has no atmosphere), and the surroundings for an Earth observer get rather dark. It is not, however, as dark as night because the Sun's corona, or atmosphere, becomes visible as a glowing light around the Moon's disk, shedding enough light on Earth to give a twilight-like appearance. This corona is usually visible to Earth observers only during total solar eclipses, so astronomers travel great distances and position themselves directly on the center line of the paths of total solar eclipses to catch these fleeting glimpses of the Sun's atmosphere for study.

Because of the astronomers' fixation with being on the center line during such total eclipses, and also because no one has ever informed them differently, amateur astronomers and the general public have also flocked to the center line of total solar eclipses. This maximizes the time to view the solar corona, but for most eclipse viewers, this is just one of several fascinating phenomena which are part of the solar eclipse experience. And for almost all other purposes, the center line of the eclipse is *not* the place to be.

Shortly before a solar eclipse begins, and again shortly after it ends, "shadow bands" are often seen wavering on the ground and on nearby buildings and objects. These rapidly moving packets of light and darkness, believed to be caused by atmospheric turbulence, create an eerie feeling and are an exciting part of the solar eclipse experience.

When the crescent of sunlight becomes extremely thin, hundreds of small images of the crescent may be seen projected onto the ground through the leaves of trees or other locations which serve as pinholes.[b]

Another solar eclipse phenomenon is called "Bailey's beads," which are beads of sunlight peering through individual valleys between mountains on the edge of the lunar disc in the sky. This can only occur in the final moments before the total phase of the eclipse begins, or in the moments just after it ends.

Rarely, fortunate observers are treated to the "diamond ring," a circle of light extending outward from the Sun's limb as the last rays of light disappear. Sharp-eyed observers may also see other special effects such as the "flash spectrum," a brief glimpse of the Sun's very red inner atmosphere (called its "chromosphere" because of its red color).

What is noteworthy about all these phenomena is that the worst place to view them anywhere inside the path of totality is on the center line, where their probability of occurrence and duration are minimal. Both probability of occurrence and duration increase gradually away from the center line, and quite rapidly as one approaches the edge of the path of totality. Indeed, observers positioned at the optimal 2–5 miles inside either path edge will see these phenomena in slow motion, with durations amplified by a factor of 10 or so.

The same is true of the onset and conclusion of the total phase of the eclipse itself. Near the center line, everything happens in a rush in the last seconds before totality. The sudden darkening, the disappearance of the last of the Sun's crescent, the formation of beads at the limb, and the appearance of the corona are squeezed into perhaps a 1- to 15-second interval. Near the path edge, the same events happen in slow motion over the course of 1–3 minutes. Near the edge one can plainly see that the corona appears well before the last of the Sun's crescent disappears.

---

[b]A bright light projected through a pinhole will form an image of the source on the other side.

Observers stationed near the path edges get these enhancements in duration of eclipse phenomena with only a modest sacrifice in the length of totality, typically 50–70% less than on the center line. A six-minute eclipse on the center line might last a full two minutes, even quite close to the edge. But the preceding and following minutes are taken up with the prolonged phenomena that precede and follow totality, especially the "shadow band" phase. And the corona is visible for most of that time too, typically becoming visible a minute before totality! (It has been noted in recent eclipses that the corona can be seen even from a few miles outside the path of totality.) So although the length of the total phase of the eclipse is shortened, the time interval during which interesting phenomena occur is actually greater near the path edge by as much as a factor of 10 or more.

The enhancement of these phenomena near the path edges for solar eclipses was not realized until observations of grazing occultations of stars by the Moon brought the enhancement possibility to mind. The latter observations, and many of the ideas about what to expect near the path edges for solar eclipses, must be credited to David Dunham and Joan Bixby Dunham.

If you are still skeptical about sacrificing some "true totality" time, especially since all the professional astronomers (who are supposed to know what they are doing) are crowding the center line, consider the logical extreme: suppose that the Moon was much larger in apparent diameter than the Sun. Total eclipses would last much longer but be far less spectacular and less interesting to everyone. Even the view of the solar corona would be partially obscured by the larger lunar disc. Astronomers would have found out long ago that to see the lower corona or any of the other phenomena, they would have to travel to near the edge. The perfect eclipse would be one in which the Moon's disc just barely covered the Sun's, and this condition was prolonged as long as possible. For both purposes—matching the disc sizes and slowing the rate of relative motion of the discs—the path edge is better than the center line for every total solar eclipse.

To be more specific, consider Table 12.1. For the July 11, 1991, total solar eclipse visible in Mexico, the duration of totality near the center line reached about 418 seconds—one of the longest total

246

solar eclipses possible from the Earth's surface. The first column shows the percentage of distance from the center line to the edge, and the second column shows the duration of the eclipse for the mean lunar limb. To visualize why phenomena are so prolonged near the path edge, note that the eclipse geometry is not very different from that of two discs of slightly different radius, where one of them pivots about a fixed point on their common limb.

%	sec
00	418
10	416
20	410
30	399
40	383
50	362
60	335
70	299
80	251
90	182
95	131

Table 12.1

From the table, note the following circumstances, which apply generally to total solar eclipses of all lengths: 1. As one moves off the center line by as much as 20% of the distance to the edge, the duration of totality drops merely 2%. So precise positioning exactly on the center line has very little value. Any convenient location in the vicinity will serve equally well. 2. The position where the duration falls to about half that on the center line is about 90% of the way from the center toward the edge.

For the July 11, 1991, eclipse we might note these additional points: 1. On the center line, the time interval within which all phenomena associated with the onset and ending of the eclipse may occur is about 14 seconds long, with most action concentrated within the middle 7 seconds. 2. At the optimal location about three miles inside the path edge of the 160-mile-wide path of totality in Mexico, the equivalent time interval for onset and ending phenomena is 155 seconds long, and the corresponding high-action period is 109 seconds long. For many purposes, observing from near the path edge is really like viewing an eclipse in slow motion. On the center line, only the period when the corona is visible but no other action is occurring is prolonged.

In addition to the prolongation of phenomena near the path edge because of the geometry of eclipses, the sliding of the Sun's disc past the Moon's adds additional phenomena not viewable elsewhere. Consider, for example, Bailey's beads, which are bits of sunlight peering between mountains on the lunar limb. On the center line of the path, only mountains which happen to be suitably located near the point where the Sun's last light disappears can produce these beads. But near the path edges, the Sun's limb slips past the Moon's limb over a considerable angular distance along both, so that many lunar mountain ranges form beads of varying brightness during the course of the last minute or so before totality begins (and after it ends), and these beads appear to "travel" along the limb as new ones form and old ones disappear.

I have personally observed four total solar eclipses thus far in my life. In 1963 my wife and I observed from the center line in Maine. In 1970, my family traveled to Norfolk, Virginia, to observe from the north edge. The Dunhams chose the south edge.[c] Those of us at the north edge were treated to a relatively rare effect—a slowly expanding ring of light off the edge of the two celestial bodies just before totality began. In 1972, my family traveled to northern Canada to again observe from near the north edge of the path, while the Dunhams again chose the south edge. Pronounced shadow bands were readily apparent several minutes before totality for both of these "edge view" eclipses, although we saw none at our "center-line" eclipse.

There is no doubt in my mind that the edge view is far more spectacular than the center-line view. Knowing that and seeing that no expeditions were planning to travel to the edge on July 11, 1991, I organized an expedition (with the help of several other astronomers, including David and Joan Dunham) which took 300 people to a small village on the west coast of the Mexico mainland for a spectacular view of the southern edge. Ours was called the "Eclipse Edge Expedition," and no one in our group was disappointed. We included a complete week of astronomical activities,

---

[c]To my knowledge, this is the first occasion where astronomers deliberately positioned themselves near the path edges to get an enhanced view of eclipse phenomena. In earlier efforts, most notably the 1925 eclipse over New York City, the astronomers generally went to the center line and stationed public viewers at intervals near the path edge so as to better define exactly where the edge was. The professionals thought the public volunteers were sacrificing the great view they would themselves enjoy at the center!

as well as a stay in the resort city of Puerto Vallarta. The beautiful red chromosphere remained visible throughout totality at our site, adding rich color to what was already nature's most magnificent spectacle. All edge effects were in evidence.

The expedition was so successful that I am already planning to lead a similar expedition for the November 1994 total solar eclipse, visible across central South America. Unfortunately, no sites could be located in the hospitable parts of Brazil with weather prospects as high as a ⅔ probability of seeing the eclipse. So I plan a week-long expedition to Peru and/or Bolivia and/or Chile, where weather prospects are excellent. From there we plan to visit interesting geological and archaeological sites, then travel to the path edge that offers the best view of the eclipse. We plan to take full advantage of the opportunity for northern-bound persons to see and learn the parts of the southern skies which they can never see from mid-northern latitudes. If this expedition sounds interesting to you, watch for ads for "The Eclipse Edge" expedition, or write to the author for an information bulletin.[d]

[d]Meta Research / PO Box 15186 / Chevy Chase, MD 20815.

13

· ·

Mercury and Venus

Summary: Mercury and Venus are unique or anomalous among the major planets in several ways. These two alone are without natural satellites. Mercury has an unusually small mass and large eccentricity and inclination of its orbit for a planet, a unique 3-to-2 spin lock, and is cratered, atmosphereless, and Moon-like in appearance. Venus is the "twin" of Earth in size, mass, and location, except for the absence of a moon of its own. And something other than the Sun has robbed Venus of most of its spin. Working deductively from the hypothesis that Mercury began as a satellite of Venus, the present planetary status of Mercury and the orbital and spin anomalies for both planets follow inevitably. If we assume that Mercury originated by fission, as has been proposed for the Earth's Moon, then tidal melting of both Mercury and Venus, massive outgassing within Venus (producing a thick atmosphere), and volcanism and upheaval (producing fissures and high mountains) are all necessary consequences. If the fission origin occurred before Venus differentiated chemically, then Mercury would get most of the iron, leaving it with a large magnetic field, and Venus devoid of one, as observed. During the inevitable tidal evolution of Mercury outward from Venus to its escape into solar orbit, Mercury would be forced to acquire a prolate shape (a bulge toward Venus). Since its spin period at escape must equal its satellite orbital period then—about 40 days—the next stable spin configuration it can achieve is the 3-to-2 lock it now has with the Sun. No other plausible formation mechanism has explained why Mercury today would have such a tidal bulge. Virtually the entire assem-

bly of odd characteristics for both planets follows as inevitable consequences of the natural, if unfamiliar, hypothesis that Mercury originated as a satellite of Venus.

Similarities Between Mercury-Venus and Earth-Moon

The ideas in this chapter have been taken largely from a paper by the author and Robert S. Harrington of the U.S. Naval Observatory.[146]

In science, if you take a single observation and reason backwards to a cause, there will usually be a multitude of possibilities, with little to distinguish among them. On the other hand, if you can find a suitable starting point and reason forward, deductions are often unique and compelling. If the starting point also makes predictions that are true and none prove false, that is good evidence that the starting point is a correct one. This deductive process is one of the chief reasons why the astronomy in this book differs from mainstream astronomy.

Mercury and Venus, the two innermost planets, are the only two major planets without natural satellites. Each has its own share of unique features. Many of these features lead us to the conjecture that Mercury may be an escaped satellite of Venus. In this chapter, we will explore that conjecture.

Mercury is small as planets go, having a mass more like the larger moons in the solar system than like the other planets. With the exception of Pluto (which may itself be an escaped satellite—see the chapter "Neptune and Pluto"), Mercury's orbit is tilted by a larger amount, and its orbit is more eccentric, than any of the other planets. Also, Mercury spins exactly three times for every two revolutions around the Sun—an unusual situation which likewise requires some explanation. And Mercury is the only major planet without an appreciable atmosphere. Hence the composite picture of Mercury seems more like the description of a moon than a planet, but for its solar orbit.

This view was reinforced by the *Mariner 10* spacecraft encounter with Mercury. The planet's surface is so like that of the Earth's Moon that the layman is hard-pressed to tell them apart. (See Fig-

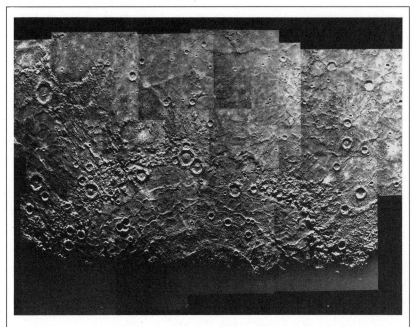

Figure 13.1. A *Mariner 10* spacecraft view of the surface of Mercury, showing its huge Caloris basin and its general similarity to our Moon. (NASA photograph)

ure 13.1.) The similarity in appearance goes further, to the extent that one hemisphere of Mercury is more heavily cratered and the other has solidified "lava seas," just as for our Moon.

We adopt as a starting point the hypothesis that Mercury originated as a satellite of Venus, just as the Earth's Moon originated as a satellite of the Earth. In size, mass, and location in the solar system, Venus is a virtual "twin" of the Earth, except for the conspicuous absence of a major satellite like the Moon. (See Figure 13.2.) Moreover, the rotation of Venus is quite anomalous in that its spin is extraordinarily slow, and backwards at that. The Sun could not have removed the spin of Venus through tidal friction because even if it were strong enough to slow Venus that much (which it is not), it would have forced Venus into a spin-lock state (one spin per revolution around the Sun), and never allowed it to reach a backwards spin state. The most obvious available mechanism for

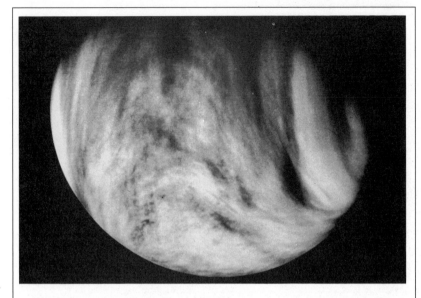

Figure 13.2. A spacecraft view of Venus, showing some visual similarities to Earth. (NASA photograph)

removing the spin of Venus so completely is through tidal interaction with a former massive natural satellite.

Formation and Evolution as a Moon

Let us examine in detail what the consequences would be of assuming that Mercury originated as a satellite of Venus. If that were so, we might presume that Mercury formed in close orbit about Venus, perhaps by fission.[a] But Mercury is four and a half times more mas-

---

[a]If Mercury fissioned from Venus due to overspin, as is suspected to be the case for the Earth's Moon, then we would expect hemispheric asymmetry on Venus, with analogs to the Earth's "Pacific basin" and "Atlantic ridges." Since there are no oceans because of the heat, these might take the form of missing crust, replaced with mantle material, in one hemisphere, and perhaps a major rift or split in the other hemisphere. Or in view of Mercury's greater mass, perhaps the entire original crust of the planet was stripped away in the fission.

sive than the Moon. So the interchange of energy through tidal friction between Venus and Mercury would have been enormous. Mercury's original spin would have been halted fairly rapidly by Venus, leaving Mercury spinning once per revolution around Venus, always keeping the same face toward Venus, as for our Moon.

We can also note that both planets would have been melted by tidal heating in the early stages following escape. Assuming this occurred before Venus differentiated (before the heavy elements sank to its core), this might explain both the high density and the magnetic field of Mercury, and the absence of an appreciable magnetic field for Venus.[b] Thus we have reason to believe that all three present-day planets with unusually high densities (Mercury, Venus, and Earth) probably melted at one time from tidal heating. This melting is then the most probable cause of their high densities.

Tides raised by Mercury on Venus while Venus was still spinning rapidly would have caused great interior heating and outgassing, and probably a great deal of surface upheaval (mountain

---

[b]If Mercury is an escaped satellite of Venus, perhaps most of the original iron in Venus (which ultimately produces the magnetic field) was forced up into the crust by an excessively high spin rate. Venus may have then fissioned from overspin to form Mercury, with Mercury getting most of the iron. Subsequently both bodies would have melted each other from tidal friction, which would cause the heavy elements (such as iron) to sink to the core. Such a scenario could explain why Mercury's magnetic field is stronger than that of Venus, since Mercury would get most of the iron during the original fissioning.

As for the Earth and its Moon, a similar scenario might apply, except that the Earth's iron was not forced to the surface, perhaps because the Earth was not as hot and molten as Venus during that phase of its formation. Whether the iron and heavy elements rise or sink depends on the rate of spin and degree of melting of the planet. For the Earth, if these elements sank to the core before the Moon fissioned, the Moon would end up without its share of heavy elements. The sinking process increases the spin of the Earth, and raises the likelihood of a fission to form the Moon.

Interestingly, for Venus, when the heavy elements rise to the surface, its spin slows. Yet a configuration with a heavy crust and light core becomes more likely to fission at lower spin speeds because it is unstable. If it does fission, the planet that remains behind will have lost a considerable portion of its angular momentum right at the outset.

"There's no use trying," Alice said. "One can't believe impossible things." "I daresay you haven't had much practice," said the Queen. "When I was your age, I always did it for half an hour a day. Why, sometimes I've believed as many as six impossible things before breakfast."
—Lewis Carroll, *Through the Looking Glass* (1872)

building). We already start to see the evolution of a planet very much like the Venus we know today: an unusually thick, dense atmosphere from outgassing to great depths below the surface; quite hot, with mountains as large as its gravity field will support; and robbed of most of its original spin. We know that 50–100 atmospheres' worth of CO_2 and other Venus-atmosphere constituents are trapped in carbonate rocks in the Earth's crust, and might have been released from tidal grinding if the Earth's Moon had been as massive as Mercury.[c]

Tidal friction would take Mercury into higher and higher orbits, just as has been happening for billions of years with our own Moon. However, our Moon will not reach a distance at which it can escape from Earth. All the Earth's spin energy will be transferred to the Moon, and the two will revolve while keeping the same side toward each other, some billions of years in the future. Mercury, however, is sufficiently massive that it takes all of Venus's spin in the first half-billion years after formation; and Venus's orbit is close enough to the Sun that complete escape of Mercury will occur.[d]

---

[c]We might also note that Venus and the Earth have the only two surfaces in the solar system with linear mountain ranges. In this model, these were presumably built during the crust-fracturing process which led to the formation of a large Moon initially in orbit around each of these two planets, and no others.

[d]It is interesting to follow closely what would happen to the spin of Venus as Mercury approaches tidal escape. For Venus or any planet that rotates faster than the mean speed of its atmospheric winds, mountains and other surface irregularities impart enough momentum to the atmosphere to ensure that it moves in the same general direction as the planet spins. But when the planet's rotation slows to below the mean wind speed,

256

While Mercury is still a satellite of Venus, its shape will tend to become somewhat prolate (elongated toward Venus). Although that condition will relax somewhat after escape, the planet should still retain a slightly prolate shape. This turns out to be an important factor in understanding Mercury's present-day odd spin state (3-to-2), as we shall see.

Post-Escape Evolution

Calculations by Harrington show that escape would necessarily occur on the sunward side of Venus, and that the new orbit around the Sun which Mercury would then occupy is both stable and non-intersecting with the orbit of Venus (important to avoid collisions or ejection from the solar system). The subsequent evolution of the orbit of Mercury takes it to higher orbital tilts and eccentricity (ellipticity)—indeed at times to the same values for those parameters which Mercury's orbit has today, even though those values are higher than for any "true" planet.

Let us consider what forces might have been operative in the early solar system which could evolve Mercury's orbit inward to its present distance from the Sun. One candidate is tides raised by Mercury on the Sun. Such tides are negligible today, for purposes of orbital

---

as Mercury would cause Venus to do, then the situation reverses. Mean wind speed can push on mountain ranges and other surface irregularities, and ultimately determine which direction the planet will rotate.

As Mercury tidally evolves outward, it must necessarily produce rotational drag on Venus, tending to slow the rotation of Venus. But it must raise even bigger tides on Venus's atmosphere, causing the whole atmosphere to circulate in the retrograde direction. After billions of years, this may produce retrograde spin of the entire planet.

Today, the largest net torques on Venus's atmosphere are due to the Earth, since its tidal forces are stronger than either Mercury's or Jupiter's. The Sun produces stronger tidal forces than any planet, but with no net torque. So the Earth will ensure that the atmosphere of Venus continues to receive slight retrograde impulses at every inferior conjunction of the two planets. This may explain why the spin of Venus today lies close to a resonance with Earth, despite the seemingly negligible strength of the interaction between the two planets.

evolution. However, these tides should be orders of magnitude larger than is usually assumed, as described in the chapter "Sunspots and Planets." And in the early solar system, the Sun is presumed to have been physically much larger in diameter than now, according to stellar evolution theory (its T Tauri contraction phase). There is no question that a Sun with ten times its present diameter would have produced major tidal evolution which could have separated the orbits of Mercury and Venus (assuming they already existed, and that Mercury had already escaped from Venus). Smaller solar sizes may well have accomplished the same feat, depending upon the rotation speed and extent of differential rotation of the early Sun.

Other forces which might have been operative, such as collisions or drag from leftover planetary formation material, would also operate in the direction of separating the orbits, taking Mercury closer to the Sun than Venus. It is often forgotten that *some* forces were likely operating to evolve the mean distances of the planets from the Sun; for if there were not, we would find leftover formation matter today in the vast number of stable orbits between the planets. In short, if the planets did not all evolve significantly in their mean distances from the Sun (changing their distances by at least a factor of two), the left-over solar system formation material would cause the solar system to more nearly resemble Saturn's rings than discrete planets with empty space between. Even in the conventional model of solar system formation from the primeval solar nebula, the planets would have collided with masses totaling 100% of their own mass in the aggregate while they were undergoing their last doubling in mass during accretion. These aggregate collisions must have had a major effect on the mean distances of each of the planets from the Sun, which could therefore not have started at their present values even in the standard model.

We conclude that the orbit of Mercury *would* evolve into one with unusual eccentricity and inclination to the plane of the other planets, typical of what we see today; and that its mean distance from the Sun *could* have evolved to today's values also. Venus *would* have lost most of its spin in the process, and its remaining slow spin *could* have become retrograde because of thermally-sustained high atmospheric winds being forced retrograde by tides from Mercury just prior to the satellite's escape.

Further calculations by Harrington showed that Mercury would have had a revolution period (and therefore also spin period, since spin is locked to Venus up to escape) of somewhat over 40 days at the point of escape, which spin period it would then retain for a time in its new orbit around the Sun. Tides raised by the Sun on Mercury would gradually slow its spin. Under ordinary circumstances, this slowing would continue until it reached 88 days, Mercury's orbital period, at which time the planet would always keep the same face toward the Sun. Instead Mercury slowed only until it reached its present 59-day, 3-spins-to-2-revolutions state. Why did its spin stabilize in that condition? Because (and I consider this the strongest argument for the correctness of the theory that Mercury was a satellite of Venus) following an escape with a 40-some-days period of spin, the *next* stable spin configuration for a Mercury-like body with a slightly prolate shape is the 3-to-2 spin condition. Mercury has the required prolateness (and no other planet does) to a necessary and sufficient degree. And this prolateness, which enables Mercury to lock into such an unusual spin configuration, is itself a predicted consequence of having been a satellite of a larger planet.

In summary, *something* gave Venus a slow backwards spin, caused it to outgas a dense atmosphere and form high mountains, and to have no natural satellites today. *Something* caused Mercury's satellite-like size and appearance, giving it a prolate shape, high density, and magnetic field, and put it into a 3-to-2 spin state. Up to now, astronomers have invented separate and ad hoc explanations for each of these anomalies. But we can instead invoke a single hypothesis, from which all these anomalies are natural, deductive consequences: that Mercury is an escaped satellite of Venus!

14

• •

The Origin of the Moon

Summary: Four theories of lunar origin are reviewed, together with mention of some recent and some as yet unpublished evidence favoring the theory that the Moon broke off from the Earth out of the Pacific basin. This is the only lunar origin theory that is not inductive in its logical motivations.

Four Theories of Lunar Origin

A question certain to arouse an emotional response from most authorities on the subject is that of the origin of Earth's companion in space, the Moon. (See Figure 14.1.) It is known that the Moon is over 4 billion years old, or nearly the same condensation age as meteorites (and presumably the Sun and planets as well). However, there is little else on which experts agree about its beginnings.

Theories of lunar origin logically divide into three categories: origin of the Moon elsewhere, origin in Earth orbit, or origin as part of the Earth. Each of these categories has had a turn at dominating the opinions of researchers.

The Moon may have originated elsewhere and been captured by the Earth. This theory was given a boost when backwards calculations of the Moon's orbit over billions of years, taking into account tidal friction, seemed to show the Moon escaping, implying that it was indeed captured several billion years ago in forward time. But it has since been shown that this calculation does not lead to a unique solution. And as discussed in the chapter "Orbits," the

Figure 14.1. Earth's only natural satellite, the Moon, showing solidified dark lava "seas" on the side permanently facing Earth, and cratered, mountainous terrain on the side never seen from Earth before spacecraft photos such as this. (NASA photograph)

gravitational capture of one body by another is a virtual impossibility under ordinary circumstances. If gravity is the only force acting, then capture cannot occur unless some other body of appreciable size is involved; and even invoking tidal interaction with the Earth does not raise capture probabilities to a significant level. This fact, taken together with considerations of how bodies such as the Moon might have formed from gas and dust in the early solar nebula, has led to the suggestion that our Moon is the lucky

262

survivor of an original population of thousands of similar bodies. This, however, is a swidget.[a]

It is possible that the Moon originated in the same manner as the Earth, at about the same time, and was already a satellite of the Earth at the moment of its formation. This is usually imagined to be the case if both objects condensed out of a cloud of gas and dust along with the Sun and other planets, and such an origin is suggested by parallels with the satellite systems of the outer planets. In whatever manner the solar system was formed, the planets developed in roughly circular (at least non-intersecting) orbits in nearly the same plane, revolving in the same direction as the Sun's rotation. The major satellites of the outer planets have these same properties (with some special exceptions, discussed in the chapter "Neptune and Pluto").

The main argument against such an origin is that tidal interaction between the Earth and Moon is so relatively large that an origin quite close to the Earth would be implied by any traceback of the Moon's orbit, and formation of such a relatively large satellite close by would be strongly inhibited by tidal forces. It may also be noted that the Earth is the only planet in the inner solar system to have a major (non-asteroidal) satellite, and that the mass ratio is relatively quite large, prompting some to describe the Earth-Moon system as a "double planet." In the most closely analogous case— Pluto and its moon Charon—a special origin for Charon (either capture or fission) seems required. For these reasons the analogy with satellites of the major planets may not apply to the Moon. Nonetheless, this mode of origin is often made the theory of choice because of the severity of objections to the other possibilities.

The third theory is that the Moon split off from the Earth long ago, originally proposed by George Darwin (the "fission" theory). One motivation for this theory is that the Earth's continents would nearly fit together like a jig-saw puzzle if the Atlantic Ocean were removed. This suggests that the Moon formed from part of the Earth's crust, formerly located where the Pacific Ocean now is, which tore off due to the Earth's spinning too rapidly. The breaking of the Earth's crust would then have split the crust (now conti-

---

[a]See Glossary.

nents) on the opposite side, producing the Atlantic Ocean basin and the jig-saw appearance of the continents.

Until the 1970s this fission theory was thought to be in conflict with dynamical and chemical evidence. However, NASA scientist John O'Keefe has shown how the dynamical conflicts can be resolved, and the German astrochemist H. Wanke has done the same for the chemical problems. We now know that the Moon shares certain properties with the Earth's crust, such as a tungsten deficiency, which are unlikely to have arisen unless the Moon was indeed once a part of that crust. More recent work by Keith Runcorn has resolved what were once thought to be other minor discrepancies in composition.

Lunar Origin from Mars-Sized Impactor Planet

Once the idea of lunar origin from the Earth's mantle began to gain ascendancy, a number of objections were raised, ultimately leading to a "compromise" theory. This hybrid fourth theory was that the Moon was made out of a combination of terrestrial mantle material and material from an outside source, generally taken to be a Mars-sized impactor planet.

Although intuitively this hybrid idea may seem unlikely, it again presupposes that many such Mars-sized candidate impactors existed in the late stages of planetary formation. Its specific motivations were problems with the pure fission hypothesis on three fronts: 1. different iron oxide contents of the Earth and Moon; 2. the greater depletion of certain relatively stable metallic elements in the Moon compared to the Earth; and 3. the physical difficulty of ejecting mantle material in such a way that it could form into a lunar-sized body in orbit around the Earth.[147]

These problems were nominally solved by assuming a Mars-sized body struck the Earth with a grazing blow. Such a body is said to bring with it enough angular energy to get itself and mantle material into Earth orbit. Its own iron oxide would mix with that from the Earth's mantle. And by assuming that the impactor was chemically similar to asteroids, one might explain the depletion of stable, metallic elements on the Moon. From these considerations, this hybrid theory has become the current model of choice for explaining the origin of the Moon.

But collisions are generally destructive not formative processes, and in the chapter on "Orbits," we argue that fragments from a collision site cannot get into orbit under ordinary circumstances. Their orbits would still intersect the Earth's surface. Even grazing fragments that miss the surface would still have part of their orbit less than one diameter away, yet have mean periods longer than the Earth's spin period. Under such conditions they would soon be eliminated by tidal forces. (See the chapter "Orbits" for a detailed discussion of tidal processes.)

"I'm sorry, if you were right, I'd agree with you."
—from the movie
Awakenings

Additionally, Newsom and Runcorn[147] showed that if the Moon formed a small core in the process, this could completely explain the element abundance differences between Earth and Moon. Newsom and Runcorn add the specific argument that the depletion of the Moon's surface materials in the element Vanadium could only have occurred on an Earth-sized planet which had melted, resulting in separation of heavy and light elements into core and mantle, respectively. This argument has been extended more recently to the elements chromium and manganese, which could not have been depleted by core formation in a Mars-sized impactor, but certainly could have been depleted as observed, for both Earth and Moon, during core formation of an Earth-sized body.[148]

So if an answer could be found to the angular-energy problem of how to get the Moon into Earth orbit, with a process that forms a small lunar core, none of the arguments for a Mars-sized impactor would any longer be required.

The Theory of Lunar Origin by Fission

In some unpublished research, Bob Harrington at the U.S. Naval Observatory and I showed that backwards integrations of the lunar orbit are unstable, and therefore do not lead to a unique solution. Very slight perturbations cause enormous variations in the end result. Interestingly, integrations forward in time have no such instability and can be followed even over billions of years. Initial conditions over a fairly broad range close to the Earth will all evolve outward under the influence of solar and tidal perturbations to a lunar orbit with an eccentricity and inclination close to what the Moon has today.

In may not be immediately evident why this is so. If a body starts out in the plane of the Earth's present-day equator, with a tilt of 23.5 degrees, why wouldn't it end up in an orbit with comparable tilt? While the Moon is close to the Earth, the Earth's gravity dominates. The effect of the Sun is to cause a precession of the plane of the Moon's orbit which is quite slow compared to that induced by the shape of the Earth. But as the Moon's orbit evolves outward over hundreds of millions of years, the Sun's influence becomes progressively stronger while the Earth's influence weakens. Gradually the Sun's efforts to get the Moon's orbit to precess about the plane of the Earth's orbit win out over the efforts of the Earth's shape to cause precession about the equator. Further outward evolution tends to be "toward the Sun's plane" on average, rather than "away from the equator" on average. Tilt angles that were large closer to the Earth become smaller when far from the Earth. The result is that a wide range of starting conditions all end up about the same: inclined about 5 degrees to the apparent plane of the Sun around the Earth.

In fact, we integrated just such a case because of its special interest: the case of a fission origin of the Moon in close Earth orbit in the plane of the Earth's equator. We made the assumption that the Earth's rotational spin had reached the critical value (about two hours) at which the Earth would be caused to fission from spinning too rapidly. We will discuss in a moment why this condition probably came about. Not only did the evolution of this early lunar orbit come close to present-day conditions (for both ellipticity and tilt), but it also had the side effect of increasing the tilt of the Earth's axis to its orbital plane. Starting tilts of only about 8 degrees (i.e., similar to the Sun's tilt) for the Earth's axis were pumped up to today's 23.5 degrees during the exchange of angular momentum by tides.[b] Greater starting tilts ended up with greater final tilts, and

---

[b]Although we have never done the calculations, clearly this "pumping" mechanism for increasing the tilt of the axis of a parent body through

vice versa. We interpreted these calculations as fully supporting the theory of fission origin of the Moon from the Earth, and as explaining the origin of the relatively large tilt of the Earth's present-day spin axis.

Our deductive model proceeds as follows. As the Earth accretes in the early solar system (in the standard model),[c] pressures and temperatures rise near its center. Eventually the core regions melt. This causes heavy elements to sink to the center and results in a general contraction, and consequent spin-up, of the Earth. This process would continue, with the spin of the Earth getting faster and faster, until either the end of significant accretion, or the Earth reached an overspin condition.

The Earth might have reached overspin more than once during its accretion. But we assume that it reached overspin at least once late in its accretion phase. Overspin means that the outward centrifugal forces due to spinning exceed the inward force of gravity. Because the Earth's crust has some tensile strength, it would not fly off immediately. But as the overspin became more excessive, eventually the crust must fracture along some weak fault lines.

When the crust fractures, whole sections are lifted wholesale away from the Earth's surface. By the meaning of overspin, everything on the Earth's surface has enough velocity to orbit the Earth, and it is being restrained only by the tensile strength of the crust. Anything not "tied down" will indeed orbit. Objects at the surface

the tidal exchange of angular momentum with bodies orbiting it has applicability elsewhere in the solar system. It may well account for the otherwise-unexplained origin of the Sun's tilt of 7 degrees to the mean plane of the planets (since the planets contain 98% of the present angular momentum of the solar system, and must have had significant tidal interaction with the Sun during its T Tauri contraction phase). It would also be interesting to determine if extreme tilts, such as that of Uranus or Pluto (near 90 degrees), or even that of Venus (near 180 degrees), could be produced through this mechanism. If so, it may be safely predicted that this mechanism is of major importance in the dynamical evolution of the small solar system bodies with satellites, such as comets and minor planets, where tidal forces have relatively even greater effects than for the major planets.

[c]We propose in this book that the Earth may have fissioned from the Sun instead.

Figure 14.2. The Origin of the Moon. Part of the Earth's crust breaks away due to overspin and enters earth orbit, while the Earth's continents split apart. (Artist: DeVita)

would experience weightlessness. Under such conditions, the Earth could not have a significant atmosphere. Pieces of fractured crust might at first remain close to the site they broke away from, but would continue to orbit the Earth even without any physical connection to it. (See Figure 14.2.)

The fractured crust would pull away from what is now the Pacific basin, splitting apart the remaining crust in what is now the Atlantic basin (ignoring continental drift).[d] But since the floating crust is not sent flying away with any significant velocity or violence, much of it easily collects into a spherical shape under its own self-gravitation. This then is how the model predicts that our Moon formed.

What little momentum the proto-Moon did get when the crust finally fractured from excessive overspin would lift it into low Earth orbit. As the Moon compresses back into a roughly spherical shape under the weight of its own gravity, its spin increases as well. But the Earth raises enormous tidal forces on a spinning Moon. Tides on such a proto-Moon might easily be many miles high!

What quickly happens is that the Moon's spin is damped out (and the Moon is eventually forced to keep one side permanently toward the Earth), while the Moon's orbit increases its distance. But while the tides last, the "tidal pumping" due to the surface ris-

---

[d]Modern geologists do not accept a connection between the continents and the origin of the Moon, because current theory has the Atlantic sea floor widening at a rate of about 2 cm/year, and the entire Atlantic basin created just within the past few hundred million years: far too recent to be caused by the Moon. This is all part of the modern theory of "continental drift," which was resisted for most of this century until magnetic anomalies were discovered on the sea floor which appeared to confirm it.

Reality cannot be both ways. The continental drift scenario and the lunar fission origin as I have described it contain incompatible predictions about the origin of the Atlantic basin. Deductively, the fission origin works well in other respects, and is a sufficient cause for the Atlantic basin. This leads me to make the following prediction. Modern techniques that measure the locations of observing sites on different continents with a precision of 1 cm or better, such as Very Long Baseline Interferometry (VLBI), will show no secular trend to spread apart at nearly the rates predicted for the sea floors. Alternatively in might be the case that the Earth is expanding in radius, which would make room for more mid-oceanic ridges without much change in the overall geometry of the Earth's surface. Either of these scenarios would surprise geologists, who would have to re-think the meaning of the magnetic anomalies found on the sea floors. But they would come as no surprise to me.

ing and falling heats the Moon's interior and partially melts it, forming a small core. Chemically, the proto-Moon was made from basaltic Earth crust and mantle material after the Earth's heavy elements (iron, tungsten, etc.) had mostly sunk toward its core. Then as the Moon formed its core, the stable metallic elements and all volatiles became depleted from its surface as well, just as observed.

Finally, the Moon raises huge tides back on the Earth, which keep the Earth's interior hot and molten for an extended period. But their principal effect is to increase the Moon's orbital height. This is a process which occurred quite rapidly while the Moon was close by, but continues to this day to a far lesser degree. The scenario then follows along the lines of the calculations Harrington and I performed, as described earlier.

So did the Moon originate from the Earth? Certainly no consensus yet exists among authorities in this field of research, and all possible origins, including several hybrids, have their modern-day proponents. My opinion is that the preponderance of evidence now favors the pure fission theory over the other possibilities. Most significant to me is that the fission theory is the only one which can adopt a starting point and derive a Moon closely like the real one by deduction alone. The other models require inductive steps. But 4 billion years is a long time over which to reconstruct the history of the solar system at the present state of knowledge.

Even today the Moon continues to recede slowly from the Earth due to tidal forces. Ultimately the Moon will be about twice its present distance, and the Earth will keep the same face toward the Moon, just as the Moon now does toward the Earth. If we still haven't reached agreement on the riddle of the Moon's origins by then, our descendants in a few billion years can emigrate to the side of the Earth where the Moon will never rise, and put the vexing problem permanently out of their minds!

15

• •

Mars and Saturn

Summary: Several ideas developed in other chapters are applied here. We discuss and propose solutions for the problem of the origins of Mars and its moons, suggesting that the latter are quite recent. The rings of Saturn are apparently quite young, and may be from a recent satellite breakup, perhaps triggered by the planetary explosion event. We extensively review the distribution of dark material all over the solar system, such as on Saturn's half-black, half-white moon Iapetus, showing how all of it seems likely to have originated from the planetary explosion event.

The Origin of the Martian Moons

Mars has two moons, Phobos and Deimos, which have all the characteristic appearances of being captured asteroids. Yet they are too deep within Mars's gravitational field for capture to have been possible at any time without the intervention of some non-gravitational forces. Phobos, the inner satellite, revolves faster than Mars rotates and is therefore tidally decaying. It should impact onto Mars in about 40,000,000 years.[149] The other moon Deimos revolves more slowly than Mars rotates and hence is tidally evolving outward slowly. Both moons are heavily cratered, but Phobos in particular shows evidence of having undergone some unusually severe collision which gouged out a major chunk of its mass and must have nearly shattered the moon into pieces. (See Figure 15.1.) Stress cracks are also visible on its surface in higher-resolution photos.

271

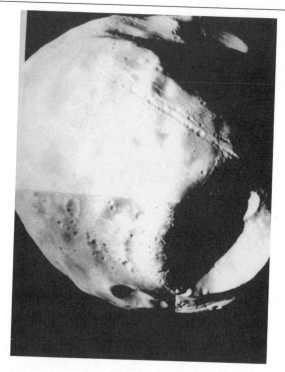

Figure 15.1. Phobos, the inner moon of Mars, and the crater Stickney. (NASA photograph)

Theories to explain how these objects could have been captured into their present orbits have generally been rather contrived, especially since it is so difficult to get Phobos inside an orbit synchronous with Mars's rotation in any of the conventional ways. In the chapter "Do Planets Explode?" I discuss evidence that asteroids originated in the explosive breakup of a planet between Mars and Jupiter within the past few million years. It is very satisfying to note that such a scenario implies an uncontrived capture mechanism that works very well to get Phobos and Deimos into their present orbits.

If asteroids originated from the breakup of a planet beyond the orbit of Mars, then Phobos and Deimos, which are certainly former asteroids, must have originated in the same way. Let us picture the breakup, and reason in an a priori manner about what must have happened next. The process is called "gravitational screen capture" as described in the chapter on "Orbits."

As the planet explodes, smaller masses are in general propelled outward with higher velocities than larger masses. The travel times to Mars are many months for the leading bits of the planet. Velocities past Mars are too high to permit gravitational capture, and as a result the blast wave simply travels on past Mars. Other masses impact on the Martian surface. But Mars has a thin atmosphere which takes up perhaps 3% of the total cross-sectional area Mars presents to the oncoming blast wave. Hence some projectiles will pass through the ultra-thin atmosphere (1% of the density of Earth's atmosphere). For a substantial range of altitudes above the Martian surface, the slowing by this thin atmosphere will be enough for capture of these projectiles into temporary orbit around Mars.

These orbits will be temporary indeed, often decaying onto Mars within just a few revolutions (because the orbits must continue to pass through the atmosphere).[a] (Note that the relative thicknesses and small scale heights[b] of the atmospheres of Earth and Venus prevent either of those planets from acting in a similar manner to capture any significant number of projectiles into temporary orbits around themselves, even for just a few revolutions.[c,150] But in the case of Mars the circumstances are just right for the temporary capture of a number of the projectiles from the explosion.)

---

[a]Their lifetimes may become somewhat prolonged by the removal of significant portions of the Martian atmosphere by many large objects passing through it at high speeds. The mean atmospheric density on Mars may have become considerably reduced in a matter of days by this process.

[b]Scale height: a measure of how rapidly an atmosphere decreases in density as a function of height.

[c]An observed example of just such an event for the Earth is the Cyrillid Meteor Shower of February 9, 1913. Apparently a cluster of meteors, as might accompany a small asteroid or comet, just grazed the Earth's atmosphere during daylight hours, causing them to circle the globe. On their next (and last) revolution, after darkness had fallen, they gradually decayed in the Earth's atmosphere over a long trajectory covering Canada to the Bermuda islands. Thirty individual bodies were widely seen by many observers, covering a span of about six minutes for each observer (see next reference).

Next we notice that by the time the somewhat slower but larger masses from the explosion arrive in the vicinity of Mars, there will be a "screen" of bodies in temporary orbits around Mars with which these larger masses may collide. Among the many such collisions likely to occur, some may be suitable to leave a few of the larger masses gravitationally bound to Mars in a permanent way. Moreover, continued collisional interaction with the temporary bodies in orbit will tend to drive the larger captured satellites into somewhat more circular and somewhat more equatorial orbits, via mechanisms well known to dynamicists who study how rings of planets for.[d]

The result of the scenario just described is that Mars would tend to capture asteroids much like Phobos and Deimos, which would each necessarily show evidence of at least one fairly catastrophic collision (the one that dropped them into gravitationally bound orbits in the first place). And it would then be no surprise to learn that one of them was decaying in 40 million years, since the capture event was also quite recent. Furthermore, evidence has been reported of an unusually large number of objects which struck the Martian surface at angles of less than 15 degrees,[151] which very nicely fits into this scenario calling for the decay of numerous temporary satellites.[e] The same researchers remark that the visible "grooves" on Phobos could be caused by running into material in

---

[d]The late presence of these smaller bodies to collide with and circularize the orbits of the larger moons suggests that some of them may remain in orbit around Mars today, but be too small for detection. Since debris that crossed the orbits of Phobos or Deimos would eventually be eliminated, the best places to search for such debris would be in the same orbits as Phobos or Deimos, and in the orbit synchronous with the rotation of Mars, which lies between them. The Russian spacecraft Phobos 2 has apparently already detected a gas torus in the orbit of Phobos. Considerable meteoroid and small satellite material knocked off Phobos during its capture into Martian orbit may orbit there as well.

[e]Notice the major scar or gorge on Mars in , called Valles Marineris. It would be a reasonable guess that this was caused by decayed former moons, some of which were perhaps of many kilometers diameter. The moons were probably massive enough to be capable of completing a few orbits of Mars even while in the Martian atmosphere. This would result in first contact with the surface being almost perfectly tangential, and on

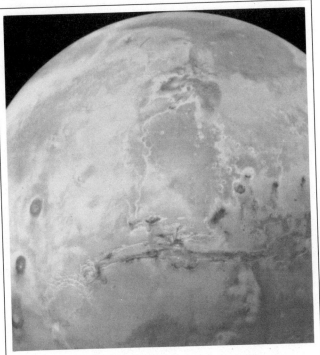

Figure 15.2. The equatorial region of Mars, showing the Valles Marineris canyon and three high volcanoes. (NASA photograph)

relatively high Martian terrain. The highest such terrain—three volcanoes—lies just to the west of the huge gorge, in the Tharsis region of Mars. (And just as this hypothesis would deductively demand, the surface in that region is scarred with long, thin fissures pointing toward Valles Marineris, marking the initial contact points for the decaying moons.) What would follow next would presumably be describable as bodies with masses of hundreds of mountains barreling along at a couple of kilometers per second (faster than a bullet). They would drag, roll, and eventually tunnel across the Martian surface until their considerable momentum was brought to a halt, probably fragmenting as they went. The sculpted rims of the gorge offer further testament to just such a history. (See Figure 15.2.) Many former equatorial Martian moons or Phobos fragments may have suffered the same fate and crashed into the same gorge.

Figure 15.3. Closeup of Valles Marineris, showing sculpting of rims. (Photograph courtesy E. Hauber.)

orbit, which would produce the parallel or nearly parallel arcs less than 180 degrees long, unlike what would be expected of ejecta from the huge Phobos crater Stickney, which apparently nearly shattered the moon.[f]

Indeed, the only link in this scenario one might question is the starting assumption of a recently exploded planet. Given that event (for which evidence is presented in the chapter "Do Planets Explode?"), the rest of the theory for the origin of the Martian moons seems altogether likely to be accurate.

[f]Although the crater Stickney appears to correspond with the predicted major impact event required to drop Phobos into Martian orbit initially, we might ask about the corresponding event for Deimos. The collision that produced Stickney nearly shattered Phobos; and Deimos, which is somewhat concave on one face, looks as though it may have been shattered and split, with the moon we see today being just the largest surviving fragment.

As mentioned, atmospheric densities of Earth and Venus are not quite so suited to this capture mechanism, since their atmospheres are so thick as to cause most high-velocity debris to burn up. Conditions are suitable for only a very narrow range of height in their atmospheres. The most suitable candidate in the outer solar system for similar captures would seem to be Titan, Saturn's largest satellite. It would be interesting to have the Hubble Space Telescope look near Titan for small captured asteroidal satellites. It is also possible that some of the inner asteroid-like moons, and probably most of the rings, of the four gas giant planets were captured and formed through this same basic process at the time of the breakup of the asteroidal parent planet.

The Origin of Mars

In the chapter "Mercury and Venus," we discussed the likelihood that the planet Mercury may have originated as an escaped satellite of Venus. Such an escape, under the action of tidal friction, would preferentially occur toward the Sunward side of the planet (i.e., Mercury's orbit would be closer to the Sun than Venus's). Mars is another relatively small planet, having not quite twice the mass of Mercury, but only about 0.1 of the mass of the Earth. The question then arises, is there any chance that Mars also might have originated as a satellite of a larger planet, and escaped under the action of tidal friction?

If so, its former parent planet would have been the next planet out from the Sun. This would seem to be the location of the "missing planet" where the asteroid belt is now. In the chapter "Do Planets Explode?" we discuss evidence that a large planet, perhaps Saturn-sized, orbited there until recently in the solar system. Let us refer to this missing planet as "Planet K," following the lead of Canadian astronomer Michael Ovenden, who argued that the appropriate name for this hypothetical exploded body, taken from modern mythology, would be "Krypton."[g] We will also discuss in the chapter "The Origins of the Solar System and of Man" the conjec-

---

[g]Superman's home planet, of course.

ture that Mars's parent was actually "Planet V" (the real "fifth planet"?)—another hypothetical former planet in this part of the solar system.

If Planet K or Planet V had formed with normal contingents of satellites, the outermost of them might well have undergone a tidal escape in much the same way that we propose Mercury escaped from Venus. That escaped satellite could then have evolved into the next available planetary orbit inward toward the Sun, becoming the planet we call Mars. This evolution would necessarily have happened quite early in the solar system's history. Evidence supporting this conjecture is mild, but not implausible. For example, Mars has no natural satellites of its own (assuming that its moons are indeed captured asteroids)—a condition shared by no other planets except Mercury and Venus, which we suspect of being a former satellite-parent pair.

Another argument arises from the slowness of Mars's spin. It can be argued that a planet ought to spin up to the point of flying apart under centrifugal forces during the accretion process (if the standard model for planet formation is right), or by heavy elements sinking to the core (if planets fissured from the Sun). Indeed, the loss of surface layers from overspin may be the chief formation process for natural satellites of planets. Certainly either accretion (collision with other small bodies) or heavy-element collection in the core during the formation of the Earth could cause it to spin at, or close to, the threshold of instability (about two hours). And we know by backwards calculation of the Moon's orbit for several billion years that the Earth's spin was near that threshold at that time. (The Earth's high spin rate is then lost to the Moon through tidal friction as the Moon's orbit evolves outward to its present-day distance.)

But why then didn't Mars, although formed in the same part of the solar system as the Earth, also reach an overspin condition? To account for its low spin rate, Mars might have had massive natural satellites of its own which escaped—but then where did they go? Or perhaps, as we suggest here, Mars might have itself been such a massive escaping satellite, losing its spin as it evolved outward from Planet K or Planet V. When chemical analyses of returned samples of native Martian rocks are available, we might see evi-

Figure 15.4. Saturn's disk and spectacular rings. (NASA photograph)

dence that Mars was formed at the same distance from the Sun as the asteroids, if its parent was Planet K. With greater certainty, we would expect to find evidence of ancient solid-body tides on Mars. Rather than indicating that Mars once had an Earth-like moon of its own, such evidence may be indicating that Mars was once a satellite in orbit around Planet K or Planet V.

The Origin of Saturn's Rings

Most of the mass from the planetary breakup event between Mars and Jupiter would escape the solar system. Most of the rest would be accreted by Jupiter. Saturn (Figure 15.4.) would get the next-largest portion. As discussed in the chapter "Jupiter and Uranus," Jupiter may have accreted a substantial addition to its previous mass from this recent breakup. The small, dark rings of Jupiter, Uranus,

Figure 15.5. A close-up view of Saturn's rings. (NASA photograph)

and Neptune would be formed from captured asteroidal material.

By contrast, Saturn's rings are larger and far brighter, being composed of icy particles, definitely unlike asteroidal material. (See Figure 15.5.) In at least one case it has now been confirmed that gaps in the rings are caused by a small orbiting satellite in the gap, as predicted by the author years earlier.[152] At that time it was believed the gaps were caused by "resonance" with larger Saturnian satellites outside the rings.

Although Saturn's mass would change by a far smaller percentage than Jupiter's from accretion following the planetary explosion, it might well have been enough to bring one or more of its innermost satellites inside the Roche limit, within which they would break up under the tidal stress of Saturn's pull and spread out into rings. Tidal and atmospheric forces would then segregate the material radially, with the innermost rings limited by the distance at which rapid decay into the atmosphere occurs.

If this suggestion is correct, then the dramatic rings of Saturn, which are its most dominant visual feature, are of relatively recent origin. The youth of the rings has already been strongly indicated by other lines of evidence—for example, micrometeoroids would erode them within 10^8 years.[153] If the rings had pre-existed before the recent explosion event, what would be the effect of the passing blast wave on them? Clearly it would disrupt the rings, causing considerable dispersion in both the radial and the transverse directions. However, mutual collisions would restore the rings to circular, co-planar, equatorial orbits in short order. The net result after a few million years would only be a much greater radial extent to the rings than they originally had. We therefore conclude that Saturn's major ring features were either non-existent or of much smaller radial extent prior to 3.2 million years ago (the deduced epoch of the planetary breakup event). But the lack of evidence for any mixture of dark, asteroidal material along with the icy material in the rings argues that the formation of the rings most likely followed the planetary explosion event.

Iapetus and the Black Axiom

Yet another inevitable consequence of the passing of this blast wave of black carbonaceous material through the solar system is the coating of all bodies without atmospheres with the same carbonaceous material. In the inner solar system, some material stays in orbit around the Sun and has the opportunity to coat bodies such as Mercury and the Moon on all sides, although both bodies do have strong hemisphere asymmetries.[h] In the outer solar system, the blast wave

[h]I assume that the hemispheric asymmetries on the Moon and Mercury are due to the impacts of relatively larger bodies, up to about 1 km in size, from the same breakup event. Because of their slow rotation, both the Moon and Mercury would be preferentially hit on one hemisphere by debris from the breakup. That hemisphere would initially be random, of course. However, impacts from larger masses might produce the lunar "mascons," the known concentrations of mass coincident with the main lunar "seas." The sudden addition of a number of mascons to one lunar hemisphere would break the stability of the Moon's rotational lock with Earth, and cause the portion of the Moon's surface with the accreted

passes just once, but with a time dispersion of several weeks. The satellites of Jupiter, Saturn, and Uranus are apparently coated with irregular splotches of such black material.[i]

It would follow, of course, that any body without an atmosphere which rotated slowly enough would

> "Good judgment comes from experience. Experience comes from bad judgment."
> —Anonymous

necessarily be coated with the black carbonaceous residue of the blast wave on one side only. Saturn's satellite Iapetus (Figure 15.6.) is a candidate for this effect, since it rotates with a period of 80 days, far more slowly than any other major satellite of Jupiter, Saturn, or Uranus. The most striking characteristic of Iapetus in optical observations is that it is black on one side and white on the other, as if one side were icy and the other side carbonaceous. The difference in average brightness of the two sides is more than a factor of five, so there is no doubt about the existence of the effect (i.e., not merely topographic variations). The explanation is usually said to be unknown.

---

masses to rotate toward the Earth's pull (to the minimum potential configuration). New librations of the Moon would soon be damped out by tidal friction from the Earth. The result would inevitably be that the hemisphere with the most mascons would end up facing the Earth, whatever its starting orientation. This explains the mystery of why the facing lunar hemisphere has all the "seas" and is more heavily cratered than the far side. The case is likely to be similar for Mercury's surface: the Caloris Basin, for example, would be the site of one of the larger impacts from the breakup event. Mercury, however, is unlikely to have lost its 3-to-2 rotational lock with the Sun on this account.

[i]A few relatively bright moons with little dark material in evidence (Io, Enceladus, Tethys) are all cases where tidal forces are unusually intense, leading to extensive reworking of their surfaces during the past few million years. This was obviously true in the case of Io, which showed several ongoing volcanic eruptions as the *Voyager* spacecraft flew by. Recent resurfacing of Enceladus is also suspected as the cause of the tenuous E-ring of material around Saturn near that satellite's orbit. All moons for which active resurfacing is not suspected contain substantial dark material.

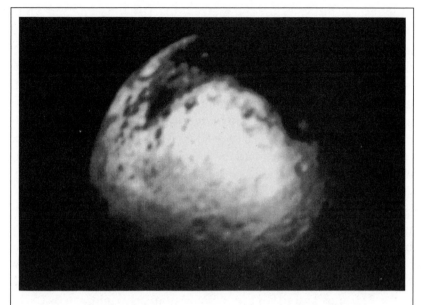

Figure 15.6. Saturn's moon Iapetus, showing some of the icy-bright and carbon-dark material on its surface. (NASA photograph)

In a discussion at a planetary science meeting, astronomer Carl Sagan raised the objection that the brightness asymmetry has a strong north-south component as well, which argues against an external source of the asymmetry lying near the average plane of the planets. The answer to this objection is that Iapetus (unlike Saturn's closer satellites) is inclined by 15 degrees to the plane of Saturn's equator, which in turn is inclined by 27 degrees to the average plane of the planets. If the rotation axis of Iapetus were also inclined by a few degrees to its orbital plane, tilts of up to 45 degrees to the average plane of the planets would occur from time to time. Hence a blast wave spreading through the solar system from a source near the average plane of the planets could indeed coat Iapetus with a strong north-south component to its brightness asymmetry because of this tilt.

I refer to the generality of this brightness-asymmetry phenomenon as the "black axiom": any atmosphereless body in the outer solar system which rotates more slowly than about one month should show just such an asymmetry—black on one side and white on the other—from the effects of the passing blast wave. It appeared at the time I first formulated this axiom that Iapetus was the only definite example in the solar system. Since then some other examples have surfaced. For example, lightcurve evidence weakly suggested that Neptune's moon Nereid is another example of the black axiom—with a rotation period of nearly a year and a strong brightness asymmetry between its two sides.[j] Moreover, the sharpness of transition between bright and dark regions and the degree of blackening are both predictable consequences of the planetary explosion hypothesis. For Iapetus, which was exposed entirely on one side, the black-white contrast is especially great. But its slow rotation during its weeks of exposure produced a grey-area boundary between dark and bright regions on the moon.

I now realize there are other classes of bodies which may show this asymmetric reflectivity as well. The orbital planes of the satellites of Uranus and Pluto are inclined at nearly right angles to the average plane of the other planets. This means that at some parts of their orbital cycles around the Sun, those satellites will face one pole (and therefore one hemisphere) toward the Sun continuously as they rotate; while at other parts of the parent planet's orbit, they will present all sides to the Sun as they rotate. In that connection, Pluto is already known to have a large, dark area concentrated toward one hemisphere; so it is already known to obey the black axiom prediction.[k] We might further predict, when such observations become possible, that the distributions of extrinsic dark material over the surfaces of Pluto and its large moon Charon will be

---

[j]*Voyager 2* was unable to confirm either the rotation of Nereid, or any hemispheric asymmetry. But if the spin period is as slow as a year, Nereid would have had only one side in sunlight the whole time of the *Voyager 2* encounter. When better-resolution pictures become available, the black axiom predicts that Nereid should have a sharp boundary between its dark and normal regions if its spin rate is indeed quite slow. This assumes that the satellite is original, not asteroidal; that its brightness changes due to surface reflectivity, not shape irregularities; and that its spin axis is only moderately inclined to its orbital plane.

[k]We might also note that the hemisphere of Pluto now experiencing "winter" is the darker one. If the light-dark regions were due to processes

surprisingly similar, because they would have had the same pole orientation toward the explosion when that material accumulated.[l,154]

In the inner solar system, the slow rotators are Mercury, Venus, and our own Moon. Mercury has been photographed by spacecraft on one side only but already shows evidence of a strong cratering asymmetry, as for our Moon. Venus has a thick atmosphere and apparently refreshes its surface every few hundred million years. Before the *Magellan* spacecraft's radar-mapping results were in, I predicted that Venus would show a hemispheric cratering asymmetry similar to that on Mercury and our Moon. The results are now in, and there is a significant asymmetry. But the interpretation is complicated by large areas devoid of cratering in both hemispheres, which have seemingly been recently resurfaced, perhaps by volcanic lava flows.[m]

Our own Moon was only recently photographed from a space perspective. It too has an appreciable hemispheric asymmetry in the distribution of its dark material. However, lunar soil samples seem to show a lot more silicaceous ("glassy") than carbonaceous material. Among asteroids, the spectra of inner asteroids tend to be more S-type ("silicaceous"), and outer ones tend to be more C-type ("carbonaceous"). Whether this anomaly means that two different types of dark material coated these bodies, or whether it

---

originating on the planet, we would ordinarily expect the winter hemisphere to be icier and brighter.

[l]Since this prediction was written, a small part of it has already been confirmed. Photometric studies have shown that Charon is variable, most likely due to changes in geometric albedo as a function of longitude (see next reference), just as is true for Pluto.

[m]On our own Moon, I have remarked that the hemisphere toward the approaching blast wave was probably the one now facing the Earth. That hemisphere contains more dark material, and the larger impacts on that side apparently punctured the lunar crust and flooded wide areas, producing the lunar "seas" on the facing side only. If I had thought more carefully about this before making my prediction for Venus, I would have realized that the facing hemisphere of the Moon actually contains *fewer* craters than the other because of the lava flows. This phenomenon complicates any interpretation which might be attempted from simple crater counts alone.

reflects some other physical difference between the inner and outer bodies, will probably only be determinable by direct chemical analysis of a variety of these bodies. In any event, the dark material on the Moon must be of fairly recent origin, because there are only a few cases where large craters appear on top of it, as indicated by the presence of bright "rays" where ejected material has overlaid the dark lunar topsoil.[n]

The Black Axiom in the Outer Solar System

In applying the black axiom to the satellites of Uranus, we need to examine the unusual geometry of the seventh planet's moons. During part of its 84-year orbit around the Sun, the moons of Uranus will all be oriented with their north poles continuously facing toward the Sun. Only their northern hemispheres will receive any sunlight at any time during the spin of the moons. Twenty-one years later, the satellite poles will be in the plane of the sky, with their equators facing the Sun. At such times, each satellite will have normal day and night as they spin with periods ranging from less than a day up to two weeks for the outermost moon, Oberon. Twenty-one years later again, when Uranus has moved along another 90 degrees in its solar orbit, the south poles of the moons will continually face the Sun, while their north poles will be in the middle of their 42-year-long night. Clearly the aspect presented by the moons of Uranus depends very much upon when we look at them.

Now if the moons had presented all faces to the incoming blast wave from the exploded planet, they would have been blackened all over, as for the Jovian moons. But if either pole happened to be facing the blast, then only one hemisphere of the moons would be blackened by the blast wave. The other hemisphere would remain icy bright. Of course, even if one pole were roughly toward the blast but was off by, let us say, 30 degrees, then that hemisphere would still be blackened, and the opposite would still be bright. But there would be a transition zone 30 degrees on either side of the equator of the moons which would face the blast wave during part of each spin and be hidden from its effects during the rest of the spin. These

---

[n]Examples are craters Copernicus and Tycho.

would then become "grey areas," partially coated with blast material to a varying degree. We would not expect "sharp boundaries" between black and white of the sort we noted near the pole of Triton.

Now here is the observed situation. The north poles of Uranus and its moons faced the Sun in 1945. In 1966, the planet's equator faced the Sun. And in 1987, the planet's south pole was sunward, with only the southern hemispheres of planet and moons visible from any direction (because only the southern hemispheres were in sunlight). Photometric observations made in the 1960s showed only modest variations between hemispheres, indicating that the moons were nearly equator-on toward the breakup blast wave. However, in January 1986, the *Voyager 2* spacecraft flew by Uranus in a few hours, collecting a great deal of new information about the planet in just a few days. Because this was so close to "mid-summer" for the Uranian southern hemisphere, only the southern side of the moons was visible, even though the spacecraft flew past Uranus and looked back. The northern sides were in total darkness.º

Figure 15.7 shows the Uranian moon Umbriel. Because of the timing of photos and location of the moons relative to the passing spacecraft, *Voyager* photographed a larger fraction of the surface of Umbriel close up than any of the other moons. The reader must judge for himself whether or not this moon shows evidence, as predicted by the black axiom, of having a dark and a bright hemisphere separated by a gray zone between them, as predicted.

One intermediate case also exists for a moon of Neptune: Triton's 20-degree tilt to Neptune's equator, combined with Neptune's

---

ºAnother consequence of the planet Uranus having its south pole nearly facing the Sun while the *Voyager* spacecraft flew by was the absence of the changes of day and night on the planet at the time. The planet's southern hemisphere was being continually bathed in steady sunlight of virtually fixed intensity at every point on its surface, even as the planet spins every 17.2 hours. This almost total lack of day-night temperature variations is surely in large measure responsible for the almost featureless atmosphere seen on the planet. We may then venture the prediction that around the year 2009, when Uranus has its equator toward the Sun and has a normal day-night pattern, we may expect to see a quite different atmosphere and visible appearance of the planet.

Figure 15.7. *Voyager 2* view of Uranus' largest moon, Umbriel. (NASA photograph)

29-degree equatorial tilt to the plane of the planets, means that *one pole* of Triton will be shielded from coating by the dark material, possibly up to as much as 49 degrees away from the pole. *Voyager* photos strikingly show this to be the case. (See Figure 15.8.) Triton's south polar region is quite bright, and there is a sharp transition boundary to much darker material at mid-latitudes.ᴾ Planetary scientists have been trying to explain why one polar region is bright, instead of why the rest of the moon is dark. This is yet another example of how model testing works: when the model is right, sur-

---

ᴾSince Triton's rotation would not expose the polar region to the blast wave, but would continually re-expose the same non-polar regions on every rotation, the boundary between bright and dark areas should be especially sharp, which is the observed situation. Moreover, nearly all impacts near this boundary from the blast wave would be grazing impacts at a high incidence angle, and all directed toward the shielded polar region. About 100 such streaks of just that description are seen on Triton, all of them near the boundary between the bright polar region and the dark material beyond!

Figure 15.8. *Voyager* photograph of Triton, Neptune's largest moon, showing the sharp boundary between its bright south polar region and otherwise dark surface. (NASA photograph)

prising new data fits right in. When it is wrong, new data "raises more questions than it answers"—a sure sign of a bad model.

In a recent study which strongly indicates that the dark material in various parts of the solar system is of the same type, a team of astronomers has now established that the surfaces of a few D-class asteroids, the dust of some comets, the dark hemisphere of Iapetus, and the rings of Uranus spectrally all have cyano-group-containing molecules.[155] It is most improbable that objects originating at vastly different distances from the Sun would all have this property. This feature suggests a common origin for the dark material on all these bodies.

In looking at a number of individual examples of the black axiom, it is important not to lose sight of the generalization which it proves: Wherever in the solar system airless surfaces were exposed to the planetary explosion, those surfaces are blackened. Wherever surfaces were hidden from the explosion continuously for weeks at a time, those surfaces are icy bright. The blackness of the surfaces and the sharpness of the bright-dark boundaries on each moon or planet are predictable from the length of exposure toward the explosion during those weeks.

Note that even if there were not specific evidence for a major breakup event in the solar system, such an event could be hypothesized purely from the existence of these brightness asymmetries. For it is only by the passage of such a wave through the solar system that one can correctly predict a priori exactly which satellites will be affected, how, and why. This is another demonstration of the advantages of forward reasoning (blast wave will necessarily coat certain satellites, and only those certain ones, on one side; argument is compelling and inescapable) over reverse reasoning (why certain satellites might have a brightness asymmetry; a multitude of possibilities, with little reason to choose among them).

I do not see how the success of the black axiom can be argued away as a bizarre coincidence.

16

• •

Jupiter and Uranus

Summary: We suggest that an increase in Jupiter's mass as a conse-quence of the planetary explosion event may have caused the cap-ture of Jupiter's outer, asteroidal moons. Tidal forces may have a significant effect on Jupiter's Galilean moons, both orbitally and physically. We also suggest that Jupiter's "Great Red Spot" was formed from an "impact." Lastly we discuss what may have tilted Uranus and its moons over by 90 degrees.

The Capture of Jupiter's Asteroidal Moons

In the chapter "Do Planets Explode?" we discuss evidence that a substantial amount of matter may have broken up relatively recently in the solar system. Because of its large gravitational field, Jupiter acts like a giant "vacuum cleaner," sweeping up or ejecting out of the solar system all bodies on orbits that cross Jupiter's orbit in any direction. Even orbits not intersecting Jupiter's orbit will meet the same fate by means of precession of the orbit until it does intersect. The time scale for eventual elimination by Jupiter for any body orbiting the Sun and able to reach Jupiter's distance from the Sun in any direction is only about 100,000 years.

We have proposed that a substantial planet, perhaps Saturn-sized, broke up. A large portion of its remnants would have been swept up collisionally by Jupiter. Let us consider the implications of such events.

291

It has already been pointed out in the research literature that Jupiter's apparently captured asteroidal satellites are presently too deep inside Jupiter's gravitational field for capture or escape to be possible under existing circumstances. It has been further pointed out that both the direct and the retrograde satellites would be simultaneously on the threshold of escape/capture if Jupiter's mass were 40% less than it is at present.[156] This would be the least contrived, and therefore preferred, theory for origin of these bodies as satellites of Jupiter if a source of so much mass for Jupiter to accrete was evident. The planetary breakup event would presumably have acted as just such a source, causing considerable accretion by Jupiter.[a]

The principal argument against this scenario, from Jupiter's perspective, is the existence of a resonance in the orbital periods of Jupiter's large Galilean satellites: Io has half the orbital period of Europa, whose period is almost exactly half of Ganymede's, which is somewhat less than half of Callisto's. If Jupiter had accreted substantial mass in the recent past, this resonance condition would likely have been disrupted, and by existing opinions, it would take billions of years to re-establish through tidal friction interactions with Jupiter. This belief is based on the lack of any known efficient tidal friction mechanism involving a gaseous planet such as Jupiter. In the chapter "Sunspots and Planets," a new mechanism for tidal friction is elaborated that actually makes gaseous giant planets a more efficient source of tidal friction than solid planets. If this mech-

---

[a]A new examination of the outer satellite capture/escape conditions needs to be undertaken in this light. The Byl and Ovenden analysis assumed a circular orbit for Jupiter and only two dimensions. But the inclinations of the captured satellites are not small. Moreover, both inclinations and eccentricities undergo quite large variations over time. The analysis also neglected changes in Jupiter's mean distance from the Sun which might accompany large mass accretions. It may well be that the increment to Jupiter's mass to arrive at the present orbital conditions could have been substantially less than 40%—perhaps as little as 5% (about 16 Earth masses). Including in the calculations the Trojan asteroids which move in Jupiter's solar orbit should permit a reasonably definitive determination about whether the mass accretion hypothesis is viable, and about how much mass is required.

anism is verified by future measurements of orbital accelerations of these large satellites due to tidal friction, then the objection just described would disappear, and we could expect enough tidal evolution of the Galilean satellites in a few million years to re-establish a mildly disrupted resonance.

We must also assume that the mass accretion by Jupiter does not occur in a time short in relation to the satellite orbital periods. For example, if no single chunk of accreted mass exceeded a few Earth masses, and successive chunks are well spread out in time (as they would be), then changes in the satellite orbits would be slow and progressive, with tidal dissipation able to maintain the resonances. In this connection, the enormous global heat flux emitted by Io appears to exceed the calculated maximum under the existing dynamical conditions, unless the moon has indeed changed its orbit substantially in the astronomically recent past.[157]

Let us assume, for the sake of continuing to draw out the consequences of the hypothesis, that Jupiter did indeed accrete substantial mass within the past 3,200,000 years. One of the consequences may be a further compression of the planet's core under the increased load from the accreted mass. This seems likely to result in the radiation of a substantial amount of heat away from the planet until a new equilibrium is established. Hence the observed excess of heat radiated by Jupiter into space, over and above the heat it receives from the Sun, may not be indicative of star-like reactions having begun in its interior, as often speculated. It may be a "short-term" adjustment from recent accretion which will die away in another few tens of millions of years.

The Nature of Jupiter's Great Red Spot

Let us look in some detail at another consequence of the accretion by Jupiter of large masses. Suppose a body with Moon or Earth dimensions approached the giant planet on a collision course. The usual opinion is that once the approaching mass was close enough (inside the "Roche limit"), it would break apart. Smaller pieces would burn up in Jupiter's atmosphere; larger ones would sink to the core. But let us look at the details of the encounter a bit more closely.

It is well known that a mass breaks up if it orbits too closely to a massive planet. This is presumably the origin of at least some of the ring systems of the outer planets. However, the same reasoning does not apply to a body approaching on a collision course. The tidal forces that would tear an orbiting body apart over a period of time cannot operate quickly enough on a rapidly approaching body. Moreover, some of the tidal forces are working to compact the body while others are trying to tear it apart. Inside the "Roche limit," Jupiter's gravitational pull on the front surface of a body is stronger than the body's own gravitational pull on its own front surface — hence the tendency to be pulled apart. However, Jupiter's gravity tends to press the "sides" of the approaching body toward the body's center, compressing it rather than pulling it apart. The result is a tendency for the body to elongate along the line toward Jupiter.

Now suppose that the body enters the atmosphere of Jupiter. The velocity of entry is necessarily quite large, and the body does not travel far before it encounters as much atmospheric mass as its own mass, so hitting the atmosphere will be not unlike hitting a solid wall. Some of the body will be heated so rapidly and suffer such high compression during atmospheric entry that an explosion must result. But for very large bodies, only the leading layers of the body would bear the brunt of the entry forces and explosion. The heat and pressure would take so long to be transmitted through the large body that the trailing portions would receive relatively gradual deceleration. Even at speeds of 20 to 50 km/s, it would take several minutes for a Moon- or Earth-sized body to move its own diameter, or to pass a given depth in Jupiter's atmosphere; pressure waves would travel at a mere fraction of such speeds.

The effect on such a large body, then, would be to flatten out and break up, but not all of it would do so explosively. The body fragments would also tend to be pushed into a large, flattened disk. The flattening tendency would be the direct result of the forces of entry and would become increasingly stable against tidal disruption. This is because the tidal forces that tend to tear the body apart are proportional to the body's thickness in the direction toward Jupiter's center; while the tidal forces tending to hold the body together increase with body width perpendicular to that direction. Although the body would naturally be trying to spread out horizontally in all directions, both the tidal forces of Jupiter and the body's own gravitational forces would effectively oppose spreading beyond some radius. Tidal forces would simply continue to increase in magnitude until the flattened body could spread no more.

The final configuration would be a large, flattened disk of loosely bound fragments, which would not be able to disperse because of mutual gravitational attraction and cohesion. However, in the course of

> "If we knew what we were doing, it wouldn't be research."
> —Anonymous

spreading out, the density of the fragmented "pancake" would decrease. Thereafter, the flattened body would sink until it reached a layer in the atmosphere with the same mean density. Considering that our own Moon's diameter is 5% of Jupiter's radius, it would not take much spreading before the "pancake" density became low enough to match the average atmospheric density at modest depths in Jupiter's atmosphere. Once this depth was reached, the "pancake" mass would float there indefinitely. Although it would eventually share Jupiter's average rotation, differential rotation at different latitudes would cause turbulent flow around this floating atmospheric obstruction.

The details of the breaking up and reshaping of the entering body are difficult to model. If a dense body simply displaced an equally dense volume of atmosphere, self-gravitation could no longer hold it together. However, it presumably undergoes some aerodynamic reshaping in the entry process, trapping lighter gases underneath as it drops. The considerable lifting forces of the very high winds, and perhaps even magnetic suspension, may play a role in supporting the body in the atmosphere. Like the hull of a heavy ship floating in the ocean, it would only be necessary that the impacting body be flattened and reshaped so that at some depth, it eventually displaces its own "weight" in the Jovian atmosphere. Self-gravitation could continue to assist cohesion.[158]

If this picture sounds familiar, there are such features in the atmospheres of Jupiter, Saturn, and Neptune. The "Great Red Spot" of Jupiter is the most famous example (Figure 16.1.), followed by the "Great Dark Spot" on Neptune. Traditional theory has it that

Figure 16.1. The gaseous giant planet Jupiter with its "Great Red Spot" and bands. (NASA photograph)

the Red Spot is a giant hurricane in Jupiter's atmosphere which has lasted for centuries. But winds are so much higher on Jupiter than on Earth, and there is so much differential flow and turbulence, it is difficult to see how a cohesive storm pattern could survive for months, let alone centuries. One would expect any major atmospheric disturbance to spread around the entire planet, as happened for the "white spot" on Saturn in 1990. For semi-permanent spots, it seems far more likely to me that something is floating in the atmosphere, producing an obstruction and therefore the appearance of a giant storm. And I propose that the "something" is the remnants of a quite large impact on Jupiter. Such a floating obstacle also may be capable of inhibiting heat transfer from the deep interior to the top of Jupiter's atmosphere.

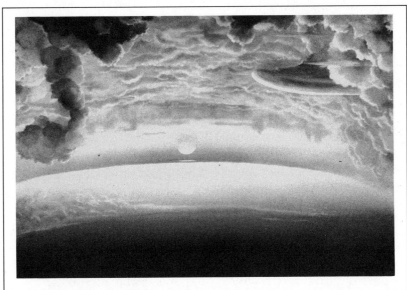

Figure 16.2. "Sunset From Neptune's Great Dark Spot." Triple image of setting Sun as viewed from Neptune's upper methane atmosphere. (Artist: Bensusen)

In the case of Neptune's Dark Spot, this provides a more natural explanation of the unmoving "lenticular" cirrus-like clouds near the spot.[b] It even provides a "surface" for the clouds to cast visible shadows on, which is easier to visualize than the "haze layer"

[b]Paul Burke of California, an observer of "lenticular" clouds in the Sierra Nevada mountain ranges on Earth, first made this suggestion to me in the Astroforum discussion section of the CompuServe Information Network. As warmer air hits the slopes in the mountains and is forced rapidly to higher altitudes it cools, condensing some moisture. This continually re-forms clouds which seem to remain "in place," not moving with the winds. The reverse process, descending and warming air, occurs on the other side of the slopes, dissolving the clouds. At Neptune, a floating obstruction in the upper atmosphere may act as a heat insulator for the excess Neptunian heat being radiated from the interior. There may be a nearly permanent zone of cooler "air" over the floating obstruction (the "Great Dark Spot"), where lenticular clouds continually re-form. (See Bensusen's concept of the view from inside the Great Dark Spot in Figure 16.2.)

whose existence has been conjectured in order to explain what makes cloud shadows visible on Neptune's Dark Spot.

If such floating "inclusions," as foreign mass concentrations within another body are called, do exist, they would certainly greatly enhance the tidal friction process evolving the orbits of the planet's satellites. (The astute reader may already have objected to my earlier suggestion: the latitudinal tidal friction mechanism I have proposed for sunspots isn't as easily applicable to Jupiter and its satellites because its major satellites all lie in the plane of Jupiter's equator. However, the Great Red Spot and other possible "inclusions" are at a variety of latitudes, making the new mechanism fully applicable.)

I am indebted to my son Brian for pointing out that it should be possible to test for the existence of solid material floating in the gaseous atmosphere by bouncing radar beams off it. This may even be possible from Earth-based radar, which can already "see" the Galilean satellites. Jupiter orbiters can also measure variations in the gravity field of Jupiter which, like the lunar "mascons," indicate mass concentrations in certain locations within Jupiter. We already have the capability of conducting these two tests, if anyone can be persuaded to look. And the day should eventually arrive when we can send probes into Jupiter's Red Spot to obtain samples of the material there. If the preceding idea is right, we might find ourselves sampling the core material from a former planet— material which would otherwise be quite inaccessible to direct sampling and study!

Uranus

The most striking characteristic of Uranus (Figure 16.3.) is that it rotates "on its side" with a tilt of somewhat more than 90 degrees. Its primary satellites and rings are in its equatorial plane, so they too revolve in orbits nearly perpendicular to the average plane of the rest of the planets. Elsewhere the author has discussed puzzles arising from the darkness and peculiar dynamical behavior of the rings.[159] Here we will take up the question of the tilt of the entire planet. If Uranus was tipped by a collision with a large body, how did the satellite orbits get back into its equatorial plane; and if not

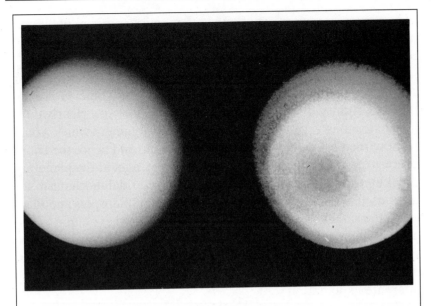

Figure 16.3. Uranus as seen by the *Voyager* spacecraft, in normal and false color. (NASA photograph)

a collision, then what caused the extreme tilt?

Tidal forces exerted by Uranus would be ineffective in changing the inclination of its satellites, as such forces have been for Neptune's moon, Triton. Mutual tidal forces among the satellites would have produced synchronous motion if they were significant, but that has not happened. Yet all four orbits of the major satellites of Uranus are very closely circular and in the plane of the equator.

If the tilt of Uranus occurred suddenly, as in a collision, it is difficult to see how the satellites could be restored to their equatorial orbits through any plausible process. However, if the tilt occurred slowly relative to the satellite orbital precession periods—say, over many centuries—then the satellite orbits could readily follow. Such slow tilts would necessarily have to arise from internal processes within Uranus, perhaps through some sort of "core-mantle" interaction of a type appropriate to a gas giant planet (which of course has no mantle, as such). One can picture, for example, the accretion by collision of a body of appreciable size by Uranus near one of its own polar regions, which might then sink to the core of Uranus and produce a strong asymmetry thereof, and begin the process of re-orienting the spin of the entire planet.

Such an event most likely would have happened near the solar system's beginning but could have occurred at any time. However, the opportunity to accrete bodies of appreciable size clearly does not come along very often. I can think of no argument which would rule out the possibility that the accretion event, and hence the entire process of tilting, began just 3.2 million years ago, at the planetary breakup epoch.[c] In particular, if my proposed tidal mechanism for gaseous giant bodies is correct (see the chapter "Sunspots and Planets"), the satellites would undergo significant tidal evolution in just a few million years. We should be prepared to recognize observational evidence for recent change in the tilt of Uranus if it arises, rather than to argue that such data couldn't be right and invent an alternate explanation.

Ten new asteroidal moons of Uranus were discovered relatively close to the planet, from the outermost ring (at about two radii of Uranus out) to a little over three Uranus radii out. The five larger moons lie from 5 to 22 radii out.[d] As described in detail for Mars, I would propose that these asteroidal moons (and rings) underwent gravitational screen capture at the time of the asteroidal planet explosion event, 3,200,000 years ago.

---

[c]If this were the case, deductions about how the "black axiom" applies to Uranus' satellites would be drastically changed.

[d]Officially, Uranus now has 15 discovered and named moons, and 10 complete rings.

17

. . . .

Neptune and Pluto

Summary: Neptune's large moon, Triton, is revolving backwards relative to Neptune's spin. For a major satellite, this condition has no other precedent in the solar system and suggests the notion that Triton formed elsewhere and was captured by Neptune. But gravity alone cannot accomplish that without outside help. Tides are too weak for capture. Drag capture would cause the decay of Triton onto Neptune in short order. Collision of Triton with another Neptunian moon of suitable size would have produced extensive destruction and left evidence on Triton's surface and in its orbit. Neptune's other moon, Nereid, is also in an abnormal, highly elongated orbit around Neptune. No other natural (non-asteroidal) moons are present around Neptune. Pluto and its "twin" moon Charon are themselves in Neptune-crossing orbits, and are tidally evolved. The situation suggests disruption of a former "normal" satellite system of Neptune by some passing mass. Calculations using thousands of random projectiles sent through a hypothetical normal satellite system show that the hypothetical disrupter was probably in the 2-to-5 Earth-mass range, with the relative velocity expected of a planet of the Sun. Larger or smaller masses, or those coming from interstellar space, cannot bring about the sort of disruption that is observed. One calculated projectile produced a disruption which resulted in orbits much like those we see today: Triton and Nereid still orbiting Neptune, Pluto and Charon escaped into Neptune-crossing orbits. The higher-than-expected densities of these bodies would then have been produced by tidal melting during their subsequent evolution. The disrupter

301

itself may yet remain in a planetary orbit around the Sun. Its implied mass and probable orbital characteristics are not unlike those proposed for the hypothetical "Planet X," which remains undiscovered.

Could Triton Have Been Captured by Neptune?

The ideas in this chapter have been taken largely from a paper by the author and Robert S. Harrington of the U.S. Naval Observatory.[160] The reader is also directed to a published debate on the subject between the author and W.B. McKinnon.[161]

The *Voyager* encounter with Neptune (see Figure 17.1.) has revived speculation that Neptune's unusual large moon, Triton, was captured early in the history of the solar system. The basis of this conjecture is primarily that Triton is the only large moon of any major planet (ignoring asteroid-sized bodies) that revolves in a retrograde direction around its primary. ("Retrograde" means in the opposite direction from the spin of the primary.) The existence of Pluto and its large moon Charon is taken as evidence for the existence of proto-planets in Neptune-crossing orbits, one of which Neptune might have captured.

There is no known way that such a satellite could have formed naturally in a retrograde orbit. It could not have fissioned (broken off) from Neptune, because Neptune's spin would have caused it to orbit in the expected direction. Nor could it have condensed from a cloud of material in orbit around Neptune, because any such cloud of material associated with the origin of Neptune would necessarily rotate in the same direction as the planet. The only remaining option appears to be that Triton formed elsewhere and was captured by Neptune into its backwards orbit.

There are problems, however, with this capture conjecture. Where are we to suppose that Triton formed, if not as a moon of Neptune? Didn't Neptune ever have any natural satellites of its own? And most difficult of all, how is it possible for Neptune to capture Triton? Note from the chapter on "Orbits" that capture has a reasonable chance to occur only under certain special conditions.

When two rigid bodies interact (i.e., no tides), and gravity is the only force involved, capture and escape are impossible. If a body

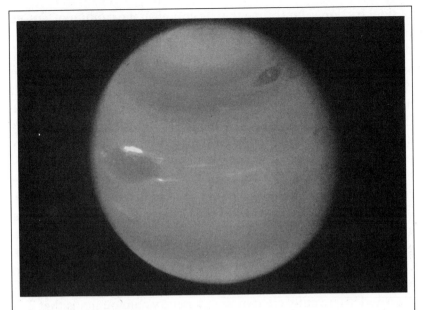

Figure 17.1. A *Voyager* spacecraft view of Neptune, showing its Great Dark Spot. (NASA photograph.)

is a satellite, it remains a satellite forever; if not, it cannot become one. The "sphere of influence" is the volume within which a mass can hold satellites permanently bound to itself. One body cannot move permanently into the sphere of influence of another body without the assistance of a third body or the intervention of a force other than gravity.

If two bodies have the same or closely similar orbits, gravitation always works to keep them apart. The motion of the smaller body is called libration: it repeatedly gains and falls back in its orbit relative to the larger body, but never approaches it. This situation exists in several instances in the solar system. The most notable examples are the "Trojan asteroids," which orbit the Sun in the same orbit as Jupiter but can never approach the giant planet very closely.

Intervention by a third mass at just the right moment to permit a satellite capture by Neptune is an extremely improbable event. Moreover, no suitable third bodies massive enough to accomplish the job are known to exist in the outer solar system today. The force

303

of tidal friction is far too weak to accomplish the capture of Triton, to say nothing of the low probability of the right circumstances occurring. Drag in a medium of gas and dust surrounding Neptune could not slow Triton enough to permit capture, unless the medium were dense enough to remove more velocity than Neptune itself adds to Triton as it approaches. A medium so dense as to remove that much velocity would cause the decay of Triton into Neptune's atmosphere within a few revolutions through continued drag.

It is true that there is an avenue of approach of a potential satellite, through the so-called "inner Lagrangian point," on just the right trajectory with just the right speed in just the right direction in all three dimensions, which would bring a potential moon close enough to Neptune with a small enough relative velocity that a nongravitational force (such as tides, drag, or collision) could then capture it. But the odds against such a fortuitous approach are so enormous as to make this loophole a practical impossibility.

An idea currently cited in the planetary community is that Triton collided with a former, smaller, natural Neptunian satellite, absorbing or destroying the natural moon and dropping Triton into a retrograde satellite orbit.[162] It is possible to make such a scenario work dynamically, but only with a quite extraordinary set of circumstances. Triton must first be altered from some stable orbit where it is formed to a Neptune-crossing orbit by some unspecified process or event. Then it must make a passage through the satellite system of Neptune in which it collides with, not just passes close to, a natural moon located at about Triton's distance from Neptune. (The ratio of the area of Triton's disk to the area enclosed by Triton's orbit, which is equal to the probability of Triton hitting a moon in a single passage at that distance, is about 1 in 20,000.) Moreover, the natural moon involved in the collision would need to have a mass of at least 0.1 that of Triton in order to affect Triton's velocity sufficiently.[a] Although that is not an unreasonable size for a

---

[a]Triton's velocity must be altered by at least 1 km/sec in order to reduce it below escape velocity from Neptune by enough that Neptune's outer moon Nereid will not be ejected from the system in subsequent encounters with Triton. The most favorable conditions are those in which Triton comes through the system in one direction with the escape velocity of

hypothetical Neptunian natural moon, it is not at all likely that evidence for such a major collision between Triton and a body with nearly half its diameter would occur and leave no trace on the surface of Triton, and no debris in Triton's orbit.

Another argument imagines that there were millions of Triton-like bodies originally formed in the outer solar system. But even if Pluto and Charon are the fortunate sole survivors from many such bodies, it is odd that their orbits cross that of Neptune, since non-crossing orbits are far more stable. Why aren't there lots of similar bodies in many of those stable orbits, which would have had a better chance of survival for billions of years? And the odds against capture are still overwhelming. The easiest way to make capture work is to have millions of Triton-like bodies and have one of them approach close to the optimal trajectory. At the same time an even larger mass impacts on Neptune, causing Neptune to accrete enough new mass that the planet's sphere of influence enlarges, capturing the nearby Triton permanently. Even this most favorable case is obviously of extremely low probability.

Competing Theories for the Origin of Pluto

Since none of these capture mechanisms seem very plausible to account for Triton's status, let us examine the alternative. If Triton was not captured, might the similar object, Pluto, be an escaped satellite of Neptune? That idea was originally suggested shortly after Pluto's discovery by the fact that its orbit crosses the orbit of Neptune.[163] It was suggested anew by more recent findings that Pluto is actually quite small by planetary standards, having only the mass of a typical natural satellite, and by physical and spectral similarities between Pluto and Triton.

At first glance, the discovery that Pluto has a satellite of its own, Charon, seemed to argue for the true planetary status of Pluto. However, it is now known that it is not unusual for minor solar system bodies (such as comets and minor planets) to have satellites of

---

5 km/sec and collides with a natural moon going 4 km/sec in the opposite direction. Then a natural moon with ⅑ or more of Triton's mass could alter Triton's velocity by the required 1 km/sec.

their own (see discussions of those bodies in the chapter "The Discovery of Minor Satellites"). Moreover, Charon is comparable in mass to Pluto, not orders of magnitude smaller, as for other planetary satellites. As we shall see, the circumstances of the hypothetical escape of Pluto from Neptune are such that both Pluto and Charon may well have been former satellites orbiting independently about Neptune.

We need to look at the overall picture in the outer solar system. Neptune has rings and small inner asteroidal moons, and a size, location, and composition that make it very much like the other gas giant planets. But it has no large normal moons, unlike the others. In addition to the abnormality of Triton's retrograde motion, Neptune's other long-known moon, Nereid, is on an extremely elongated orbit, far more eccentric than that of any other moon in the solar system, and quite close to the threshold of escape.

Add to this picture two moon-size bodies: Pluto and Pluto's own large moon, Charon. This pair orbits the Sun in a planetary orbit that crosses the orbit of Neptune. This in itself is an extraordinary situation, since crossing orbits are usually unstable (i.e., eventually these bodies either collide with Neptune or are ejected from the solar system by it). Indeed, backwards calculation of planetary orbits suggests that Pluto could not have occupied its present orbit for more than the last one billion years.

The other gaseous giant planets—Jupiter, Saturn, and Uranus—have large natural satellite systems with more or less circular, coplanar, equatorial, regularly spaced orbits. The only exceptions are small satellite bodies which appear to be captured asteroids. Although Neptune's two outer satellites, Triton and Nereid, appear typical in respect to mass and physical characteristics, their orbits are most abnormal and seemingly could not have evolved to that condition. It seems altogether fair to suggest that Neptune may have started with a normal system of satellites, similar to the other gas giant planets, but then something disrupted that satellite system, making the orbits abnormal.

The Disrupted Satellites of Neptune

To consider the plausibility of the hypothesis of a disruption, let us first take a closer look at the existing satellite system of Neptune. Triton is a large natural satellite revolving retrograde (backwards) around Neptune. There is no other example in the solar system of such retrograde satellite motion, with the exception of certain "captured asteroid" satellites of Jupiter and Saturn. Natural evolution into such an orbit does not seem possible for a large natural satellite like Triton. Moreover, Triton's orbit is inclined to Neptune's equator by 160 degrees. Even if we look at this as only a 20-degree inclination of a retrograde orbit, there is no other example in the solar system of a natural satellite so highly inclined to its parent's equator. Although Triton's orbit is nearly circular, this circularity is apparently caused by tidal friction, with Triton's orbit seemingly decaying toward Neptune's atmosphere at an appreciable rate. This is an indication of the instability of Triton's present orbit over the lifetime of the solar system—i.e., it seems impossible for Triton to have come to its present orbit without the intervention of forces external to the present Sun-Neptune system.

> "There are some strings. They're just not attached."
> —Victoria Roberts

Neptune's other natural satellite, Nereid, is in an extremely elongated, almost "comet-like" orbit with respect to the planet—again unlike any other natural satellite in the solar system. Its distance from Neptune varies from 1,300,000 km (four times Triton's distance) to 10,000,000 km. When Nereid is closest to Neptune, its orbital velocity is 3000 m/s; another 200 m/s would be sufficient to push it over the threshold of escape velocity. Nereid's orbit could never have extended outside Neptune's sphere of influence through natural evolution, ruling out a possible capture origin of the satellite unless some other outside massive body assisted the process.

So the hypothesis of an outside disrupting body might account for the unusual features of both Triton and Nereid, as well as the absence of other natural (non-asteroidal) moons of Neptune. Could

307

that disrupter have been Pluto? Pluto's mass is too small to change Triton from prograde to retrograde under any circumstances. Moreover, Pluto could not have escaped into an orbit with so much greater a mean distance from the Sun than Neptune's without the intervention of a far more massive body. The existing situation can be efficiently brought about, it would seem, only by the intervention of some mass larger than either Pluto or Triton—in fact, larger than any existing solar system moon.

To test whether a larger mass could in fact bring about the existing situation, Harrington calculated test encounters with hypothetical bodies of varying mass, encounter distance, inclination, and velocity. He started with a regular four-satellite system for Neptune, modeled on Jupiter's four Galilean satellites. The findings were illuminating: to produce disruptions of the observed sort, the encountering body needed to have a mass in the probable range of two to five Earth masses, and a velocity in the range of the outer planet velocities (but not as high as that of bodies coming from outside the solar system).[b] In other words, the only hypothetical encountering bodies that worked well in disrupting the Neptune satellite system as observed were what we might call "Planet X"-type bodies, previously in planetary orbits around the Sun beyond Neptune. Harrington's computer calculations eventually, by trial and error, found an encounter by a 3-Earth-mass body which could simultaneously reproduce a Triton-like, a Nereid-like, and a Pluto-like post-encounter orbit for three of Neptune's original normal satellites. (See Figure 17.2.)

A fourth original satellite, which goes off with the 3-Earth-mass disrupter in the figure, could have been placed in its orbit in such a way that it would go off with Pluto instead, becoming Pluto's satellite Charon. Despite its small mass, Pluto's gravitational sphere of influence is 10,000,000 km, as long as it stays away from Neptune's sphere of influence. So if Charon were pulled away from Neptune in the same general direction and with a similar velocity to Pluto

---

[b]Any body coming from interstellar space could have a velocity relative to the Sun of no less than 7.5 km/sec when it reached Neptune's orbit, even if it started with zero velocity. But typical velocities of neighboring stars relative to the Sun are even higher: 25 km/sec or so.

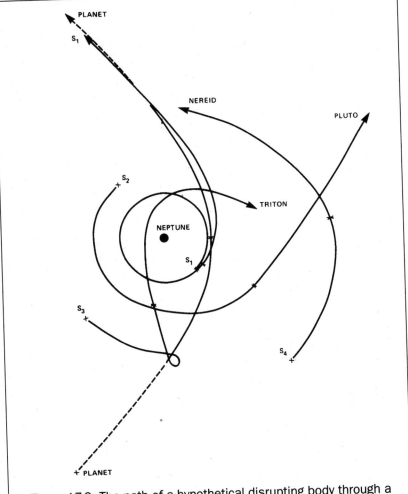

Figure 17.2. The path of a hypothetical disrupting body through a system of four regular Neptunian moons. The disrupter strips off a "Pluto" and leaves behind a "Triton" and a "Nereid."

(something a disrupting body of that mass would tend to do), it would become permanently gravitationally bound to Pluto, because it would necessarily start out *inside* Pluto's sphere of influence.[c]

[c]The relative velocity between Pluto and Charon must also not exceed escape velocity, which is presently about 350 m/s. To reach their present

(This is capture through expansion of the sphere of influence, as described in the chapter on "Orbits.")

Charon would initially enter a highly elliptical orbit around Pluto because of its relative velocity. Tidal forces would then circularize Charon's satellite orbit by reducing its maximum distance from Pluto, and would synchronize the spins of both bodies. This is precisely the situation we observe today. Moreover, as McKinnon has pointed out,[164] the angular momentum (energy) of Charon about Pluto is greater than can be accounted for by an origin of Charon from Pluto, unless there had been a collision of a massive third body with Pluto to add such energy; or unless Charon originated in an orbit with far more angular energy, as we propose here.

It has also been objected that Pluto was quite unlikely to have entered an orbit with a period almost exactly 1.5 times the period of Neptune.[165] However, that condition is forced by the orbital dynamics, and represents only the long-term average period of Pluto. The period of Pluto's instantaneous solar orbit varies over a wide range. Correspondingly, a broad range of starting conditions would all end up with Pluto's average period being related to Neptune's in this or some similar way. When orbits intersect, such a period relationship improves the stability, so that close approaches between the two bodies are infrequent. In short, such a period relationship is likely, not improbable, to result from a wide range of starting conditions.

Implications for Neptune, Pluto, and Planet X

Richard Binzel, in an excellent review article on Pluto,[166] notes that Pluto's actual density is slightly more than 2 g/cc. He says, "This implies that Pluto contains substantial rocky material in addition

---

inclined, eccentric solar orbit from Neptune's solar orbit requires a velocity impulse of about 4000 m/s. So the original relative velocities between Charon and Pluto needed to be less than about 1700 m/s, so that when vector-added to a 4000-m/s impulse, the resultant velocities will be the same to within 350 m/s. [E.g. $(4000)^2 + (1700)^2 = (4000 + 350)^2$.] 1700 m/s is a reasonable differential velocity between two Neptunian moons in orbit around Neptune but farther out than Triton.

to ices." He goes on: "This [density] would make Pluto a rockier body than the satellites of Saturn and Uranus. These bodies formed near protoplanets, where the relatively high temperatures and pressures destroyed carbon monoxide. In these regions the formation of methane and water ice was not inhibited, and so the satellites have high proportions of these light-weight materials. The low densities typical of the satellites of the outer planets eliminate the old hypothesis that Pluto is an escaped satellite of Neptune."

"Triton's diameter (2700 km), density (2.08 g/cc) and atmospheric thickness closely resemble those of Pluto (diameter 2300 km). The similar densities suggest that both Pluto and Triton formed as independent bodies in the cold outer regions of the protoplanetary nebula dominated by carbon monoxide."

This argument, which Binzel has adapted from the work of Mc-Kinnon & Mueller,[167] ignores that methane, but probably not carbon monoxide, has now been detected on Pluto; so the idea has no direct observational basis other than Pluto's density.[d] It also fails to recognize that Pluto, Charon, and Triton have all undergone substantial tidal evolution, probably including melting, which would surely have "chemically differentiated" these bodies. In a molten condition, heavier elements sink to the core and the radius of the body shrinks, increasing the mean density of the body. Jupiter's innermost large moons, Io and Europa, are also relatively high in density, surely for precisely this same reason: tidal melting by virtue

---

[d]The proposal of "the large-body impact which created Charon from Pluto," discussed by McKinnon & Mueller, is also not very plausible. If such a large body had a similar orbit to Pluto's, librations would prevent collisions between them. If such a large body had a dissimilar orbit, collisions would be extremely improbable and could only occur at high relative velocities. High-velocity collisions between such large bodies would be catastrophic and highly destructive. Matter from such a collision cannot re-accrete in orbit because debris particles either escape immediately or return to the site of the collision and re-accrete on their parent body. Even if perturbations prevented immediate re-accretion by the parent body, tidal forces would ensure that re-accretion by the parent would occur for chunks of any significant mass after relatively few revolutions. In short, collisions cannot provide the angular momentum which would be essential to accreting a new, permanent major satellite.

of their nearness to Jupiter. Io and Triton both show evidence of present-day volcanic activity, consistent with the ongoing tidal evolution of those two bodies. Pluto and Charon not only may have been tidally influenced by Neptune, but also must have undergone substantial tidal evolution from each other to get into their present synchronized situation, with spin and orbital periods locked together.

When Pluto and Charon are finally visited by spacecraft, we can predict that the known hemisphere brightness asymmetry will affect both bodies symmetrically, since the source of the dark carbonaceous material is external to the Pluto-Charon system.[e] We also expect both Pluto and Charon to have physical and chemical make-ups appropriate to origin as moons of Neptune.

Although the body doing the disrupting might have escaped the solar system following the encounter, the statistical odds are that it would have remained in a highly eccentric and inclined solar orbit with a long period. This is just the sort of body which has been suggested as a hypothetical undiscovered planet beyond Pluto, based on unexplained disturbances in the orbits of the outer planets. Certainly if such a "Planet X" were to be discovered in a highly inclined and eccentric orbit that approached Neptune's orbit at perihelion and has a mass near the interesting range of 2-to-5 Earth masses, its existence would argue strongly for the essential correctness of the whole scenario just described.

We conclude that there is one plausible explanation for the unique irregularities in the satellite system of Neptune (the retrograde motion of Triton and a "comet-like" orbit for Nereid) and also for the existence of moon-sized planet Pluto and its satellite Charon in Neptune-crossing planetary orbits. This explanation is that an as-yet-undiscovered trans-Neptunian planet (whose existence is also suggested by other data) had a close encounter with the Neptune system sometime in the past. If so, Pluto and Charon are most likely to be escaped former satellites of Neptune.

---

[e]We are making the implicit assumption that the disruption event that caused Pluto and Charon to escape from Neptune preceded the planetary breakup event, 3.2 million years ago, which was the source of the dark carbonaceous material.

In private correspondence, Binzel has questioned the advantage of replacing one improbable event with another, since all theories of origin for Triton and Pluto seemingly involve an improbable event. However, the disruption event is not improbable in the same sense as the others. In fact, given an original solar system with planets out to, say, 20 or more times Pluto's distance, the rest of the scenario (or something quite like it) is virtually inevitable. The process is triggered by passing stars. Statistically, a few passing stars would approach within 40 times Pluto's distance of the Sun over the life of the solar system. They would tend to perturb the outermost planets, those at 10 to 40 times Pluto's distance, into planet-crossing orbits. Eventually the crossings would result in close encounters between planets. Sooner or later the encounters would eject one of the encountering planets from the solar system. Through repetition of this process, eventually at most one such planet-crossing rover would remain. It too would either be ejected from the solar system in an encounter with the outermost planet unaffected by passing stars (Neptune), or else necessarily evolve into an orbit synchronous with Neptune's to avoid additional close approaches, just as Pluto does at present. But either way, it must have made one or more close approaches to Neptune, during which Neptune's satellites would have been disrupted. The rest of the scenario then follows easily. Although the particular outcome we observe is improbable after the fact, some such disruption and strangeness for the satellites of the outermost "normal" planet seem highly probable, given only the starting assumption of three to five more planets beyond Neptune in the original solar system.[f] As we have discussed, a theory that follows deductively from a plausible starting point and resembles reality has a high probability of correctness in its essentials.

Finally, we note that Triton's orbit around Neptune has been circularized by tidal friction from a far more elliptical orbit. That fact plus recent *Voyager* indications that Triton is currently undergoing geologic activity suggests that the rate of tidal evolution may well

---

[f]When planetary systems are discovered around other stars, we then expect that the outermost remaining planet in each such system will show a similar disruption of its natural satellites.

be greater than usually assumed. The ultimate fate of Triton under the influence of this tidal activity, perhaps in as little as a few tens of millions of years, is to decay into the atmosphere of Neptune and eventually be assimilated by the planet. Now *that* will be one spectacular satellite reentry!

18

. . . .

Planet X

Summary: Urbain LeVerrier successfully predicted the location of Neptune from deviations in the orbit of Uranus. But LeVerrier also inadvertently showed that not all orbital deviations are due to undiscovered planets. His search for the cause of the advance of Mercury's perihelion proved fruitless. It was left to Einstein to find that a modification of Newton's law of gravity was needed to explain that anomaly. Near the end of the nineteenth century it was realized that Uranus was again deviating from its predicted trajectory. Percival Lowell was one of the astronomers who made unsuccessful predictions for the location of the ninth planet. But his efforts eventually led to the beginning of a systematic search of the entire sky by Clyde Tombaugh at the Lowell Observatory. Tombaugh found Pluto in 1930 as a result of the careful search. No other planets down to magnitude 16 were detected during the 15-year program. It was assumed that Pluto was the cause of the deviations in the orbit of Uranus. However, determinations of the mass of Pluto kept getting smaller, and the unmodelled orbital deviations kept getting larger. Then in 1978, Jim Christy discovered Charon, a moon of Pluto, which proved that Pluto's mass was too small to affect Uranus measurably. The story of Christy's discovery at the U.S. Naval Observatory, and how the discovery first became known to the author and other staff astronomers, is recounted. This finding compelled the astronomers to look elsewhere for an explanation of the deviations in the outer planet orbits. By then, the deviations were detectable in Jupiter, Saturn, Uranus and Neptune, and in six periodic comets seen at more than one appari-

tion whose orbits go out beyond Neptune. A "Planet X" was hypothesized. Harrington's prediction approach using numerical integration and the author's analytical approach to predicting the location of Planet X are described. However, it remains possible that a portion of the deviations may be explainable by corrections to the laws of gravitation instead.

History of the Planet X Search

Contributors to the research summarized in this chapter include G.H. Kaplan, K.F. Pulkkinen, E.J. Santoro, and P.K. Seidelmann, all from the U.S. Naval Observatory.

The major planets Mercury, Venus, Earth, Mars, Jupiter, and Saturn were known to the ancients. The seventh planet, Uranus, was discovered quite by accident by William Herschel in 1781. But by the time it had made ¾ of a revolution around the Sun 63 years later, calculations showed clearly that something unknown was pulling Uranus away from its predicted orbit. Those calculations led both the English astronomer John Couch Adams and the French astronomer Urbain Le Verrier to make predictions of where the unknown body (assuming it to be a single unknown planet) was located.

Based upon Le Verrier's prediction, the eighth planet, Neptune, was discovered in 1846. This discovery based on a mathematical calculation was a triumph for the field of celestial mechanics, the field of the precise calculation of the trajectories of bodies moving under the influence of gravitation. (For more details about this discovery, that of Pluto, and the Planet X search, see *Planets Beyond.*)[168]

Le Verrier was fortunate, of course, that the unknown cause of the deviation of Uranus from its expected path was almost entirely due to a single large, relatively nearby planet. He was not so fortunate with his next venture, which was an attempt to explain the cause of the excess rate of advance of the perihelion of planet Mercury's orbit. Le Verrier spent 15 years making predictions and searching for a planet closer to the Sun than Mercury, which might have been the cause of the departure of Mercury from its predicted path. Belief in its existence ran so high that the hypothetical inter-Mercurial planet was even given a name: Vulcan. But Le Verrier never

316

discovered Vulcan, nor did anyone else. The cause of the excess advance of Mercury's perihelion was explained half a century later by Albert Einstein in his General Theory of Relativity. In effect, the explanation was a failure of the law of gravitation as then understood, rather than an undiscovered planetary body.

But by the beginning of the twentieth century, it had become apparent that Uranus was still deviating slightly from its predicted path, even after allowing for the effects of all eight then-known planets. Moreover, a surprise development involving Neptune suggested that the eighth planet was also off course. Two observations made more than 50 years before the planet's discovery were brought to light. In 1790, the astronomer Joseph Lalande had been measuring the positions of stars and happened to measure the planet Neptune by chance on two different occasions. Of course he had no idea at the time that he had measured anything but a star. However, his other star observations were accurate to within a few arc seconds. The two pre-discovery positions of Neptune deviated from the planet's predicted trajectory by an uncomfortably large 10 arc seconds.

Percival Lowell, the founder of Lowell Observatory in Arizona, began his historic search for planets beyond Neptune early in the twentieth century because of these small irregularities in the motions of Uranus and Neptune. Again, predictions were made and searches conducted. Once again there was competition, as several other astronomers entered the prediction game. William H. Pickering used a variety of approaches, including a study of comets, to make a number of predictions regarding the location of the ninth planet. None of these predictions led directly to any discovery. However, the astronomers at Lowell eventually commissioned a photographic search of the entire sky for undiscovered planets. That search was begun in 1929 by a young astronomer hired for the purpose, Clyde Tombaugh.

Within a year, Tombaugh's painstakingly careful and thorough search came up with its most important discovery: the planet Pluto. The object was detected in a location only 7 degrees in longitude from one of Lowell's predicted positions; so despite its unexpected extreme faintness, everyone assumed that the cause of the deviations in the orbits of Uranus and Neptune had at last been found.

317

Its mass was estimated to be about five to seven times that of the Earth from the strength of the perturbations it was assumed to be producing, so it had to be an unusually dense and dark object to be so faint.

Tombaugh's search continued over the following 15 years until nearly all the sky visible from Lowell Observatory had been photographed at least three times and searched for moving objects which might be planets. No further planets were found, although the search was complete for the sky visible from Lowell Observatory down to roughly magnitude 16. But evidence began to accumulate that Pluto was neither so dense, nor so dark, as had been assumed. New observations of both Uranus and Neptune not only continued to deviate from predictions, but started to show less and less possibility of being brought back into agreement with predictions by forces of any size emanating from Pluto's direction. Calculations began to suggest smaller and smaller estimated values for the mass of Pluto, while the unexplained part of the deviations in the planets' trajectories grew. By the early 1970s, it was painfully evident that Pluto could not possibly be the principal cause of the deviations in the orbits of Uranus and Neptune, because its calculated mass could not exceed one-tenth that of the Earth.

The Discovery of Charon

The slowly accumulating evidence was explosively brought to the attention of the entire astronomical world when in 1978 U.S. Naval Observatory astronomer James Christy discovered a satellite of Pluto. The satellite enabled Pluto's mass, and later its size, to be measured directly, instead of estimated from its effects on the other far-away planets. It was learned that Pluto had only a fraction of the mass of our own Moon, which itself has only 1% as much mass as the Earth. Pluto was actually quite a tiny body, consistent with its faintness. Indeed, it was smaller than quite a few of the major satellites of the eight major planets of the solar system.

If Pluto were discovered today, it seems quite unlikely that it would be designated as the ninth major planet. It would instead be classified as a minor body orbiting the Sun, not unlike the minor planets between Mars and Jupiter, or the small body Chiron orbiting between Saturn and Uranus, although certainly in a class of its own. Pluto's satellite Charon has nearly half the diameter of Pluto itself, making the pair essentially a "double satellite" in a planetary orbit. In the chapter "Neptune and Pluto," we discuss the conjecture that both members of this pair are escaped satellites of Neptune.

I was present at the Naval Observatory when this important discovery of Pluto's satellite was made by Christy, and I participated in the excitement of the unfolding story as it happened, so I would like to share a few recollections here before continuing with the Planet X saga.

One day Robert Harrington walked into my office, quite excited over some photographs of Pluto taken by the Observatory's fine astrometric telescope in Arizona. He said that James Christy had been measuring the photographs, some of which showed elongation, and some of which did not. What was exciting was that the appearance of the elongated images occurred at regular time intervals, suggesting that the elongations were caused by a body orbiting Pluto. We went downstairs where Christy and Harrington showed me the images. They patiently went over for my benefit what they had already examined—that the images of stars on the same plates showed no elongations, so the cause of Pluto's elongation was not movement of the telescope during the photographs. The images were elongated exactly like a close, unresolved double star would be. But the data showing the regularity in the timing of appearance and disappearance of the elongations meant that the cause was a large, close body orbiting Pluto apparently every 6.4 days.

Some of the elongations they showed me were extremely subtle effects, and it was evident to me that only a trained eye could recognize them as abnormal images in any way. However, Christy was a trained and experienced double-star observer, so I had to trust his judgment. But in no case were the images clear enough for the untrained eye to be certain that two separate bodies were actually present. And the 6.4-day interval was the same as the known period of rotation of Pluto, suggesting perhaps some sort of spot on the planet or related phenomenon as the cause of the elongations. We all agreed that more photographs needed to be taken the next evening, when the elongation was predicted to be at its extreme again. With the cooperation of the weather, perhaps a much clearer picture could be obtained.

We awaited the new photographs with considerable eagerness. When they finally arrived, they were indeed elongated, in a roughly north-south direction as predicted, whereas what little elongation there was in the stellar images was entirely east-west. The confirmation was exciting, but the images were not so clear as to be more convincing than the others. What we had here was a predictable phenomenon having to do with Pluto—but was it a satellite?

> "Don't wait for your ship to come in, paddle out to it."
> —Anonymous

Harrington began to make some orbital calculations, and I played around a little with some of the other implications. We had to be sure we had the correct period, and not some multiple of it. Harrington assumed right from the start that the orbital period of the satellite would turn out to be identical to the rotation period of Pluto, since tidal locking would produce such a result for such a relatively large satellite. His assumption was easily verified as correct. We then derived the implied mass of Pluto from the known period and estimated separation, assuming the elongations were caused by a satellite. We were amazed, but excited by the implications of how tiny Pluto must be. At first it seemed too small to be plausible, but the low mass gave reasonable values for the density and reflectivity of the surface of the planet, which the higher mass estimates did not. So we soon convinced ourselves that the conclusions were reconcilable with other knowledge, and even helpful in explaining some things. A visiting colleague tape-recorded some of these brain-storming sessions in the belief that they might someday be of historic interest.[a]

By this time we were getting pressure from the military command, and from the Observatory's Astronomical Council, to decide whether or not Christy had a discovery, and whether or not to call a press conference to announce it. We still had many questions and doubts, especially since the images were all unresolved. But we responded to the pressure by dropping everything else and working full time on this project to meet a deadline two days hence,

---

[a]These recordings are preserved in the Naval Observatory archives.

which we were given. Christy went to the archives and found many more older photographs of the planet showing the elongations, some dating back to the 1960s when that telescope had first been put to use. Some of the photos had never been measured but had merely been archived with the notation: "Pluto images elongated and unsuitable for measurement"! Christy had not been the first astronomer to notice an elongation in Pluto's images, but he was the first to recognize that the anomaly was not an artifact, and needed to be followed up. He therefore deserves, and has received, full credit for the discovery.

Harrington used the new data to refine the orbit and to make some better size, brightness, and mass estimates for the pair. I spent my time testing the hypothesis that dark, irregular surface markings on Pluto, or an extremely irregular shape for the planet, or other exotic hypotheses, might be causing the elongations. I was able to produce calculations and satisfactory arguments to the effect that only two separate bodies could replicate the elongations that were seen.

We met at the appointed hour in the captain's office. Since so many reservations had been expressed two days earlier, the captain was quite surprised when he polled us, and the decision was unanimous to go forward with the announcement of the discovery. A press conference was convened shortly thereafter, and the astronomical world was informed. Christy chose the name Charon because of that mythological being's association with Pluto, god of the Underworld, and because it was similar to his wife's name, Charlene.

New Predictions of Planet X

The most important implication of the discovery for us was that we could no longer use Pluto as the cause of any of the perturbing effects on the orbits of Uranus and Neptune. Those two planets continued to show significant deviations from their predicted trajectories, and more subtle effects could be seen in the orbits of Jupiter and Saturn as well. Oddly, when only twentieth-century observations were used, the orbits stayed fairly close to prediction, but projections of their orbits back to the nineteenth century were quite discordant. Some astronomers tried to blame the accuracy of the older observations, but the deviations did not display consistency in the same parts of the sky—as errors in the star positions would produce—and they were too large.

Today we have twice as long a span of observations of Neptune as Lowell had when he first judged that a deviation was taking place; and although the deviation is smaller in the 1980s than it was in Lowell's time, there is little reason to doubt its existence. But we cannot be certain that the cause of the observed irregularities in the motions of the outer planets is another undiscovered planet. Recall that Tombaugh photographed ⅔ of the sky (including all of it within 30 degrees of the ecliptic), searching for just such a planet, with nothing besides Pluto ever found. Recall also that Vulcan never existed. Some astronomers have hypothesized that the deviations might be caused by a new asteroid or comet belt, or by causes other than a single, undiscovered planet. But the form of the deviations is highly suggestive of the perturbations by a single body beyond Neptune, since their size gets progressively greater as one goes further out in the solar system; and the periodic character of the deviations is reminiscent of single-body perturbations, rather than those from a ring or other continuous distribution.

Despite these uncertainties, the result of our preliminary investigation was that a single undiscovered planet could entirely explain the observed irregularities in each of the outer planets. For example, a planet in the two-to-five Earth-mass range, as suggested by the Neptune satellite evidence (see the chapter "Neptune and Pluto"), could explain the observed irregularities in the planet orbits if it were presently located 50 to 100 times further from the Sun than the Earth's orbit. (Neptune is 30 times as far from the Sun as the Earth.)

Both Harrington and I began using the planetary observations to attempt predictions of where to look for the unknown planet. Harrington used numerical integrations combined with the constraints provided by Tombaugh's search about where the planet is *not* to make several predictions, some of which have been followed up with search photographic plates. No discovery has yet resulted. My approach was to take advantage of the full potential of modern computers by using an algebraic manipulator to calculate the effects of the unknown body on all the known ones (Jupiter through Neptune) in analytic (formula) form, then solve for the unknowns with full generality.[b] This approach, although computationally very difficult, was inspired by the belief that the undiscovered planet probably had a close encounter with Neptune at some time in the past, and therefore might be in an elongated orbit of high inclination.

---

[b]As a technical note for my colleagues in Celestial Mechanics, permit me to elaborate a bit on the method I was planning to use to find "Planet X." Orbits with high inclination and eccentricity that come close or cross, such as the conjectured orbit for Planet X with respect to Neptune, are traditionally the most difficult to handle with an analytic approach, because the perturbation series do not converge. Hence, numerical approaches have always been preferred for such cases. The difficulty with a numerical approach is that it requires trial and error, and lacks generality. It was not possible, using a numerical approach, to solve for Planet X's direction, but only to guess likely directions from the effects of a great many trial orbits.

The goal of the analytic approach was to use computers to develop a general formula for the perturbing effects of a "generalized" planet, represented by orbital elements which were symbolic variables rather than specific numbers. Then one could compare the predicted perturbations to the observed ones and solve for the best-fitting values of the generalized planet's orbital elements. The fatal flaw, using traditional methodology, was that the series for the perturbations were non-convergent, yielding meaningless results.

My idea was to combine the strengths of both the numeric and analytic approaches to avoid convergence problems. Instead of assuming a specific elliptic starting reference orbit in the analytic approach, I planned to adopt a starting position and velocity for the unknown body—as in the numeric approach—but using variables (symbols) rather than numbers for these starting parameters. Then the computer could go through all the same steps as in the numeric approach, moving forward one time step, predicting the next positions, calculating mutual forces, and correcting the positions back to the actual trajectories—but all done with symbols instead of numbers! I coined the term "numalytic integration" to refer to this hybrid approach.

The end product of this numalytic integration would be expressions for the perturbations of an unknown body on the planets and comets of interest, which could be evaluated at times of interest. These evaluated

I had further hoped to utilize information from the orbits of six comets of long period which go out beyond the orbit of Neptune, yet have been observed making more than one return to the vicinity of the Earth. Comet orbits are perturbed anyway by so-called "non-gravitational forces" arising from solar radiation pressure, but only within their orbital planes. All six of these comet orbits also show deviations perpendicular to their orbital planes, which seemingly could not have been caused by any known forces. No other comets display significant deviations perpendicular to their orbital planes except these six. A study of these comets may therefore add significant information to the "Planet X" prediction process.[c]

The goal of further research with these planetary and comet observations is to be able to predict the direction of the hypothet-

---

expressions would be algebraic formulas in terms of the unknown body's starting coordinates, or its orbital elements. Part of their effect would be taken up by an adjustment of the orbital elements of the planets and comets themselves, and this amount could be calculated and removed from the expressions. The remainder could be compared to the observed perturbations and solved for the parameters representing the orbit of the unknown body.

Although there may well have been a fatal flaw in my plans which would have become evident to me only after trying out this approach, I have not yet been able to imagine why it could not be made to work and accomplish the goals of the "Planet X" project. This approach would likewise have potential applicability to a number of other Celestial Mechanics problems, so I hope that it will be investigated further in the future.

My most recent proposal to NASA for funding to pursue this approach was turned down for what appeared to me to be insubstantial reasons. But NASA officials made no response to my appeal of their negative decision. Non-responsiveness on the merits of the scientific issues has left me to assume that other factors were operative in NASA's decision. But I have long known that there is a heavy personal price to be paid by anyone who criticizes mainstream theories as much as I have done.

[c]The rediscovery of Comet Swift-Temple in late 1992 adds a seventh comet to this set. With a 134-year period, this comet has spend more time beyond Neptune since its discovery (two revolutions ago) than any other comet. Correspondingly, its orbital deviations are greater than for any other known comet.

ical new planet accurately enough to photograph and discover it, if it exists. It is not yet known whether the existing observations are accurate enough to permit a sufficiently precise prediction, since there are hundreds of millions of stars with brightness comparable to the suspected planet. (A true planet would betray itself by moving slowly along an orbit relative to the "fixed" stars.) A principal limiting factor in the accuracy of calculations done up to now is our knowledge of the mass of Neptune. The *Voyager 2* encounter with Neptune in 1989 has eliminated all ambiguity about the precise value of that mass. Now that it is known, the calculations for the direction of "Planet X" can be completed. The chapter "On Gravity" also suggests one way in which a modification of the law of gravity (due to its finite range) may be needed to successfully complete the prediction process.

Why do we call this the "trans-Neptunian" planet search, rather than "trans-Plutonian"? One of the reasons is that we are explicitly renewing the efforts of Percival Lowell, which began before Pluto was discovered. There is also the factor that Pluto is actually a minor body, rather than a true primary planet. However, we can avoid the controversial matter of Pluto's planetary status by noting that Pluto's egg-shaped orbit takes it occasionally closer to the Sun than Neptune, which is its present condition. It is therefore technically correct at this time to say that Neptune is the most distant of the known planets, and therefore we are indeed renewing Lowell's trans-Neptunian planet search. As for calling the hypothetical body "Planet X," the ambiguity in the meaning of "X" (Roman numeral for "ten," or "unknown") serves the same purpose.

19

. . . .

The Origins of the
Solar System and of Man

Summary: We begin with a discussion of how tidal forces are likely to be involved in the process of accreting particles into larger masses, as the Meta Model would imply. This seems to make more dynamical sense than the concept of "sticking." We also note the important point that bodies of any size in the same orbit tend to avoid collisions, and to "librate" rather than to accrete. This is why planetary rings are stable and do not eventually accrete into one or a few isolated masses. We examine many of the problems with the primeval solar nebula hypothesis and hint at the sort of replacement model deductive reasoning would suggest: planetary origin by fission from the Sun. Then we present a synopsis of all the preceding theories about the evolution of the solar system, leading to a new model of what the original solar system may have looked like—quite different from the present solar system. Next we use our deductive perspective to argue for the inevitability of extraterrestrials. The exploded planet hypothesis is then used as a basis for a speculation about the origin of man, not greatly dissimilar from that pictured in certain translations of ancient historical texts. Finally we consider the great pyramids on Earth and speculations about their possible counterparts on Mars. We conclude that the attitude of scientists toward such hypotheses is unscientific.

How Stars and Planets Get Started

In traditional theories of cosmology, the fundamental particles (say, the baryons) of the universe either condense out of the initial Big Bang explosion or are continually created as the vacuum expands to make room for new matter (the "Steady State" model). In both cases, the details are vague and mysterious. In the chapter "On the Composition of Substance," we see how the Meta Model deals with the quantum world. Here we need note only that there is an infinite range of smaller entities from which baryons may form, and also an infinite number of media and forces of nature available to help assemble them.

Indeed, the Meta Model would expect that larger matter assemblages tend to arise where numerous smaller ones already exist. To observers on our (or any) scale, this process would resemble the so-called "multiplicative creation" proposed by P.A.M. Dirac, in which new matter appears to come into existence wherever old matter already exists. But whereas the idea seemed almost magical when Dirac proposed it, the Meta Model makes the process understandable and the idea plausible.

Current astronomical literature has it that stars and planets condense out of massive clouds of gas and dust in space. Indeed, star formation does seem to be occurring at the present time within certain large gas clouds, such as the Orion nebula.

The means of getting the entire process started has always been rather vague, but in its essence, it involves particles colliding and "sticking" together. At first, the sticking results in pairs of molecules here and there. Eventually, some of these collide with each other and stick, and bodies of larger and larger size ultimately are built up. Insofar as I have seen, the literature supposes that high velocity collisions are destructive, whereas low-velocity collisions are "constructive," i.e., result in sticking. Naturally small bodies that collide with much larger ones will tend to accrete there. But exactly why there should be a stickiness between bodies of comparable mass always mystified me—partly because it didn't seem natural for relative particle velocities to be so low as to permit it, and partly because "stickiness" isn't one of the fundamental forces of nature. Hydrogen gas isn't "sticky," so why should any two hydrogen atoms that collide decide to stay together rather than rebound and go their separate ways?

As we explore in the chapter on "Orbits," intuition denies that gravitational forces from tiny bodies can ever be significant, because they never are in our everyday experience. But our experiences all take place inside a strong gravitational field (the Earth's), which prevents small bodies from influencing each other noticeably. Isolated in space, the gravitational forces of small bodies on each other can indeed be significant. As we see in the chapter "Do Comets Have Satellites?" indefinitely small bodies can hold other like bodies as captive satellites, out to distances limited only by the proximity of other bodies. Such captures must occur often within a cloud of small particles because of n-body interactions, just as would occur in a globular star cluster. Moreover, when satellite capture occurs, tidal forces are even more significant on smaller distance scales than they are on larger distance scales. And the Meta Model tells us that there must exist an analog to tidal forces caused by gravitation on the atomic level, where electromagnetic forces dominate. Tidal decay of small satellites will occur relatively quickly, with the inevitable result being a low-velocity grazing collision between the particles mutually orbiting, and finally a "sticking" together, bound by gravity.

I conclude that the accretion of small masses into larger ones is a process in which gravitational and tidal forces play a role along with collisional and electrostatic forces (the latter being the reason why like atoms tend to get together more often than dissimilar ones). Accretion probably involves very little in the way of "stickiness" as such.

How a Solar System Gets Started

Once somewhat larger masses have evolved by this process, the larger ones can sweep up smaller masses in the usual collisional way. Collisions are destructive only when the masses involved are comparable and/or the relative velocities are quite high, such that the energy transferred is enough to break up the larger body. Collisional sweep-up and self-gravitation will soon mold the accreting bodies into roughly spherical shapes.

329

The accretion of many of these larger spheroidal bodies into still larger masses is once again influenced by both gravitational n-body interactions and tidal forces, with collisional accretion between masses of non-comparable size simultaneously acting. The traditional model of what happens next is called the "primeval solar nebula hypothesis," in which a huge cloud of cold hydrogen gas eventually accretes into the Sun and its planets and their moons. I am not alone in having several problems with this traditional scenario.

It is often spoken of as intuitively obvious that moons and planets, while forming, would eventually sweep up all the material in or near their orbits. Actually, that is not possible in the simplest, intuitive sense. Objects in the same orbit as a larger mass are forced to "librate" back and forth, always avoiding collision with the larger mass. The most outstanding example of this libration phenomenon is the Trojan asteroids in Jupiter's orbit. And it is obvious that the various planetary rings in the solar system are not tending to accrete into larger bodies. Even a gradual change in period of a larger mass in a ring would not enable collisions to occur. The smaller masses would still librate to avoid collisions until the period of the larger mass had passed completely through the range where collisions might have been possible.

It follows that the "solar nebula" out of which the planets are said to have formed—and similar clouds around the planets to form satellites—could not have consisted of material revolving uniformly in co-planar, circular orbits, because such material could never get accreted. Accretion is effective only when orbits are moderately chaotic.

Another problem with the hypothesis is that 98% of the angular momentum ("energy") in the solar system is in the planets, not in the Sun. Yet these planets account for only a bit over 1/1000 of the mass of the Sun. That at first seems like a very unnatural state of affairs. One would expect that if the cloud from which the planets accreted had that much angular momentum, then the Sun would reflect evidence of it and would spin very much faster than it does, especially after contracting to its present size. Moreover, it is now recognized that accretion from a solar nebula would not necessarily cause the planets to spin in the same direction as they orbit. One

330

would expect as many backward-spinning planets as forward, because collisions have an equal chance to increase or decrease the spin. Yet planetary spins are dominantly forward.

When multiple stars condense from a common cloud, their mutual orbits generally have high eccentricity and are seldom co-planar. So assuming that planets originated from these same clouds still requires a completely different formation process and subsequent evolution to get them all into circular, co-planar orbits.

Still another plausibility problem with the whole solar nebula hypothesis is the volume of space involved. The volume enclosed by the orbit of Pluto is so great that all 200,000,000,000 stars in our galaxy could fit inside it without touching! The volume of space near the orbit of, say, Neptune is so great that it is quite difficult to imagine the process by which Neptune could have accreted from hydrogen gas anywhere near its present location.

Finally, if one looks at the chemistry of planets and moons, their compositions suggest formation under a far smaller range of temperatures than the solar nebula hypothesis would allow. Especially striking is the presence of abundant carbon dioxide in the outer solar system, e.g. on the surface of Triton.[69] It is most difficult to account for this if that frozen body were never much hotter than at present.

So how did the solar system form? I have not worked on any specific model here. But it seems clear in what general direction deductive reasoning would take us. Elsewhere we argue for the origin of the Moon by fission from the Earth. Occam's Razor ("invent no unnecessary hypotheses") suggests that the same formation mechanism operated for the other planets and their moons, unless some evidence compels us to accept a different origin. So I would conclude from this reasoning that fission of the planets from the Sun as the Sun contracted and spun up, and fission of planetary moons from their parent planets under the same circumstances, may be the dominant mechanism for the original formation of solar system bodies in the planet and satellite mass range.

This would simultaneously account for all major problems with the present model: The planets don't accrete in their orbits; they originate in the proto-Sun. The proto-Sun must reach an overspin condition numerous times during its contraction phase. Each time it fissions, much of its excess angular momentum from spin would be transferred to a new orbiting planet. Planets fissioning in such a way would start out with the forward spin of the proto-Sun they fissioned from and would contract, overspin, and form their own moons by fission as they cooled. Most of the angular momentum of the solar system would end up in the planets. Tidal forces operating on the planets from the huge proto-Sun would further enlarge their orbits soon after fission. The theory certainly has no problems with the compositions of the planets, which are basically made of solar photospheric material, less volatiles and/or heavy elements to varying degrees.

The principal reasons why this idea was rejected earlier are that the Sun's present spin is well below an overspin condition; and its equator is tilted about 7 degrees to the mean plane of the planets. But both of these conditions can easily arise from subsequent evolution,[a] especially if (as it appears) the Sun's interior presently spins much faster than its surface. This is indicated by different latitudes on the Sun having different spin rates. And the tilt of the Sun's spin axis will be altered during its contraction, both by interactions between its faster-spinning "core" and its slower-spinning "mantle," and by the same sort of tilt-changing interaction with the planets we proposed for the Earth-Moon system following the Moon's fission from the Earth.

Since it seems clear to me that counter-arguments are too insubstantial to rule out a fission origin of planets from a proto-Sun, and since that model solves many problems the solar nebula model is currently experiencing, and since it readily arises from deductive reasoning which makes far more specific predictions than the present model, I am convinced that the fission idea is very much worth another careful look.

A View of the Original Solar System

The usual view of the solar system is uniformitarian, in which it was formed 4.6 billion years ago, and little of interest has happened since. By contrast I propose a dynamic solar system with a rich and

---

[a]For example, by magnetic breaking.

varied history, whose appearance has changed drastically as recently as within the last 3.2 million years.

In regard to the inner solar system, we have discussed reasons to conclude that Mercury was originally a satellite of Venus. Adopting the possibility that the mean distances of those two planets were then evolved by tides raised on the Sun following the escape of Mercury, this might imply original solar distances of perhaps more like 0.35 au for both planets.

The Earth-Moon system then probably originated at about 0.7 au. Additional planets might have been prevented from forming inside the original Mercury-Venus orbit by whatever mechanism slowed the Sun's rotation to well below orbital speeds.

If Mars were originally a satellite of Planet K[b] at about 2.8 au, at that time there would have been a gap in the spacing of planetary distances at about 1.4 au, near where Mars now resides. We would have expected a planet intermediate in mass between Earth and Planet K (the latter presumably being comparable in size to Saturn) to have evolved in that location (say, 5–20 Earth masses). All traces of such a planet may have disappeared, if it ever existed. Perhaps it met the same fate as Planet K, but much earlier in the solar system's history. The principal reasons for the conjecture of the existence of this hypothetical "Planet V" (the real "fifth planet"?) are to fill the possible gap in the reconstructed planetary distance distribution, to provide smoothness in the mass distribution of the original planets, and (most importantly) to provide a mechanism for removing most of Mars's original spin.[c]

---

[b]We refer to the planet missing from the asteroid belt region as "Planet K" for reasons mentioned in the chapter "Mars and Saturn."

[c]It seems likely, from what we know about planetary formation processes, that all planets reached or approached an overspin condition (spinning so fast as to throw off surface layers) at least once, perhaps several times, while being formed. This spinning-up process is a natural by-product of the planet contracting under the force of its own gravitation, and of the heavier materials sinking to its core (like an ice skater spinning faster by pulling in her arms—contracted bodies spin faster, expanded bodies spin more slowly). Throwing off surface layers during overspin is a natural mechanism for the formation of both planets and planetary satellites.

Mars also has a density only a little greater than the Earth's Moon but completely lacks a magnetic field of its own.[170] This may indicate merely that it never melted, since melting would have allowed its heavy elements to sink and form an iron core. But it could also indicate that like the Earth's Moon, Mars may have formed from mantle material of a planet that had previously melted and was depleted in heavy elements. We presume that this hypothetical Planet V disappeared early enough that its own "asteroid belt" and "comets" have long since disappeared too.[d]

Next out from Planet V and its hypothetical satellite Mars we would have found Planet K, originally at about 2.7 au, presumably with satellites of its own (e.g. Ceres, the largest minor planet?). We would predict that physical and chemical studies of Ceres would

---

[d]There is some evidence that two separate populations of asteroids still exist today. Simon Newcomb argued a century and a quarter ago against the idea that minor planets could have originated in a planetary breakup. His reasoning was that certain minor planets (primarily S-class inner-belt asteroids) are in orbits which do not now, and could never in the past, intersect with the orbits of main-belt asteroids. And inspection of the distribution of minor planet orbits shows that two discrete populations of orbits exist. Also, chemical evidence suggests the same thing: the inner-belt asteroids are mostly S-type, the main-belt ones mainly C-type (by far the dominant type). Moreover, there is a sharp drop-off in the number of asteroids crossing the orbit of Mars: far sharper than Mars itself could have produced in just 3.2 million years.

The most logical explanation, given the rest of the planetary explosion scenario, is that the population of asteroidal moons in temporary orbits around Mars—which we have hypothesized as responsible for the capture of the Martian moons Phobos and Deimos—was extensive enough and lasted long enough to collisionally affect many Mars-crossing asteroids. In addition, asteroids of high inclination and eccentricity would have been more frequently involved in collisions than those in more stable orbits. The principal effect of collisions would be to remove both eccentricity and inclination from the asteroids involved. (See the chapter "Mars and Saturn.") Then the S-type asteroids would be the remnants of those asteroids which were involved in such collisions, and for which Newcomb's argument no longer applies. Spectral and photometric evidence do suggest that S-type asteroids have had their dark regolith material stripped off, and they are somewhat smaller and more irregular than main belt asteroids, consistent with the idea they have been involved in collisions.

reveal its former status as a satellite body—for example, a prolate shape and hemispheric asymmetries. We would also expect an almost complete absence of satellite bodies in orbit around it, since it would not have had the same opportunity to capture debris from the planetary breakup event that bodies from the breakup would have had (through increases in the sphere of influence—see the chapter "Orbits").

Original Jupiter would have had no rings or asteroid satellites, or even Trojan asteroids associated with it. There would have been at least the four remaining Galilean satellites in orbit. But there might have been a few more satellites in Jupiter's original family of natural satellites whose orbits have since decayed while Jupiter's mass accreted—perhaps in discrete jumps following the Planet K and/or Planet V explosions. Jupiter's original mass was surely far less than its present value.

Original Saturn would have been like original Jupiter—ringless, with a number of natural satellites, and somewhat less massive. We would anticipate that the gap in Saturn's satellite system between Rhea and Titan may have been occupied by some other satellite, perhaps no longer existing due to some past encounter with a large comet or asteroid (such as Chiron). Similar remarks would apply to Uranus, which would not yet have tipped over. Neptune's satellites would have included Triton, Nereid, Pluto, and Charon, possibly among others. And Planet X would have orbited beyond Neptune, presumably with satellites of its own which it no longer retains (because of its close encounter with Neptune—which would likely have removed them all). We may someday find other Pluto-like bodies which are actually former satellites of Planet X, but their gravitational perturbations are too small to discover them through their perturbing pull, so other methods of discovery will be required.

Although there may have originally been other planets beyond Planet X, it seems likely that their orbits were disrupted, probably to the point of escape from the solar system, even before Planet X's orbit was disturbed. I imagine that the disrupting agents were most likely passing dwarf stars. It is true that we can calculate that in the lifetime of the solar system and at the density of stars at our distance from the galactic center, probably no star came closer than

PLANETS IN THE ORIGINAL SOLAR SYSTEM			
#	NAME	MASS	DIST.	SATELLITES (present planets in *italic*)
1	Venus	1	0.35	*Mercury*
2	Earth	1	0.7	The Moon
3	Planet V	10	1.4	*Mars*
4	Planet K	100	2.7	Ceres
5	Jupiter	200	5	Callisto, Ganymede, Europa, Io,...
6	Saturn	80	10	Iapetus, Titan, ?, Rhea; no rings
7	Uranus	15	20	Oberon, Titania, Umbriel, Ariel; no tilt
8	Neptune	15	40	Nereid, Triton, *Pluto*, Charon
9	Planet X	3	80	Undiscovered; now in planetary orbit?

Table 19.1.

about 1000 au or so, which is insufficient to cause such disruption. However, that assumes the Sun originated in a region with typical stellar density. I think it more likely that the Sun originated as part of a compact cluster of stars; or even that it originated in or near the galactic center, if it turns out that stars continually spiral out from the centers of galaxies, as is suggested by certain observations of stellar velocities difficult to explain with conventional models (see discussion in the chapter "Stars, Galaxies, and the Universe"). In either case, the 1000-au statistical limit does not apply, and a more severe limit is placed on the distance of stable planets.

Finally, there would have been no "Oort cloud of comets" in the original solar system, the present cloud seemingly having been added in just the last 3.2 million years.

The Idea of Extraterrestrial Intervention

Many authors have raised the speculation that the evolution of the human race has been modified by the intervention of extraterrestrials, or through some natural catastrophe. Erich Von Daniken[171] comes to this hypothesis through the existence of ancient wonders on the Earth which seem unlikely to have been created by primitive man, since their reconstruction would be difficult or impossible today. Zecharia Sitchin[172] concludes that ancient writings tell a story of extraterrestrial contact. All the familiar Bible stories have their counterparts in the ancient writings of other cultures, and Sitchin argues that their interpretations are consistent if one does not impose the constraint that they could not have been speaking of extraterrestrials. Many forms of natural catastrophe have also been suggested as influencing the development of life on Earth—for example, asteroid or cometary impacts, global floods, the explosion of a nearby supernova, passage of the solar system through interstellar dust clouds, giant solar flares, and the like.

I take it as intuitively obvious to any mind without religious convictions to the contrary that the chances are negligible of this being the only planet in the universe on which intelligent life happened to

> "If you can't change your mind, are you sure you still have one?"
> —Anonymous

develop. This was already true in a "Big Bang" universe three times older than the Earth. It is quite undeniable in an infinitely old universe. And in a universe in which life is also possible at many levels in an infinite range of scale too, life elsewhere becomes a certainty.[e] It is therefore of interest to speculate about why we are not in obvious communication with extraterrestrials, rather than about whether or not such beings exist.

It is usually argued that the time needed by a species to propagate its presence throughout an entire galaxy is short enough in

---

[e]The obvious term to describe intelligent life here on Earth at scales too small for us to have yet detected it is "intraterrestrials."

comparison with the age of the galaxy that any such beings must have had an opportunity to "be here"—that is, visit Earth. It may be, of course, that a "non-interference principle" for developing civilizations is in effect, or it may be that some tiny portion of UFO sightings are real, but they have never left behind credible evidence of their visits.

Another possibility is suggested by trying to place ourselves in "their" position and think deductively: What good are we to them? I submit that if we are to be any good to them, it can only be in the form of some uncontaminated experiment involving a developing civilization. Once we have extraterrestrial contact and assimilate their knowledge, our own evolution and development are forever aborted in favor of a co-development with them. As long as we evolve independently, we will make discoveries and mistakes unique to our species, with perhaps illuminating results for onlooking extraterrestrials.

To me the most exciting speculation is the idea that extraterrestrials have indeed visited this planet in the past, which is what deductive logic would dictate. Then perhaps they are not here now simply because it takes a long time to make interstellar journeys, and there are 100 billion suns in our galaxy to visit. Perhaps they come along only every 10,000 years or so. Indeed, if there is any element of truth to the ancient writings of various cultures, all of which tell somewhat similar stories about the beginnings of man, perhaps extraterrestrials were directly involved with the origins of man on this planet. Sitchin makes the point that if ancient writings are translated with the conventional procedures, but removing the constraint that they couldn't possibly be talking about spacecraft or extraterrestrials, the most natural translations for the many references to "the gods" (plural) and "fiery chariots" is indeed "extraterrestrials" and "spacecraft," respectively.[f]

---

[f]Sitchin has translated the Sumerian texts, which pre-date and apparently are the basis of the "sacred" writings of many cultures (the Bible, the Koran, the I Ching, and many others), all of which tell stories of the ancient world which have elements in common. In a few cases, there has now been verification that these writings are not totally mythological; for example, there is scientific evidence of a major flood event, and ruins of ancient cities have been found in the described locations. The rest of the

While speculating along these lines, I must admit to my fascination with the idea that the rough correspondence between the time of origin of man on Earth and the date of the planetary breakup event, which we discuss in the chapter "Do Planets Explode?" is perhaps not at all coincidental. Both can be approximated at about three million years ago. This rough coincidence begs the intellect to wonder if the two events could be causally related. One might even go so far as to wonder if the missing planet is not in fact the origin of the legend in ancient writings of a "Garden of Paradise," lost to mankind. I find Sitchin's writing about the interactions of "the gods" and early mankind most interesting in connection with such speculations. By meshing what little survives of ancient legends with the latest discoveries about our solar system's active recent history (over the last several million years), anyone can suggest fascinating scenarios about how it might all have come about.

---

story is subject to interpretation, but Sitchin argues that it is not intellectually honest to translate a word that literally ought to mean "those who had come down" as "giants," to take just a single example.

In Sitchin's more literal rendition, mankind was genetically engineered ("made in the image and likeness of God") to serve the labor needs of the advanced visitors. Humans were instructed to serve only their makers, and not any of the other gods ("I am the Lord thy God; thou shalt not have [serve?] strange gods before me"). The humans were forbidden certain knowledge ("the knowledge of good and evil"), which they eventually acquired anyway, resulting in a great casting out. But humans continued to multiply, sometimes mating with the gods themselves. Eventually they became so numerous and disobedient of the rules ("sinful") that the gods felt a need to exterminate them and start over (the flood). The survivors were hand-picked from among the superior (more god-like) humans. Later, the descendants of these humans sought to imitate the gods by building a conveyance that could take them to the heavens where the gods came from (the "tower" of Babel). When the gods discovered this, they became greatly concerned about mankind's imitativeness. To prevent further development of technology and keep humans under control, the gods caused the partition of languages and scattered humans widely over the Earth. Eventually their inability to control the human race was one of the reasons for the gods' departure. Their spaceports and centers at seven locations, including Sodom and Gomorrah, were destroyed by nuclear weapons before departure. The Dead Sea, with its

A Speculation about the Origins of Man

Now I am entering a domain where the evidence is too incomplete or uncertain to support my ideas (this is called "conjecture"), or where I am simply using guesswork or speculation—a haphazard process at best. We have abandoned strict Scientific Method and are therefore proceeding at our own very considerable risk. The purpose of proceeding is nothing more profound than that man has an insatiable curiosity about his own origins and that of the world around him. So, in the same spirit as the science fiction writer, we may find it stimulating to guess at some of the most interesting possible outcomes of our search for the "roots" of our species. Such conjectures, though insupportable on the basis of available evidence, may provide the hypotheses for testing new observational results when they become available.

I was suggesting the possibility that the explosion of a planet between Mars and Jupiter three million years ago may have been causally connected with the first appearance of man on Earth at about that time. The connection might have been passive: the extra cosmic radiation reaching Earth might have sped up evolution; or some natural enemy of the primates may have been killed off.g

25% solid content, is said to be a surviving by-product evidencing the destruction.

Other than such controversial translations, there is little credible evidence to support this fascinating story. However, it does meet the requirements to be considered a serious scientific hypothesis: it is contradicted by nothing known, it provides insight and aids understanding, and it makes testable predictions. For example, if extraterrestrials have visited the Earth in the past, the concept of the Great Pyramids as a nuclear bomb and fallout shelter makes ever so much more intuitive sense than the concept of a tomb for a pharaoh, considering how labor-intensive the project was. And sediment samples from the bottom of the Dead Sea should be quite definitive in determining whether or not nuclear weapons were used on the Earth long ago. I can think of no legitimate reason for the irrational reaction most of my colleagues have to serious consideration and further testing of hypotheses such as this.

gMy son Kevin, in discussions about this, pointed out that evolution must proceed more rapidly on land than in the sea because there is more solar

340

Or the connection might have been active: intelligent inhabitants of the dying planet might have intervened directly in the evolution of species on Earth, so as to produce an intelligent species here.

We first argue by suggestion that there could have been life on the planet before its destruction. Such a notion is, of course, sheer speculation—but not altogether insupportable speculation. From comets we know that water was present in abundance. Tektites are the melted glassy condensations of sedimentary material so Earth-like that many scientists maintain they originated on Earth, despite their global distribution and aerodynamic evidence of entry through the Earth's atmosphere. With an internal heat source and the proper type of atmosphere, temperatures could have been very mild on the other planet. And we are sure that oxygen was abundant in that atmosphere based on other properties of meteorites. Most significantly, cells which might have biological significance have been found in certain meteorites that presumably were once part of the planet! And recently, Fred Hoyle advanced the possibility that outbreaks of influenza on Earth at random sites over the globe show enough correlation with the sunspot cycle that an origin of those viruses from space (pushed into our atmosphere preferentially at times of sunspot and solar wind maximum) seems indicated.[173] One way for viruses to get into the near-Earth space environment is from the planetary explosion event.

Now we imagine that an intelligent species living on the planet realized the end was near. Some of its members selected the most nearly similar planet: Earth. Perhaps a colony of them actually transferred here in spacecraft before the end. But their days were numbered because the atmosphere, environment, food sources, etc., would have been too foreign for their survival once their supplies were exhausted. Anticipating the inevitable, they might have used their advanced knowledge of genetics to speed up the evolution of primates to produce early humans—perhaps in some ways resembling themselves. They would teach them about hunting, harvesting, fire, tools, etc., and tell the story of their origins back in another world, which by comparison was a veritable "garden of paradise."

---

and cosmic radiation to affect genes, and land gets greater exposure to extinction events from volcanic eruptions, storms, meteoroid impacts, etc.

Eventually they would all die in our inhospitable environment, leaving humans with their legends to pass on generation after generation.

Interestingly, the most ancient tradition about the Great Cheops Pyramid in Egypt is that it was erected to memorialize a tremendous cataclysm in the planetary system that affected the globe with fire and flooding.[174]

I developed this "intelligence" speculation for two reasons: 1. To show that theories argued by association in this way are quite weak, in contrast to the exploded planet hypothesis itself, which can be argued by deductive reasoning. 2. In furtherance of my opinion that even extraordinary speculative hypotheses are worthy of consideration by mainstream science as speculations, so long as they are internally consistent, not contradicted by data or observations, and make testable predictions. Is this particular speculation likely? Not at all. But as science progresses we will eventually unravel the mystery of our origins, and it will happen sooner if our minds are prepared to accept the truth when it is found, however fantastic that truth may be. If we are guided by our Scientific Method rather than by emotion, if we let the universe describe its wonders to us rather than telling it how it ought to be, then human beings will soon come to learn the answers they seek, perhaps even within our own lifetimes.

Pyramids on Mars?

Let me cite an example to illustrate both the typical behavior of present-day scientists confronted with an extraordinary idea, and why I think this prevalent behavior is so counter-productive. At a meeting of the American Astronomical Society in the late 1970s, two astronomers (DiPietro & Molenaar) presented high-resolution pictures taken by one of the *Viking* Mars-orbiting spacecraft showing certain interesting formations on the surface of Mars.[178] These formations have since been widely publicized by Richard Hoagland[176] (who cites numerological coincidences), and Mark Carlotto[177] (who has done computer enhancement of the images). (See Figure 19.1.) The objects in the photographs were apparently rock formations with dimensions of about one or two kilometers. They were all located in the same region of the planet. Some of the objects appeared to vaguely resemble pyramids—unusual for nat-

Figure 19.1. The "face" on Mars in a region of odd formations.

ural rock formations. One of the objects was shown at a low Sun angle and appeared very much like half of a human face, reminiscent of the Sphinx next to the Great Pyramids in Egypt.[h,174,178] The

---

[h]If the Martian formations turned out to be pyramids and a face, this might imply that those similar formations on Earth in Egypt were likely also built by traveling extraterrestrials. I have always suspected that the arguments to explain how the Egyptians built the pyramids were contrived and extremely ad hoc. The Egyptian scrolls which purport to detail the building of the pyramids were not contemporaneous with it, but rather were written about 900 years after the alleged fact. It is easy to imagine how they could have been an attempt by the writers of the time to explain the building of the pyramids in the most plausible way they could think of, rather than a report of what actually happened historically. Moreover, alleged stellar alignments in the pyramid are not unique in their interpretation; e.g. precession brings about the same star alignments every 25,000 years.

On the occasion of a recent visit to the great Egyptian pyramids, I was struck by some additional facts which I was previously unaware of. While many of the numerous smaller pyramids clearly built by the Egyptians as tombs (perhaps in imitation of the Great Pyramids?) contained bodies,

Martian rock formation appeared to have an eye, a nose, and a mouth, with the other side of the "face" hidden completely by shad-

---

treasures, and detailed histories in hieroglyphics all over the walls, none of these have ever been found inside the three Great Pyramids. Certain interior corridors are only three feet high, while one is 30 feet high, with walls made of multi-ton blocks placed along a 30-degree incline (the flat bases of the blocks lie at 30 degrees to the horizontal!). Merely working on the pyramid must have been a difficult and hazardous affair even without the need to lift some 30-ton blocks into place, since the height of the blocks at the base (i.e., the first step up) is five feet, and the full unencumbered ascent on foot can take hours. The Cheops pyramid contains about 3,000,000 huge multi-ton stone blocks.

The case that the Great Pyramids were built by Egyptians can be summarized as follows (from first following reference, describing the exploration by Col. Howard-Vyse, 1836, on pp. 64–65):

"As some of the quarry marks found in the chambers are hieroglyphs signifying 'year 17,' Egyptologists deduced that the building had reached that stage in the seventeenth year of the king's reign. Most of the marks were roughly daubed in red paint and appeared upside down, indicating they were quarry marks and not decorations.

"Similar marks, mostly red, but occasionally black, were also found on the first five or six courses of the Pyramid, behind the casing blocks.

"Howard-Vyse sent copies of the crayon marks to Samuel Birch of the British Museum, who identified one of the ovals as belonging to King Suphis, or Shofo, or Khufu."

"The most interesting discovery was not so much the [5] chambers [over the King's Chamber] themselves but some red-paint cartouches daubed on the inner walls of the upper chambers. Thanks to the Rosetta Stone and Champollion's successors, one of these cartouches was recognized by Egyptologists as belonging to Khufu, believed to be the second Pharaoh of the Fourth Dynasty, called Cheops by the Greeks, whose reign was thought to have occurred in the third millennium before our era.

"There was, of course, no way to prove that this Khufu was indeed the Cheops who had reigned in Egypt. But the fact that similar cartouches had been found in the quarries of the Wadi Magharah hills, from which much of the stone for the Pyramid was derived, added weight to the assumption.

"One thing seemed clear. Whoever had daubed the cartouches on the inner walls of the upper chambers must have done so before the chamber was sealed and the Pyramid completed; there appeared to be no entrance or exit other than the one blasted by the colonel.

344

ows. The resemblance to a face was striking—beyond what one's intuition considered plausible for a chance happening.[i,179]

"Doubt still lingered that there might have been a far earlier king with a similar cartouche, quite unknown to Egyptologists; but until further evidence could be adduced, it seemed hard to go against the theory of the Pyramid having been built in the reign of the historic Cheops, as reported by Herodotus and other classic authors."

This is rather mild evidence for a point of such major importance. Indeed, Z. Sitchin (see second following reference) presented strong evidence that Col. Howard-Vyse himself placed the markings there to resurrect dwindling financial support for his explorations. It would seem a most valuable undertaking to determine an absolute age for the building of the pyramids, or perhaps equivalently, for the date when its rocks were quarried. The only direct dating methods available require the presence of either organic or radioactive materials, neither of which is available in these three Great Pyramids. Dating them or learning their purpose may have to await the discovery of additional chambers in the interior which have been undisturbed since the original construction. Finding such undiscovered chambers deep inside a massive granite structure will be no easy undertaking, although there is easily room for hundreds of them. I am indebted to astronomer Carol Williams for the suggestion of using sonic waves to probe the interior. Travel times for long and short waves between many pairs of points could be analyzed to give a picture of the interior in much the same way that earthquake tremors are analyzed to determine the structure of the Earth's interior.

Insofar as I have seen, most serious scientists have been unwilling to test the hypothesis that such dates might be far older than the ancient Egyptian civilization. It may be that the pyramids were built in Egyptian times, and by the Egyptian people. I only hope that I live long enough to see a serious test of that theory performed by scientists fully prepared to grapple with the implications if the pyramids turn out to be much older than the ancient Egyptians.

My purpose here is not so much to advance the conjecture that the Cheops Pyramid may have been built long before the Egyptians came on the scene, but to criticize all people, especially scientists, who offer resistance to asking such legitimate questions as "What solid evidence is there about when the Cheops Pyramid was really built?"

[i]Since the preceding footnote was written, a news story broke in the *Los Angeles Times* on October 23, 1991, citing results presented by geologist Robert M. Schoch of Boston University (see next reference). Speaking to the Geological Society of America, Dr. Schoch presented new

Clearly the astronomers had come upon one of two situations. Most probably they had found natural rock formations which by chance had taken on forms of interest to humans, the way a cloud in the sky might occasionally do if one is looking for shapes. The less likely possibility is that the shapes were actually what they seemed—pyramids and a face—thereby providing us with proof of the existence of extraterrestrials (presumably not present-day Martians, but rather those same once-every-10,000-years traveling ones). With stakes that high, why not investigate further?

This was a nearly ideal case for follow-up, since a distinction between the two situations could be made with further observations. The radical hypothesis, that the formations were made by intelligent beings, predicted that the other side of the "face," hidden in shadows, would be a mirror image of the visible side. The chance formation hypothesis predicted that the other side of the "face" would be random. The chances of another perfect half-face formation occurring by accident were clearly minuscule. All one had to do was point the spacecraft when the Sun angle was right and look. Although the original discovery was made while the Mars-orbiting spacecraft still had a few months of useful observing left, no scientist was willing to do that! Each feared facing a no-win situation: ridicule for even looking, and criticism for wasting the spacecraft's valuable resources if the formation turned out to be random; or the greater fear of discovering that the radical hypothesis was true. The idea was clearly too radical for most scientists to be willing to deal with, despite the potential for a great discovery. What a terrible shame; *they should have been willing to look.*

---

evidence that the Great Sphinx (an immense sculpture with a human face and the body of a lion) adjacent to the Great Pyramids may be about twice as old as had been thought, or perhaps even older than that. Schoch conducted the first seismic studies ever allowed at the site. They showed that the limestone bed surrounding the monument had weathered far longer than expected, and also far longer than other nearby structures known to have been built in the era of Cheops (who was thought to have built the largest pyramid). Both porosity and erosional differences in the rock were consistent with this conclusion. Schoch indicated the Sphinx may be about 9000 years old. This was disputed by archaeologists, who argued that human society of that era could never have built such an advanced monument.

346

20

●●●●●●●●●●●●●●●●●●●●●●●●●●●●●●●

The Scientific Method

Summary: Reasoning must begin with assumptions. We first justify the assumption of the existence of a unique, external reality. Because our senses and our thought processes are both subject to error, we must develop procedures (called the Scientific Method) to test reality, if we wish to avoid falling into error. But the Scientific Method is itself a theory subject to error. We review some of its procedures and the reasons for each. "Occam's Razor" tells us to invent no unnecessary hypotheses, the importance of which is illustrated with a playing card demonstration. Experimenter bias must be guarded against by using "blind" techniques and "controls." But we take exception to the axiom "extraordinary hypotheses require extraordinary proofs," arguing that it retards progress in science, and proposing that more hypotheses be admitted for testing than is presently done. Then we examine the techniques of the "Unscientific Method," such as the ad-hominem attack, discrediting by association, the "run-and-shoot" tactic, the sneak attack, and the widely-used appeals to authority. It is permissible, we argue, to appeal to authorities for information, but not judgment. We then compare the values of inductive and deductive reasoning and argue for the latter over the former whenever it is available to us. We conclude that theories contradicted by no observation or experiment, which aid understanding of phenomena, which make successful predictions (or are falsifiable if their predictions are unsuccessful), and which are deductive in nature (i.e., without unnecessary degrees of freedom beyond the starting assumptions) have a high probability of being correct, even if extraordinary.

Introduction

Eclipses, comets, supernovas, meteor showers: these are some of the unusual events that occur in the sky from time to time. To the ancients they are said to have caused fear, because the nature of the events was unknown, and so were their implications for mankind. Imagine the ancient shepherd standing on a hillside at night during an intense meteor shower, such as the famous Leonid showers of 1833 and 1866, when it "rained meteors." It would be only natural for him to fear for his life. In 1999, when the Earth next encounters the cloud of debris which causes these historic showers, many of us may look up in awe and wonderment at a beautiful spectacle of nature. What differentiates our reaction from that of the ancient shepherd?

The answer is that modern man not only understands the cause and consequences of most events in the sky; he can even forecast their occurrence years in advance. That is the goal of the so-called Scientific Method: to arrive at theories which explain and predict the phenomena of nature. It is a set of rules which experience has shown to lead to theories offering correct explanations and predictions more often than when the rules are ignored. But paradoxically, the rules of the Scientific Method are themselves a theory, subject to verification, change, and improvement. They sometimes fail us, leading us to develop false theories that make incorrect predictions. As long as that continues to happen, there will still be room for improvement in the set of rules which constitute our Scientific Method for understanding reality.

About Truth and Reality

Like many words, the word "reality" has more than one meaning. Our efforts will be facilitated if we can agree to use the same meaning for this and other key words.

I therefore propose that we use "reality" for the unique, common, shared experience of the external world. Then the way individuals experience that reality would be called a "perception of reality," which is no longer unique. And a theory or model attempting to describe or predict reality would be a "description of reality."

With these definitions, the job of defining "truth" becomes less difficult. Let a true perception or description be one that agrees with this unique external reality, and a false perception or description be one that does not match reality. (Truth, of course, is not always determinable.)

This starting definition of reality makes an assumption, the truth of which may not be obvious: that such a single, unique, external reality does exist. Here is a justification for making this assumption.

1. The process of reasoning or logic requires premises or assumptions. It is impossible to prove or derive anything without starting assumptions. Ordinarily the question of the existence or reality of *everything* lies outside the domain accessible by reasoning, because no prior assumptions are available. Such propositions are therefore knowable only by experience or observation.

2. To observe and experience the external world, the tools available to us are our senses and our thought processes. But we already know that each of these is subject to occasional error. Not only can sensory input data be in error (as in the extreme case of hallucination, but more commonly, simple misperception), but even thought processes can be disordered (as in the extreme cases produced by drugs or mental illness, but more commonly from the influence of emotions).

3. Given that our only means of perceiving and describing reality are occasionally flawed, we must provide a means to check each input and each thought for error, or else we will be unable to tell correct input and thinking from wrong.

4. Some perceptions can be tested by looking for consistent input data from different senses, or a repetition of the original input data. But often such tests are not available or may be subject to the same error process as the original. So we must look to tests we can perform on the external world, and to the perceptions of others, to check up on our own thoughts and senses.

5. In using tests of the external world and the perceptions of others to check for error in ourselves (a process called "real-

ity testing"), we are implicitly making the assumption that there is a unique, common, shared experience available for this purpose. The alternative is to rely exclusively on our own senses and thought processes, which is illogical given all the evidence that these are occasionally faulty.

So although we cannot prove there is such a unique, common, shared experience that we can name "reality," we are logically compelled to make that assumption, because the alternative is known to lead to erroneous conclusions; whereas the assumption of a unique reality is not known to lead to any error.[a]

Forming Hypotheses

When I was much younger I once participated in an astonishing playing card demonstration. A friend told me he was going to test my psychic abilities. He pulled out what appeared to be an ordinary deck of cards, placed them lengthwise and face down on the table between us, and turned over the top card. It was black, and he placed it face up on his side of the deck. The next card he turned over was red, which he placed face up on my side of the deck. He then instructed me as follows: "Concentrate on the back of the card at the top of the deck, until you form a mental impression of whether it is a red or a black card. If you decide that it is red, place it face down on the red pile toward you. If you decide that it is black, place it face down on the black pile toward me. Continue in this way through the entire deck, and when you are finished, we will see how good your psychic powers really are."

After I had followed his instructions through about midway in the deck, he called out to me that the card I had just placed on the black pile was in error—my "first mistake," he told me. To prove the point, he turned over the card, a red one. He left the red card face up on the black pile, and turned over the next card from the deck, a black one, placing it face up on the red pile. He then admonished me: "You were starting to lose concentration. To aid you in

---

[a]Quantum physicists may wish to read the chapter "On the Composition of Substance" to see how their special objections about this point can be addressed.

concentrating on color rather than position, I have reversed the color of the card on top of the two piles. For the remainder of the deck, place the cards you determine to be red on the pile toward me, and those you determine to be black on the pile near you." I did as he instructed, yet near the end, he called out one additional error as I placed a card I thought to be red on the pile toward him. He showed me immediately that the card was black, placed it face down on the pile toward me, and let me finish.

After the last card, he told me to examine how well I had done. I reached for the pile toward me, turned the cards over, and found that all the cards between the two inverted ones were in fact red, and all the cards following the inverted black card were in fact black! As I was doing this, he reached for the other pile, flipped over the inverted cards, and showed me that the top half was all black, and the bottom half was all red. The demonstration was astonishing because it had all been under my own control, except for the two mistakes he corrected for me.

I was confronted with a definite observation of an extraordinary event. It called out for an explanation. I formed the hypothesis that this was truly a card trick despite the hype, and despite the fact that it seemed to be done entirely under my own control. Without realizing it, I was starting to use the Scientific Method.

Occam's Razor

"Invent no unnecessary hypotheses." This principle of the Scientific Method is known as "Occam's Razor."[b] It means that phenomena should be explained, if possible, using established theories rather than by inventing new ones. The reason why this principle helps us is fairly obvious: if something *can* be explained with accepted theories, then any new theory invented for the purpose would be unnecessary, which usually implies unlikely. But the rule is not absolute. It might be that a new theory adds understanding to a phenomenon which existing ones do not. Or it might be that a new theory makes successful predictions, while an existing one does not. But lacking such powerful reasons for making exceptions,

[b]In its original form: "Plurality is not to be assumed without necessity."

Occam's Razor remains a good guideline that saves us from going down innumerable false paths.

If we apply Occam's Razor to the card demonstration example, we must rule out psychic phenomena, subliminal suggestion, mind control, and other possibilities outside the domain of accepted theories. One must adopt the hypothesis that the performance was with certainty a trick, which leads to specific ways of thinking that help unravel the mystery. We might then reason as follows.

Let us assume, as is often true in tricks, that things are not necessarily as they seemed when events were out of our own control. What do we know for certain as true? At the first moment where we take control in the scene, there is a deck of unseen cards face down, a red card turned up toward us, and a black card turned up away from us. We take an unknown card from the top of the deck, think about its color, and place it on the pile of the color we thought of. But according to our hypothesis, that "thought" color is random; or more specifically, our choice of pile is random. Yet without anyone or anything else touching that card before we inspect it later, it will turn out to be on the correct pile. This seems to be a contradiction, which would invalidate our starting hypothesis that it was done as a card trick.

We look back over each premise carefully, searching for the incorrect assumption; and we find one. No one else touched the pile in front of us before we examined it later, but our friend did touch the other pile first. So let's revise the data to what we are sure is correct: if we had chosen to place the card on the pile near us, it will turn out to be a correct choice. We cannot be absolutely certain that the same is true of cards placed on the other pile, even though we cannot yet imagine a way it could fail to be true there also.

Once we have simplified the problem down to its essentials, we have filtered out the false data and assumptions. The complete solution may now become evident. How can it be that when we choose to place an unseen card on the red pile, it will be a red card? That is only possible if all the cards are red cards. Then after the midpoint in the deck, it must be that all the cards are black cards. This is possible only if the deck was pre-sorted with red cards on top and black on the bottom, which could have been done, so far as we know. If so, then all the choices on our side are correct, and all cards placed on the other side are wrong. But even the cards on the other side would appear to be correct at the end after a simple flip of the black and red cards by the person conducting the trick. We were deceived by assumptions we thought we *knew* to be true that were actually false.

In science, as in the example, false theories arise, receive support, and sometimes thrive, not so much because of false data or invalid reasoning, but because scientists take for granted assumptions that are actually untrue, and they neglect to re-examine all assumptions whenever significant new information becomes available.

Try the card trick yourself until you have mastered it. You will need to practice a bit to make it go smoothly.[c] Then try it on someone else. The effect can be dramatic because the trick seems impossible. Quiz your subject afterwards: ask for a description of what just happened, but do not answer any questions, at least until you get his description. Note how many false assumptions are made, and how sure your subject is that they are nonetheless true. In card tricks, the best results occur when people fool themselves. The same thing happens in science, but we do not refer to these occurrences as the "best results."

---

[c]You must secretly pre-sort the deck, red cards on top and black underneath. Remember to then place one black card on top of the deck so it will be available for the trick setup. Then place the top (black) card toward yourself, since that pile will contain all "errors," and the next (red) card toward your subject. Now 25 red cards remain on top of the face-down deck. You must count them carefully as they are placed onto either pile by your subject. At any time throughout the trick you can point to any card placed on your side of the deck as an "error." Whichever pile the last red card is placed on, you should use any excuse you wish to justify turning it up and placing it on the pile toward you. Then turn up the next (black) card and place it on the pile toward your subject. Finally when your subject finishes, he will reach for the pile near him and be amazed by the results in his pile. While this happens you must reach for the pile near you and quickly flip over the set of black cards from the top to the bottom. Everything in your pile will then also appear to be correct.

Extraordinary Hypotheses

The hypothesis suggested by the conductor of the card trick was that he was testing my "psychic powers." That is what is known as an "extraordinary hypothesis": one which lies entirely outside the domain of accepted knowledge, and does not merely extend existing theories. Psychic phenomena, astrology, spiritualism, and UFOs are examples, because the core idea behind each of these hypotheses has yet to be demonstrated by the Scientific Method.

This may come as a surprise to some. Testing has shown that no one to date has demonstrated the ability to perform almost any psychic feat under controlled laboratory conditions.[d] The major claims of Sun-sign astrology have been tested and proved false. And no extraterrestrial artifact proving visitation of the Earth by intelligent beings has yet been found. Regular investigations of ongoing claims in these areas are conducted—for example, by the Committee for the Scientific Investigation of Claims of the Paranormal (CSICOP), whose quarterly journal is the well-known *Skeptical Inquirer*.[180]

Yet even a committee of eminent scientists utilizing the tools of the Scientific Method is not immune to error or human failing. One of the CSICOP committee members accused three others of intellectual dishonesty in connection with an obscure astrology-like claim. Apparently the obscure claim was unexpectedly supported by the data. According to the accuser, D. Rawlins, the three scientists felt that admitting this would undermine the goal of nullifying public belief in astrology in general, so the results were "laundered" to show a negative result. This reminds us there are no human institutions immune from error, no matter how lofty their goals or prestigious their members.

The Scientific Method includes provisions to remove experimenter bias, such as requiring that some types of experiments be performed "double-blind." This means that neither the experi-

---

[d]Certain conscious controls of otherwise random processes have been alleged to be demonstrated at a very small, but possibly significant, statistical level.

menter nor the subjects know which are test subjects and which are "controls" until all results are final. The Scientific Method further requires that all such test results be independently verified by other scientists using other subjects or data. Unfortunately, limitations on research funding and time rarely permit independent verification of *negative* results. But as may be seen from the CSICOP example, failing to do so risks leading science away from true hypotheses, some of which are extraordinary.

The investigation of extraordinary hypotheses is important to science because the most extraordinary new theories are likely to come from this set, by definition. But clearly, most extraordinary hypotheses are wrong. This is one area where I believe the rules of the Scientific Method need clarification and/or correction to improve the results we get from it.

Occam's Razor is sometimes taken as "invent no extraordinary hypotheses." It seems obvious that one should use ordinary hypotheses in preference to extraordinary ones when the former will explain the data. It seems equally obvious that we would be doomed never to discover some of the most extraordinary things yet to be learned if we used no extraordinary hypotheses. Indeed, the occasional extraordinary hypothesis which turns out to be true is sure to have little supporting evidence at first (or else it would not be extraordinary).

Some scientists have also adopted as part of the Scientific Method the axiom "Extraordinary hypotheses require extraordinary proofs." The motivation for this axiom is to make it more difficult for false hypotheses to get into mainstream science. But at the same time this axiom has the effect of making it more difficult for *true* extraordinary hypotheses to get into mainstream science, thereby inhibiting the advancement of knowledge. That bad effect is obvious, but justified by the belief that there are few, if any, truly extraordinary hypotheses still to be discovered. Hence it becomes a self-fulfilling prophecy.

The rules of Scientific Method are subject to adjustment so as to optimize the results we obtain with it. This is one place where adjustment seems called for, in my opinion. If we do not tentatively accept (for further testing and consideration) extraordinary hypotheses that meet *ordinary* standards of proof, we are doomed never to learn some of the most interesting things about our universe.

Certainly many extraordinary hypotheses are discussed in this book. I do not make this argument to bolster confidence in theories for which the supporting evidence is weak. Many hypotheses we introduce here do meet the "extraordinary proofs" criterion—especially the Meta Model and the exploded planet hypothesis. But even these might have been accepted, or at least investigated, years or generations sooner if the proof requirements had not been so stringent.

In this book we discuss the possibility of faster-than-light travel in forward time. Suppose for the sake of argument that this extraordinary hypothesis is true. What criteria should be met before scientists consider it seriously, and what criteria should be met before it is taken as an "accepted theory"?

Whatever criteria you have set in answer to this query, you surely see the point: If the criteria are too rigid for an idea to even be considered seriously, it has no chance to get such consideration, *even if true!* And scientific progress is greatly impeded as a direct result.

The Unscientific Method

In 1950, I. Velikovsky published a sensational book[181] in which he hypothesized (based on new translations of ancient texts) that Biblical events could be explained by events in the heavens. For example, his hypothesis included the scenario that Venus was born in Biblical times in an eruption from Jupiter, and made a close approach to the Earth causing the parting of the Red Sea for the Israelites. The astronomers were outraged at the publicity given to Velikovsky's book, which became a best-seller for a time. Led by H. Shapley at Harvard, they threatened a worldwide boycott of the publisher, Macmillan Press, and all its textbooks. The publisher was eventually forced to sell its publication rights.

It was 24 years before astronomer Carl Sagan helped organize a serious scientific consideration of Velikovsky's hypotheses at an AAAS symposium in San Francisco titled "Scientists Confront Velikovsky," because of continued high interest by the public in the matter. Since the symposium, interest in Velikovsky's ideas has virtually disappeared.

Velikovsky's hypotheses were certainly extraordinary. But wouldn't scientists worldwide have been better off accepting them as hypotheses, testing them, and using the Scientific Method to rate their usefulness, than organizing a boycott of the author's publisher? Indeed, can the ideas of any sane man be so extraordinary as to make them unworthy of consideration?

I consider the Velikovsky incident a twentieth-century example of what happened to Galileo when Church authorities forced him to recant his findings, or in general of what may happen to anyone who advances a hypothesis too extraordinary for the times he or she lives in. It seems to matter not whether the hypothesis is right or wrong, but only that it is completely unacceptable to the "authorities" of the times for it to provoke an unscientific response.

You may look for this phenomenon whenever you hear someone espousing a new idea. Do his opponents stick to the hypothesis and use scientific principles in their replies? Or do they switch to the "Unscientific Method," with its most useful weapon, the "ad-hominem" attack? This is where one tries to discredit the man himself, his institution, his motives, or anything associated with his ideas, rather than addressing the ideas themselves. This is most often seen in political debates, where the participants really do not wish to be pinned down on controversial issues, or perhaps have no substance to back up their positions.

> "Trying to find an open-minded scientist is like trying to find a Fundamentalist Christian who loves his enemies."
> —John Anthony West

Another popular principle of the Unscientific Method is "discrediting by association." E.g. "My opponent associates with organized crime figures, so don't listen to what he says." It is most effective when your audience is predisposed to make the association anyway. E.g. "Speed kills." But a survey on the New York Thruway showed that while 85% of the drivers were exceeding the posted speed limit, only 50% of fatal accidents involved vehicles which had been exceeding it in the minute before the accident. This is because drugs and alcohol, weather conditions, and mechanical failure were more important causes of accidents than speed, as further evidenced by countries with much higher speed limits than in the U.S. without proportionately higher fatality rates.

Discrediting by association is often promulgated effectively through the use of ridicule. Its purpose is to dissuade potential allies of an idea when a meaningful scientific response is not readily available. The mark of the insecure layman posing as a scientist is the regular use of ridicule, particularly when it replaces substantive responses and critical thinking. Even a truly crankish idea deserves better than ridicule from one who would call himself a scientist.

Another common form of discrediting by association is to point to one or more other errors that a scientist has made as a reason for dismissing some new statement. The "reasoning" is perhaps along the lines: "He's been wrong before, and it would be a lot of work to prove that he's wrong again this time. But because of past errors, it is not worth the investment to prove him wrong again now; so we'll just assume it." In astronomy, new ideas are sometimes discredited by simply referring to them as "Velikovskian." A case could be made for such an attitude if someone had been guilty of intellectual dishonesty, such as manufacturing or altering data. But the ideas of sane and honest men should never be unworthy of consideration, and each must be addressed on its own merits.

Scientists especially should know the rules of logic. While it is true that someone with a higher error rate than normal has a higher probability of proposing an incorrect idea, the converse is not true. A specific idea under consideration does *not* have a lesser (or greater) probability of being correct because its proposer has a higher (or lower) than normal error rate. The validity of an idea can be determined solely by an examination of its merits, and not at all by an examination of its proposer.[e]

---

[e]A common form of "discrediting by association" is one which makes this same error of logic. As an example, let us assume we are given the following as a fact: "96% of heroin users previously smoked marijuana." Can we conclude that it is likely that smoking marijuana leads to heroin use? Can we conclude there is the slightest tendency in that direction on the basis of the given hypothetical fact? By the rules of logic, we cannot. The conclusion is entirely an association in our minds and cannot be derived to the slightest degree from the given fact. To see this, consider a second hypothetical fact: "99% of heroin users previously drank milk."

Most scientists recognize unscientific approaches when they see them. But one approach, the "appeal to authority," is so commonplace that scientists suppress their knowledge that it is unscientific, even when challenged on that point. The excuse is often that science is complex, and one cannot look into everything for oneself. So when "authorities agree," that's good enough for most scientists. Besides, there is a certain reciprocity implied in this arrangement: "If you accept me as an authority in my field of specialization, I will afford you the same courtesy in yours."

Now this arrangement has its place, but only up to a point. Each field has its specialists, and these individuals generally know more than others about their specialties, and therefore should be in the best position to make informed judgments. Naturally we look to specialists to write articles and books, to review papers, and to present seminars and colloquia. And we invariably wish to hear what they have to say about their specialty whenever we are interested in that topic. The problem arises when we cross the line from respecting their superior knowledge in an area to accepting their judgment as superior.

It is true, as already remarked, that specialists should be in the best position to judge new ideas, the relative merits in controversies, and the solutions to problems, as well as to make decisions or recommendations, in their fields of expertise. But these same people are ultimately human. They may have vested interests. They certainly have egos. They may be concerned about saving face, or obtaining funding or tenure. Or they may simply have prejudices, areas of ignorance, or experiences which bias their thinking. While respecting them for their superior knowledge and experience in an area, *we should never impute superior judgment to specialists.*

Since we have no association between these two items to impose on the fact, it becomes clear that the fact alone implies nothing whatever in the way of a connection. By examining the parallel with the first fact, we can now see that any implications drawn about a causal connection were entirely from the association already in our minds before reading the fact. But to begin to draw such implications, we logically would need to know the percentages of marijuana users and of non-marijuana users who go on to use heroin. The first fact tells us neither essential correlation; it merely exploits and falsely reinforces an association we already had.

Specifically, we should listen to what each specialist has to say about some question, and all arguments he can bring to bear for one side of it and against the other. Then we should make up our own minds, and not simply accept his conclusions. Of course, we may lack the background and knowledge to substitute our own judgment for that of the specialist. But as a general rule, educated people are usually only a few sets of logical syllogisms away from being able to understand the argument at the forefront of any field of interest. And if a specialist fails to communicate enough information to allow us to make our own judgments about the conclusions, then his own conclusions are thereby automatically suspect. No specialist should be saying, "Trust me; I'm an expert." He should be communicating the basis of his conclusions so clearly that other interested parties can understand them as well.

One of the chief ways in which important new insights are lost to science occurs when an authority makes an offhanded dismissal of an idea, and others then lack the courage or self-confidence to pursue the idea further for themselves. I refer to this approach as the "shoot-and-run" tactic. Its most common form is to allude in passing to something taken out of context or something irrelevant as grounds for dismissing a substantive idea. Once again it has its counterpart in politics, the "sound byte," in which catchy one-liners are permitted to substitute for the critical discussion which Scientific Method demands. The resulting waste of taxpayer money, the toll in careers, and the squandering of talent are all part of the incalculable cost of the use of such tactics.

An all-too-common shoot-and-run comment is "That person is a crank" or "That person can't be believed because. ..." In the "Introduction" to this book, we used the term "disputers" for persons who challenge accepted ideas, and "defenders" for persons who criticize the disputers. These terms do not carry the emotional baggage and incorrect meanings that terms such as "crank" do. Having been wrong on some previous occasion should not be grounds for dismissing a person's new ideas. Disputers immediately recognize that the shoot-and-run tactic of the defender is unscientific, and they tend to interpret the use of such tactics as displaying a lack of substantive grounds for objection to their new idea.

If any of us were asked detailed questions about mental skills, we would concede that what we call "intelligence" usually consists of a superior skill at one or more mental functions, but not all of them. For example, someone with a superior memory, or with better abstract reasoning, or greater creativity, or sound judgment, or exceptional communication skills, or any particular mental skill, is respected for what he or she can do well. But clearly such people are not gifted in all areas at once. In fact, it often appears that people gifted in one area of mental function are deficient in one or more other areas. The stereotype of a scientist is of someone maladapted to society despite his brilliance. In the extreme case, we refer to this phenomenon as "idiot savant," where someone may have genius skills in a narrow area and idiot-level skills in other areas. The important corollary is that a scientific expert has that status by virtue of the facts he commands in his area of specialization. Nothing about his expert status implies that his judgment is in any way better than average, or better than our own. Relying upon experts to excel in areas in which they have no special skills is inappropriate. An expert who withholds his facts so that we have no choice but to rely on his judgment is not to be trusted. An expert who asks that we respect his judgment simply because he is an expert is being naive and egotistical.

Informed judgment has the potential to be better. That potential will not be realized unless the information is placed before someone whose judgment is excellent. That person may be, but more likely is not, the scientific expert who has the facts.

The last unscientific principle I will mention is the "sneak attack." This simply means catching your opponent by surprise with a question or challenge he has had no time to prepare for. In science, where we seek truth, not victory, it is important to give someone plenty of advance notice about challenges that will be mounted to his ideas, to give him the opportunity to think, research, and prepare his best defenses of the ideas. But scientists are humans too, and enjoy the sweet taste of victory. That is why some of the most famous debates in the history of science, such as the Scopes "Monkey Trial" debate over evolution or the Curtis-Shapley debate on the nature of "island universes" (galaxies), were perceived to have been lost at the time by the person whose ideas ultimately prevailed.

Forward Thinking

Deduction is one of the most powerful principles in scientific reasoning: "If A implies B and B implies C, then A implies C." Its great power comes from its certainty. If the premises are true and the reasoning valid, then the conclusion may be trusted absolutely. So using deduction, we may constantly learn new things that are as certain as the assumptions we make to deduce them.

To reason deductively, it is only necessary to have a "starting point": a set of premises whose truth may be relied upon. In the preceding example, "A" is our starting point, from which we eventually deduce "C." If we had started instead with some other starting point "Z," it is most improbable that we would be able to derive the same conclusion "C" by deduction alone, since deductive steps are generally unique. Wrong starting points have little chance of leading to descriptions of reality.

The logical deductions from a theory or model are its "predictions." They must be compared with reality at every opportunity. It is of paramount importance for any hypothesis which purports to be of value that it be "falsifiable"; that is, that it be able to make predictions which if false invalidate the theory. Predictions that support a hypothesis if true, but do not contradict the hypothesis if the opposite (or nothing at all) happens, are generally of low value. For a hypothesis to gain acceptance, it must predict things seemingly of low probability that will invalidate the theory if the predictions are wrong. The convincing power of the predictions will be proportional to how much at risk the theory is placed by them. This is why it is usually a sign of a bad theory if it must be "patched" as a result of a bad prediction, or even a prediction it simply failed to make at all.

Scientists today have fallen into the very bad habit of no longer demanding that theories be falsifiable. It comes from the frustration of having no reasonable alternative theories readily at hand. So when the prediction of a theory fails, the easiest course of action is to patch the theory, rather than to go back to fundamentals and devise a whole new theory. This "easiest course of action" does not justify the procedure; it merely explains its prevalence.

362

Of course, we are not always able to reason deductively, as we should. Often in science we are given an effect (data, or an observation), and must seek the cause. Given "C," we seek to learn "A." We are obliged to reason from a particular instance to the cause of the whole phenomenon. This process is called "induction." Sometimes induction is the only method we have available to us, so we must use it. Although induction usually gives the illusion of uniqueness, it is often not widely appreciated how divergent are the numbers of pathways which might have led from the general cause to the particular effect.

The hazard of induction might be illustrated with this example. When I visited my daughter Connie in England one summer, she took me to see Stonehenge and the Roman ruins at Bath. In driving from the first to the second destination, we had to make many turns on small country roads, all well marked with road signs "To Bath." After an enjoyable visit, we realized we did not recall much about the route we had taken to get there. I jokingly suggested that we just look for the road signs saying "To Bath" and go in the opposite direction to retrace our steps. This is analogous to induction. Of course, even if we managed to start out in the right direction, it was inevitable that this process would eventually diverge from the route we had come in by, because of the great number of possible routes all converging on the same destination. (Yet at each step of the way it would appear to us that we were taking the only course which met our criteria.) What we needed to do was to remember that we had originated at Stonehenge, and to follow road signs saying "To Stonehenge." That process, like deduction, leads to a unique solution, with the possibility of error only if our starting assumption were wrong.

The "Big Bang" theory for the origin of the universe is a product of inductive reasoning. Astronomers started out with data suggesting that all galaxies were moving away from us with velocities proportional to their distances. From there, astronomers conceived of the Big Bang scenario for the origin of the entire universe, including space itself, in a gigantic explosion. Later, other data suggesting the existence of a cosmic fireball were added as supporting evidence. But both of those observations that serve as the basis of the theory are subject to interpretation.

Notice that if we use the reasoning method we developed in the card trick example—making only assumptions we are certain are true—then we cannot assume either the expansion of the universe or the background nature of the microwave radiation, for reasons elaborated in the chapter "Stars, Galaxies, and the Universe," because neither assumption is at all certain. And no theory can be more certain than the assumptions it is based on.[f,182]

There is a danger of the important point here becoming lost in semantics. Every theoretician thinks he has "deduced" his theory from the observations. And even in the procedure I recommend, one must use induction to guess the starting point. So the emphasis should be not so much on "deduction" versus "induction," but on what is deduced. "Deducing" theories from observations is the wrong way around, the non-unique way; and it is truly a form of induction, despite the common use of the word "deduce" when describing the process. The unique procedure is to deduce the observations from the theory. Then, since the theory had to pre-exist and have a reason for being true other than the observations, we can use that fact as a litmus test: Does a theory predict observations and data (without help from secondary hypotheses) other than those used to formulate it? If the answer is "no," then it will be a lucky happening indeed if the theory has been guessed correctly.

---

[f]Interestingly, astronomer Halton Arp, while decrying the lack of open-mindedness of astronomers to new ideas, has made a somewhat opposite argument about reasoning. He writes (see next reference): "It is clear that I espouse here the Baconian principle of induction of general laws, from a body of observed facts. It would seem obvious that if a scientist only reasons deductively from known laws then he or she can never do more than recover those laws, and will never discover anything fundamentally new." It seems safe enough to me to reason from known laws *within their known range of applicability*. But Arp and I are in full agreement when he says (p. 179), "It may sometimes be that not to know one thing that is wrong could be more important than knowing a hundred things that are right." So deductive reasoning, I think Arp would agree, is the superior choice if it is available, and if one makes no errors in the starting assumptions. Never assuming that a law is true outside its verified realm (not even a "universal" law such as gravitation) seems a good safeguard against the hazard Arp warns us of.

The law of gravity is an example of a good model. When we discover a new planet or a new star cluster, we don't have to "explain" why the new system needs a patch to the law of gravity; the law simply works as is. If we press the precision of the law farther than ever before, we may find weaknesses. When Newcomb looked at the problem of explaining the advance of Mercury's perihelion, he showed that it can be explained by modifying the inverse square force to the inverse $(2+\epsilon)$ power, where ϵ is a small number of order 10^{-7}. That "explains" the observations of Mercury but leaves you wondering, "Why should the universe be that way?" Einstein's theory is a fundamental model improvement from first principles, which explained the Mercury perihelion advance and a lot more in a way that made sense. No ad hoc helper hypotheses were needed. Nonetheless, I would not expect Einstein's theory to continue to apply over distance ranges or for mass densities many orders of magnitude greater than the domain in which it was derived.

The Big Bang model is an example of the opposite kind. Its first premises were induced from observations and left us asking, "Why should the universe be that way?" As we learned new things, we kept having to patch and add helper hypotheses. And as we do, the same question keeps coming up.

I have no doubt that astronomers will be able to keep "explaining" whatever we observe in the universe using the Big Bang model as a basis, for example, by just modifying the laws of physics a little bit. After all, they well assure us, changing to the inverse $(2+\epsilon)$ power isn't too much to ask, is it? I just don't buy the whole principle of doing science inductively that way: using the observations as an ad hoc driving force. Theories should be motivated by theoretical or logical or observational considerations other than the ones they are trying to explain. When we get the model right, the rest will be explained as a natural by-product, and everyone will say, "Oh, of course. Now it's clear. Why didn't someone think of that sooner?"

Such a priori theories have a significant credibility advantage over ad hoc theories. This does not arise purely from the direction of the arrow of time, but from the number of degrees of freedom consequently in the theory. When working backwards in time, there are many possible causes and pathways that might have led to the effect one is examining. But when starting with a single cause and working forward in time, there are often many effects, some of which are predictable with great specificity. If that unique set of effects all exists to the degree predicted, one can impute them to the hypothetical single cause, rather than to multiple independent causes, with considerable confidence.

When creating ad hoc theories and working from effect back to possible cause, one often has the distinct feeling that clever theoreticians could come up with a theory to explain any effect, no matter what it was. Often such ad hoc models can be recognized by making no specific, quantitative predictions, but only describing a phenomenon qualitatively, and vaguely enough that a wide range of effects might be made to fit the model. For example, distant objects in the universe appear to be redshifted. We guess that the cause is a velocity of recession and conclude that the universe is expanding. But if the distant objects had all been blueshifted, we would instead probably have derived the theory of a contracting universe. And if they had no redshift, or if they had mixtures of red and blue shifts, we would correspondingly have come up with models that explain what we see, no matter what that was. But however well the "explanation" appears to work, it nonetheless is unmotivated other than by what we see. It doesn't even begin to answer "Why should it be that way?"

But imagine a model of the universe motivated only by fundamental logic and reasoning. If this model made no prediction about the shift of the light of distant objects, we would conclude that it did not provide much insight and was not very useful. If it predicted something contrary to what we observe, we would dismiss it as having an incorrect premise or invalid reasoning. But if it insisted that the universe must be a certain way, and that happens to be in accord with what we observe, then we would gain confidence in the premises and reasoning behind the model. If many such predictions were fulfilled, including some we hadn't known about before, we would gain a great deal of confidence in the model. Our powerful confidence in the law of gravity arises from its predictive success in case after case under vastly different circumstances wherever we can observe its effects.

Suppose the prevailing paradigm is, say, that the redshift observed in cosmological objects is due to the velocity of expansion of the universe, and therefore tells us the distance of the objects. Assume that we also have a second paradigm, that nothing may travel faster than the speed of light. Then one day we observe jets moving away from high-redshift objects called "quasars." If the quasars are as far away as their redshifts indicate, then the calculated velocities of the jets would be faster than the speed of light. We are therefore confronted with a nominal contradiction to one of our paradigms. It would seem that either the jets do move faster than the speed of light, or that they are not as far away as their redshifts indicate.

But instead of accepting that a paradigm must be dispensed with, astronomers instead developed an elaborate "helper theory" called "relativistic beaming," which basically says that the observed effect is an illusion, so we can keep both of our paradigms. There is absolutely no a priori reason why quasar jets should behave in such a way. The idea simply allowed the astronomers to save the paradigms, rather than to face the difficult task of building new models from first principles. Surely an objective person would conclude that such a "save the paradigm" process using ad hoc helper hypotheses unmotivated by anything except explaining unexpected observational results is a hazardous scientific process, unlikely to lead us to a true understanding of nature.

Since I have proposed a number of paradigm changes, I have sometimes engaged my colleagues in conversation, asking them what it would mean to them personally if some particular paradigm (usually one they were professionally involved with) were to be overthrown in favor of some new model. I have been dismayed to find that the most common response I hear is, "I would do something else for a living." Further probing makes it clear that many of these individuals would change professional specialties, and in some cases entire fields, rather than accept a radically different fundamental model in their areas of specialization. I think that reflects poorly on the entire body of people who have chosen to pursue science as a profession.

Someone might argue that the pan-theory "God made things that way" qualifies as an a priori model. But in practice, it is always invoked ad hoc, when no other explanation for a phenomenon immediately presents itself. The problem with the "God" theory as a scientific model is its lack of specificity. No useful understanding or predictions can come from it because "we can't know the mind of God." Both the value of a theory and the confidence we can have in it are functions of the degree to which it adds understanding and makes specific, testable predictions that are fulfilled, the failure of which would have falsified the theory. Theories adaptable to any observational results are of minimal practical value.

In most chapters of this book, we begin with a new, logical starting point, unrelated to the usual observed "facts," and try to "deduce" the observed situation. If we achieved some success with this effort in our examination of cosmology, then we have shown that the Big Bang theory is not a unique starting point to arrive at the observed universe. Indeed, we will have seen throughout all the chapters how deduction, or reasoning *forward* in time from premises not derived from observations, can lead to conclusions in which we can have more confidence than those arrived at by induction (or deductions from observations), even among some of the most widely accepted theories in astronomy today.

21

• •

Peer Pressure
and Paradigms

Summary: We critique the theory of the Scientific Method itself. We begin with the concept of "scientific peer pressure" and how it interferes with the objective examination of extraordinary ideas on their merits. We argue that extraordinary ideas should be more freely examined if science is to make progress, and we critique Occam's Razor. We examine how science deals with threatened paradigm changes. This leads to the formulation of "catastrophe theory" for the advancement of knowledge. We conclude with a discussion of the Scientific Method and scientific arrogance, and look at the major conclusions of this book in that light.

A Note about Scientific Peer Pressure

Why have I arrived at models so different from the existing conventional models? I disagree fundamentally with one popular tenet of the Scientific Method, "extraordinary hypotheses require extraordinary proofs." Sometimes (although admittedly not often) the extraordinary hypothesis will be the correct one. If we continue to apply "Occam's Razor" and eliminate extraordinary hypotheses when ordinary ones can be made to do, this is fine as long as we do not strain plausibility. But in modern science, this preference for ordinary hypotheses over extraordinary ones is continually used to ignore plausibility, and to not give serious consideration to the merits of extraordinary ideas.

We have also seen throughout this book that the present system, in which extraordinary hypotheses are excluded without extraordinary proof, is still very much fraught with error, even in the fundamentals in many fields of knowledge. Very often we find the situation that a mediocre hypothesis has been adopted as "fact" on no better grounds than that no better hypothesis has come along for many years. I am convinced that admitting extraordinary hypotheses tentatively when circumstances justify it would advance science in two distinct ways: 1. Some of those hypotheses are true; and because they are extraordinary, they are unusually important. Even the effort of disproving them enriches the body of scientific knowledge. 2. By admitting hypotheses with less claim to certainty than usually required, all scientists will become more aware of the fallibility of all hypotheses, and perhaps be less resistant to giving up on those bad hypotheses they have already accepted.

As readers of this book may come to appreciate, the human problem with extraordinary ideas is that they often undermine the fundamental assumptions upon which so much other research work has been based. If an extraordinary idea with merit comes along, there is usually only one or a few people promoting the new concept, whereas there are many who have read, experimented, taught, published, and invested funds, time, and energy in consequences of the old theories which would need to be revised, if they are not outright rendered obsolete.

It is not so much that these individuals are intellectually dishonest as that they take the path of least resistance. Most of the time they lack the background or cannot invest the time to determine for themselves the merits of claims and counter-claims; so because of vested interests, they become "rooters" that one of their peers will shoot down the new hypothesis. They often leap to the defense of an esteemed colleague whose reputation would be "blemished" by the acceptance of the new idea—a thinly disguised excuse for failing to be scientifically objective. Most of this "rooting" takes place quietly: by ridicule in private discussions, in peer reviews by referees and editors, in decisions on grants by funding officials (who may have previously put millions of dollars into what would now be "obsolete" research).

What happens if a scientist has enough influence to get to speak

370

in front of a large body of his peers about an extraordinary idea? This happened to me at an International Astronomical Union Colloquium in Lyon, France, in 1976, where I first spoke to my peers about the exploding planet hypothesis. I had widely circulated lengthy preprints for comment prior to that talk. Unbeknownst to me, a number of colleagues arranged with the meeting chairperson for three specialists to be called on in the discussion period after my talk to give prepared rebuttal remarks.[a] Afterwards, the chairperson tried to cut off further discussion, although dozens of additional attendees still wished to ask questions or make comments. So one prominent specialist stood up and declared, "Based on what we have just heard, this paper is surely without merit and can be dismissed!" The response was emotional applause and cheers (without precedent for that scientific body) and the immediate adjournment of the session, postponing the remaining scheduled presentations. So much for the pretense of objectivity!

The term for what we are describing here is "peer pressure." We have come to see how effective peer pressure is in getting people to try alcohol, cigarettes, drugs, coffee, etc.—things with deleterious health effects not in their own interests to try. But peer pressure operates throughout life, not just among the young;[b] and it is prevalent among scientists, who would even mount an international boycott of a publisher of a radical hypothesis (Velikovsky's) rather than address its scientific merits (which didn't happen for a quarter of a century, because of peer pressure). *The ridicule of scientists who present extraordinary hypotheses* is scientific peer pressure in its most blatant form. It usually accomplishes its intended goal—

---

[a]An example of the "sneak attack."

[b]To see its effects, consider cases of peer pressure in which almost everyone participates. Suppose someone chose to defy social conventions about clothing, hair-style, or public behavior in some non-intrusive way. They might be shunned and avoided, ridiculed, scorned, perhaps even threatened, in proportion to the degree of their defiance. Much of this will be done by people who believe they are acting in the defiant one's best interests. Everyday peer pressure from one's family, friends, and acquaintances may differ in degree, but not in kind, from this example. That is why it is so devastatingly effective in acting on all of us. The unified withholding of communication is always a powerful motivator!

to prevent otherwise neutral scientists from being willing to speak out publicly with any favorable remark about such an idea.

This environment in which scientifically counter-productive peer pressure flourishes is created and encouraged by modern society. It probably stems from our basically religious, and therefore authority-oriented, heritage. It also arises from the huge numbers of people who either are, or have been trained to think they are, judgment deficient, and who therefore rely on "experts" and "authorities" to form their judgments for them. Finally, this counter-productive climate is fostered by society's resistance to change, especially rapid or radical change. It is literally true that many people *do not wish to know* that reality differs from their present conception of it. Such people will always be a source of inertia to change, and an inhibitor to those of us who do wish to know. We might accommodate them by describing even the most certain of new models as tentative, allowing them to maintain their illusions. It should not be forgotten that there are some people who truly do not have the personal resources to cope with drastic change.

As for my ideas presented here, I have attempted to provide some testable implications of each hypothesis. The chief value of any hypothesis, extraordinary or not, is in its ability to predict things not yet known or understood. I would be content to have that criterion measure the value of my own ideas. But only readers such as yourself can help ensure they will be afforded the opportunity to be judged objectively in that way, rather than treated with unscientific methodology.

Paradigm Change

Once a paradigm (a standard model with far-reaching implications) becomes widely accepted, most scientists acquire incentives to keep it in place as is (see the Preface of this book). In addition to all those incentives, modern knowledge has become so vast and accumulated so quickly that it is becoming increasingly difficult, approaching impossible, for a single person to challenge a paradigm. This is most unfortunate for progress, since the motivation to challenge a paradigm usually originates from a single person.

Consider that in order to discuss and defend the exploded planet hypothesis among my colleagues, it was not sufficient that I simply put forward the evidence I found within my own field of special expertise, dynamical astronomy. I had to become familiar with dozens of sub-disciplines, many of them in areas so remote from my training that I initially had no knowledge or experience in them. Yet I had to become familiar enough with each subject to make comparative tests of how well the standard and alternative theories fit the data in each. To emphasize the point, since it is my intent to suggest an explanation about why so few scientists can successfully criticize the fundamentals within their own fields, here is the list of sub-disciplines I had to study to address just the exploded planet hypothesis:

The history of the conflict over the past 200 years, especially Olbers, Lagrange, Newcombe, Brown & Patterson, Carter & Kennedy, and Ovenden; the Titius-Bode law of planetary spacing; Ovenden's alternative "least-interaction action" hypothesis; dynamics and spatial distributions of asteroid orbits; collision theory and probabilities; explosion signatures among artificial Earth satellite orbits; Kirkwood gaps; gravitational spheres of influence; tidal forces for small bodies; observations of asteroidal secondaries from occultations and radar; resonance theory; meteor streams; properties of meteors entering the Earth's atmosphere; bands of zodiacal dust; asteroid families; the Oort cloud; the "inner core" theory; the "Kuiper Belt" theory; the solar nebula hypothesis; theories of comet origins; dynamics of passing stars; galactic tidal forces; giant molecular clouds; physical properties of comets, such as formation and brightness of coma and tails; chemical abundances; statistics of orbital elements; correlations of physical and orbital properties; spectra and albedos at all wavelengths; lightcurves; Sun-grazing comets; comet splits and the velocities of fragments; tensile strengths of materials; non-gravitational forces; coma dust and OH bursts; spacecraft encounters; infrared trails in comet orbits; jets; solar magnetic sector boundaries; distribution of dark material throughout the solar system; cratering distribution and statistics; meteorite types, physical and chemical properties; theories of meteoroid origin; geology and climate of the Earth; "mascons" on the Moon; librations; magnetic and radiogenic character of all extraterrestrial materials; erosion rates; flow properties of water on various surfaces; capture and escape mechanisms; "spots" in outer planet atmospheres; accretion; rings; lenticular cloud formation; hurricanes; cosmic ray exposure ages; fission tracks; chemical differentiation; cooling rates; shock and pressure effects; isotopic anomalies; carbon isotope formation and diamonds; fireballs; interstellar hydrogen clouds; X-ray and extreme ultraviolet backgrounds; gamma-ray bursts; matter-antimatter interactions.

It is my opinion that when so much evidence for a hypothesis is brought forward, either the hypothesis deserves a place on the scientific table for further evaluation, or other scientists acquire an obligation to show cause why it should not. "Showing cause" implies open discussion of the merits, not unilateral declarations of error.

The Value of Extraordinary Hypotheses

Some of the ideas set forth in the chapter "The Origins of the Solar System and of Man" are sheer intellectual speculation. Yet I feel certain there is nothing wrong with them as viable hypotheses about our origins, and that they are entitled to the same scrutiny from the Scientific Method as other, more conventional theories of origins. It is a perfect example of why the axiom "extraordinary hypotheses require extraordinary proofs" is harmful to scientific advancement: since the extraordinary hypotheses are, by selection effect, necessarily those we least suspect to be true, it follows that they are the ones with the least surviving evidence.[c] We shall be condemned never to discover the most extraordinary truths unless we are prepared to make exceptions to the rigorous application of the "extraordinary proofs" criterion.

This approach does imply a willingness to accept many more hypotheses for investigation than one otherwise would do, in the full realization that most of them will be false. The point of doing so is that we may expect the occasional true extraordinary hypothesis will be of considerably greater importance to the advancement of knowledge than most ordinary hypotheses. A further aspect of our more liberal approach is a tolerance of ambiguity. We admit that knowledge is often tentative and incomplete, and that all our

---

[c]Extraordinary hypotheses discovered to be true become accepted into conventional science and are then no longer extraordinary.

accepted hypotheses have a certain probability of correctness attached to them. We are here expressing the desirability of lowering the required probability of correctness before accepting a hypothesis for serious consideration. Although we may take a higher risk of accepting false hypotheses into our body of knowledge by so doing, we may also include a greater number of the most important true hypotheses for which proofs are not presently possible, or may never be possible, because of data destruction. The origin of the human race is a hypothesis of this sort, since hard data is virtually nonexistent.

In a perverse way which frustrates conservative scientists, the preceding premises will alter the balance of proof fundamentally in numerous cases of research on the frontiers of science, where inadequate data exists. This is because a cataclysm or other extraordinary event will often suffice to explain a multitude of phenomena, all of which would otherwise require individual causes and explanations. This is sometimes referred to as "catastrophe theory."

The case in point is the origin of the human race. By either Von Daniken's approach or by Sitchin's, Occam's Razor argues that the single hypothesis of earlier contact with extraterrestrials to explain the wonders of the ancient world and the remarkable agreement among ancient texts in speaking of visitations by "the gods" should be preferred to the multitude of separate and ad hoc explanations others have offered. If mainstream science were not so preoccupied with avoiding extraordinary hypotheses, it would surely be agreed by most parties that the evidence, severely lacking though it is, mildly favors the extraterrestrial visitation hypothesis over most others. However, it cannot be argued that the evidence is anything approaching compelling, especially since it is all indirect (i.e., no definite extraterrestrial artifacts have been found). And since the hypothesis is certainly extraordinary, science prefers to reject it until and unless some extraordinary proof comes along.

But what if the hypothesis were true, but most of the evidence has been destroyed? I wish to argue for the legitimacy of accepting such hypotheses for serious consideration on the basis of preponderance of evidence, even though the idea is extraordinary and the evidence far from conclusive. In other words, I am arguing for the admittance of a body of "tentative" knowledge to mainstream science, labelled as such, which has some lower than usual probability of correctness attached to it, or some ambiguity of interpretation. And, I contend, the benefit of so doing will be a more rapid advance of science, because the truly significant breakthroughs will often be represented among these tentatively accepted hypotheses. We would not call such ideas "facts," as we tend to do with conventional theories. Instead we would refer to them simply as hypotheses under investigation, having both supporting and contrary arguments. It does not threaten the integrity of science to state that among other hypotheses under consideration for the origin of man is the possible intervention of extraterrestrials. The pro and con arguments would make interesting reading for all. And the hypothesis does make testable predictions, some of which we examined in the chapter "The Origins of the Solar System and of Man." Why should it be disreputable to engage in such a discussion?!

Catastrophe Theory

The most elegant example I have encountered to illustrate catastrophe theory as applied to the advancement of knowledge (and by extension, to other areas as well) is based on a mathematical analogy first brought to my attention by S.V.M. Clube. Imagine that we are making observations of some phenomenon. When the phenomenon is first discovered, nothing is known about how it changes with time, so let's represent a quantitative measure of its magnitude by the constant 1. Later, a change is perceived as a function of some independent variable x (perhaps the time; let x be measured in units such that it is a fraction less than 1). We then represent the phenomenon by the expression $(1 + x)$, and make predictions of its future behavior from this "theory." Still later we detect some deviation from our predictions, which remains mysterious until one day a learned scientist discovers that the deviations can be represented by a quadratic term, and that the corrected "true" theory should be $(1 + x + x^2)$.

After much time elapses, new discordances with the observations (the existence of which are at first denied) become too great to ignore. Yet another learned person investigates the problem and discovers a cubic term. The theory $(1 + x + x^2 + x^3)$ now represents the observations so well that the validity of the new theory cannot be denied by "reasonable" men, and it soon replaces the old theory in all the textbooks. The process may continue indefinitely, perhaps spanning generations of learned researchers, each adding his own significant new refinement, as important in his time as was his predecessors'. The theory becomes ever so complex: $(1+x+x^2+x^3+x^4+x^5+\dots)$. Though all students learn how to make correct calculations with the theory, only a few minds fully understand it.

Of course, it never succeeds in making correct predictions very far outside the domain of the observations used to formulate the theory.

Then one day, a radical scientist, reasoning from an entirely different perspective thought to be irrelevant, makes a startling suggestion: the real theory for the phenomenon is $[1/(1-x)]$. The new theory looks nothing like the old one and makes radically different predictions about the expected ultimate behavior of the phenomenon far from the domain of the observations, so it is not given serious attention. It may even be forgotten altogether and have to be rediscovered many times. One day, however, a compelling fact forces a confrontation: the radical new theory continues to represent the observations better than the old theory, however many terms are patched onto the old one. In fact, it passes the most important tests of any radical new hypothesis: it has correctly predicted the future when other theories failed, while adding insight and understanding of the phenomena.

Once this is realized, the entire body of science based on the old theory may be overthrown. The discoverer of each new power of x in the old theory is lowered in prestige by the revolution. Textbooks must be rewritten. Whole fields of investigation based on the old theory become obsolete. All the consequences of the new theory must be carefully redeveloped from first principles. Scientists are not at all pleased by these developments (except young, new ones, who have no vested interest in either the correctness of the old theory or in its application), but eventually, the last of the discontented "old-timers" dies off. Then it becomes difficult to imagine a time when it wasn't obvious that such a well-known phenomenon can be predicted so accurately in such a simple way.

I refer to the discovery of each new term in the old theory as ordinary scientific progress. I call the discovery of the new theory a "revolution" or "catastrophe" of knowledge. Nothing about scientific progress demands that the revolution ever occur. Ordinary scientific progress may continue, quite literally, forever (through an infinite number of powers of x). But if a catastrophe of knowledge does occur, it makes obsolete most of what has gone on before it, however many "powers of x" may have been added.

> "Censorship is the only form of Obscenity. (Wait, I forgot government tobacco subsidies...)"
> —Tom Horsley

And so it is, I strongly suspect, with all human affairs, wherever evolution is operative.

Scientific Arrogance

There is one last point of considerable importance to this whole topic of the advancement of knowledge and the issue of evolution versus revolution: I call it the *arrogance* issue.

Everyone who would espouse an extraordinary idea and take unilateral action based upon his own belief that what he does is good is acting arrogantly; and most of the time, the rest of us wish to be spared from the "good" such a person thrusts upon us. So when are such actions justifiable, if ever? Scientifically, is it ever justifiable for a man to conclude that he is correct and everyone else who doesn't agree with him is wrong?

Individuals can deceive themselves almost without limitation. But it is possible to "reality test" and tell the difference between self-deception and improbable reality. In fact I have mentioned cases in this book where the universal opinion of relevant authorities is almost certainly wrong. Now let me review one case where I am confident that I am correct, against the opinion of almost all authorities in a particular field, and why I think such a conclusion is supportable by objective criteria.

In brief, I maintain that there is only one reality; and to know it, one must objectively test reality. Such a test must distinguish the truth of the hypothesis one is testing from the condition that it is false; and both results must be *possible* results of the test—i.e., the hypothesis must be falsifiable. One might add the further condi-

378

tions that in order for a hypothesis (whether true or false) to have value, it must aid understanding and be able to predict things not already known.

My example is the nature of comets, discussed in detail in the chapter "Do Comets Have Satellites?" The first distinguishing characteristic of comets is the appearance of a "coma," or bright area, usually accompanied by a tail, always pointing away from the Sun. Astronomers trying to explain comas and tails finally settled on Whipple's "icy conglomerate" model, in which frozen water and other volatiles are heated as they approached the Sun and driven off the nucleus. It was expected that comets therefore reflected most of the light that hit them from the Sun, as ice and frozen volatiles would do. But it was then discovered that the material of comets reflects very little light, being in fact darker than coal dust.

So the theory was amended to accommodate that observed fact, and comets became known as "dirty snowballs." But then it became known that "new" comets (approaching close to the Sun for the first time) lost an order of magnitude in brightness in doing so; whereas comets making their second or later approach had no detectable further changes in brightness. The theory did not anticipate this development but could accommodate it: comets must be dirty snowballs which underwent extensive surface melting on their first approach to the Sun, then froze into a hard "crust" as the comet receded, thereby preventing such extensive further losses on subsequent passes.

When it was observed that comets sometimes split, it was concluded that comets have very low internal strengths, are quite fluffy, and fall apart easily. Still more recently, comet expert Zdenek Sekanina, analyzing the way in which comets appear to yield so easily to the relatively gentle solar radiation pressure, undergoing significant non-gravitational accelerations away from the Sun, concluded that comets were more like dirty, "flat, fluffy pancakes!" When other observations suggested more normal densities, there was discussion of violent internal processes in comets, and strong outgassing jets were invoked.

All these conclusions were derived from the observational data and seemed compelling to the authors at the time they were proposed. Concerning the nature of comets, this is what I mean by

$(1 + x + x^2 + x^3 + x^4 + x^5 + \ldots)$ in the mathematical analogy: the theory keeps getting patched to accommodate new data, no matter how intrinsically clumsy or absurd the model becomes.

This illustrates the general hazard of reasoning inductively. There are sometimes many causes that can produce the same effect. By examining the effect, we are led to guess what seems the most probable cause. But if the effect happened to be produced by some other cause, we may be unable to reason backwards to derive that fact. It is an unpleasant reality that inductive reasoning from effect to cause will sometimes appear to be unique when in fact it is not at all so.

The Intrinsic Value of Deductive Theories

Forward reasoning, by contrast, is not subject to that hazard. Time behaves like a non-reversible dimension, and cause-effect relationships always proceed in forward time; hence deductions that proceed in the same direction as time are potentially unique.

I do not see how one could easily have reasoned inductively to the satellite model for the nature of comets from the observational data available. But when the idea that comets are multiple-body gravitationally bound systems proposed itself as a corollary of the "exploding planet" hypothesis[d] and from the observations that minor planets have satellites, it became possible to derive the logical consequences which would follow from such a comet model using forward reasoning. Let us see how well these hypothetical consequences fit the data.

As discussed in the chapter "Do Comets Have Satellites?" the gravitational sphere of influence of a comet, within which it holds satellites stably bound, increases in size as the comet recedes from the Sun, and decreases as the comet approaches the Sun. The gravitationally bound cluster of bodies, complete with gas and dust, would appear as a "coma" around a central dominant body, or

---

[d]The value of any hypothesis must be judged by the predictions it makes. If the satellite model for comets is ultimately confirmed in its essentials, then the "exploding planet" hypothesis which predicted that model will have accrued additional credit.

"nucleus." Solar radiation pressure would drive some of the gas and dust away from the Sun, forming a tail. But the material is not required to come from the surface of the nucleus; rather, it may already be orbiting the nucleus or residing on very small bodies in orbit, and can easily be pushed to the threshold of escape.

Since comets in this model are made of carbonaceous rock, just like the minor planets, we expect that comets will reflect very little of the light that hits them, just as for minor planets. The first time the comet comes near the Sun, its sphere of influence is forced to shrink in size to a new minimum, which in turn forces much orbiting coma material to undergo gravitational escape, leaving the vicinity of the nucleus forever. But on subsequent returns, the comet would have no further losses of material so extensive, since the minimum size reached by the sphere of influence would be essentially the same as that reached on the first approach. These natural descriptions of comets derived from the satellite model happen to also be just what we observe.

In the satellite model, satellites can escape from the nucleus, primarily through the action of tidal forces, but only while the sphere of influence is shrinking as the comet approaches the Sun. This is in agreement with observations of what are called "splits" of comets. In the satellite model, the entire surface area of the coma feels the effects of solar radiation pressure, so accelerations away from the Sun are relatively large, even though the densities of the constituent orbiting bodies are those appropriate to rock.

The essence of the new model is the presence of satellites of significant mass orbiting the nucleus of all comets and comprising the coma. The essence of the old model is that all the mass is concentrated in the primary nucleus, which is the source of the gas and dust in the coma.

This new satellite model is the $[1 / (1 - x)]$ in the mathematical analogy: a revolutionary way of looking at the same data that fits as just well but which makes drastically different predictions about the nature and evolution of comets. For example, this model predicts a relationship between velocity and solar distance for components of split comets that is quite different from the prediction of the dirty-snowball model in any of its current variations. In fact, the observations have shown that the prediction of the satellite model is correct, and that of the dirty-snowball model is wrong. Other examples of successful predictions are given in the chapters about comets.

At this moment, I am not trying to argue again that the satellite model is correct and the dirty-snowball model wrong. I was discussing "reality testing" of ideas, using this as an example. The satellite model of comets makes a number of specific, a priori predictions about the nature of comets which happen to be an almost exact description of what is known about comets from observational data. None of these observed characteristics were predicted by the dirty-snowball model; instead, that model was patched after the fact to accommodate them. A specific prediction that could distinguish the two models was made. A failure of the prediction would have falsified the satellite model. The observational data strongly agreed with the satellite model prediction and disagreed with the dirty-snowball prediction. Moreover, the satellite model has already been successful at predicting other comet phenomena which were previously unknown.

I submit that these criteria, carefully and objectively applied, are both necessary and sufficient to conclude that an idea is correct and has merit, regardless of the strengths of opinions or numbers of authorities who oppose the idea. Naturally it is implied in the testing procedure that those authorities have also had a chance to consider the idea and to make their best arguments why it isn't so. If no substantive counter-arguments appear, I submit that it is not at all *arrogant* to conclude that one's own reasoning is correct and almost everyone else's is incorrect; rather, it is logically compelling.

The chapter "A Synthesis of Evidence for a Recent Planetary Breakup" provides yet another example. With so much evidence favoring the breakup theory, I am not at all embarrassed to advocate it, despite the almost universal opposition it has received from colleagues, largely because it is an extraordinary hypothesis. Of course, it is not quantity of evidence that counts, but quality; but on that point also, the evidence is excellent. Looking at that evidence as objectively as possible, I have simply concluded that it is more probable that the judgment of most of the world's experts is wrong, than that I have been deceived by the evidence. Each reader, including those same world experts, must of course make that judgment anew for him- or herself after reading this book.

Having the courage of one's own convictions is the opposite of succumbing to peer pressure. Someone who appreciates the fallibility of human reasoning but nonetheless applies the Scientific Method with brutal objectivity and lets the results speak for themselves has nothing to fear from the judgments of peers, or of history. Only those who fail to recognize reality for what it is, and instead try to tell reality what it must be, need fear that judgment.

We have all experienced at one time or another an inspiration or a flash of insight. A scientist regularly comes up with inspired ideas in connection with whatever problem he is working on. He carefully examines each of these against the data or an experiment and determines which ideas work out and which must be discarded. Almost all scientists have learned to live with the disappointment that follows when a particularly excellent idea proves unworkable.

But they also know the joy of seeing an idea work well, even beyond the scope of what it was supposed to do. Such joy may be experienced when one comes upon a good starting point for a deductive model. By its nature, the deductive theory usually has little or no latitude. Its conclusions are predetermined by the starting point and the rules of logic. When such a model has a motivation other than the observations, and predicts and explains all the significant independent facts in a logically compelling way with no loose ends, and provides a new, simpler understanding of a phenomenon than anyone has previously elaborated, and when discussion before experts turns up no fatal flaws of logic or oversights of fact, one may hold to and use the model with a confidence that cannot compare with the assurances of numerous world experts that some other model is "the correct one."

The "exploded planet" hypothesis was such a model for me. When I read of the idea in Ovenden's papers, I was certain that applying it deductively would soon lead to contradictions with observations, as deductions from a bad starting point invariably do. But one of its first deductions was a new, plausible explanation for the origin of the logically absurd "Oort cloud" of comets. It made so much more sense than the conventional theory that I immediately knew the model had some merit. But then the model made prediction after successful prediction, offering new explanations for so many disparate phenomena throughout the solar system (as summarized in the chapter "A Synthesis of Recent Planetary Breakup Evidence"). It eventually became inconceivable to me that the model could be fundamentally wrong, no matter how many colleagues withheld their approval even after their objections were answered.

The promise of the extended Scientific Method recommended here is that we are more likely to arrive at true descriptions of reality by accepting tentative hypotheses and using deductive reasoning than by polling the authorities on these subjects. That is itself a theory to be verified, but with the potential rewards so great, no time should be lost in experimenting with it!

I conclude with a question that is a challenge to every reader, and to every person who seeks the advancement of human wisdom. In his five books discussing literal translations of the most ancient surviving texts,[172] Sitchin discusses how the extraterrestrial "gods" who engineered the human race as slave labor became alarmed at the imitativeness and inventiveness of humans. One of them is alleged to have bemoaned that nothing seemed beyond the capabilities of the humans, and that if left unchecked, someday the distinction between the "gods" and the humans would disappear. (The Bible story of the "Tower of Babel" is a conventional translation of later renderings of the same texts.) To prevent this merging, the superior beings planned deliberately to interfere with the advancement of the human race. One of the steps they supposedly took was the partitioning of the species into segregated groups dispersed over the continents, each with a different language to inhibit communication among them.

Just now, at the end of the twentieth century A.D., humans have made serious strides in finally overcoming the handicap of partitioning by continents and languages, however that circumstance came about. Advanced communications and networking are accelerating the pace of discovery and advancement globally. It might be argued that the largest remaining impediments to progress are the presence of false hypotheses within our collective body of knowledge, and the resistance to change on the part of many humans.

The presence of false extraordinary hypotheses is a problem exacerbated by the overly credulous. Such people have little influence on others, but the bad name they give to extraordinary hypotheses is harmful. At the other extreme, most of us have experienced the frustration of dealing with humans who resist knowledge, progress, new ideas, or change. I carefully distinguish this emotional resistance from healthy scientific skepticism, although the former often masquerades as the latter. The skeptic must ask himself, given reasonable evidence for an unlikely thesis, if this skepticism would disappear willingly, or if he will experience emotional resistance to its departure.

Consider the thesis that the tendency to engage in such counterproductive behavior (excessive skepticism and excessive credulity) was genetically inbred into the human race by the hypothetical "gods" to further slow human progress. An insidious idea, but potentially very, very effective! Suppose we learned that it was true. How would we respond?

Well, shouldn't we respond that way, anyway?!

Epilogue

● ●

Calela and her father arrived home. Calela's mother, Jorelle, had not gone to the royal hall because she had no patience with the notions of scientists. "I never understand the things that scientists say," she had commented, "so I pay them no mind." But Calela knew that her mother was wise in her own way. She had learned to trust her mother's judgment implicitly.

Calela excitedly began to relate to her mother all that she had seen and heard. When she came to the part about light, she explained that light seemed to behave like waves when it propagated. "Ah, then it must propagate through a medium. Even I know that waves are just the disturbance of a medium," Jorelle said.

Calela thought it best to explain to her mother the part about space and time, and how masses curve space and slow time. She began, "Well, did you know that light passing by a mass bends its path and travels more slowly?"

Jorelle immediately retorted, "I am not completely ignorant on these matters, Calela. You say light behaves like waves, so it must be propagating through a medium. Any mass has gravity, which would increase the density of the nearby medium. When the density of a medium increases, waves traveling through it will bend their paths and slow their speed."

"But part of the puzzle is that no such medium has ever been found," Calela responded slowly, as she reflected on the simple truth her mother had just spoken.

"No one has seen the wind, but all feel its force on their faces while standing at the top of a hill," Jorelle explained. "So why should it be necessary to see this light-carrying medium, if one sees all its effects?"

Now Calela suddenly realized what truly made light special. "But for light, the speed of the wave is not changed by the speed of its source. In fact, the speed of light is the same for all observers, no matter how fast or what direction they move in."

But Jorelle was not impressed by this revelation. "And so it would be for any wave in any medium, if one uses only waves of various types in that medium for measurement," Jorelle answered.

Calela thought it best to skip ahead to the main point of the revelation she had heard earlier that day. She patiently explained, "But the great sage, the wisest of all the scientists, has told us that space and time themselves are changed by the presence of masses. And this is why light propagates in such a peculiar way."

Jorelle, sensing a return of the frustration she always felt when trying to understand the pronouncements of scientists, exclaimed, "Well, you haven't yet told me anything about light that seems the least bit peculiar, since masses would change any nearby medium so as to make it appear that way. But about this scientist you call the 'great sage,' who says that space and time must themselves be changed...." Pausing reflectively for a moment, she continued, "Such a man must be blind."

Glossary

• •

(Note: Italic words in definitions are themselves defined in this Glossary.)

A Priori: "Before the fact." In science, a condition that is set before the results of some test or observation are known.

Aberration: A change in the apparent source direction of starlight by virtue of the velocity of the *Earth* (or by motion of the observer in general). Analogous to vertical raindrops seeming to stream at a slanted angle on the window of a moving train.

Accretion: The assimilation of a smaller mass by a larger one through collision.

Ad Hoc: For the particular case, not the general one. Often used in the sense of "after the fact" (opposite of a priori). In science, a condition that is set after the results of some test or observation are known.

Aether: Hypothetical medium pervading the universe through which light propagates, giving light its wave properties. As usually understood, the existence of an aether would provide a standard of rest for all moving bodies.

Albedo: A measure of the reflectivity of a body. The percentage of the light hitting a body that is immediately reflected back into space. The rest is absorbed, and usually re-radiated later at *Infrared Wavelengths* as heat.

Angstrom: A unit of length equal to 10^{-10} meters $= 10^{-8}$ cm. Used primarily to measure the Wavelengths of *Photons* of visible light.

Angular Momentum: A measure of the "energy" one body has relative to the line joining it to a second body. Technically, the product of the mass, tangential velocity, and distance of one body relative to another. It can be in the form of spin or orbital angular energy, i.e., *Rotation* or *Revolution.*

Antimatter: Particles with the same mass but opposite charge as their matter equivalents. When matter and antimatter meet, they annihilate into pure energy.

Aphelion: The point in a planetary orbit farthest from the *Sun.* (Farthest from *Earth* = "apogee"; farthest from a general body = "apocenter.")

Aquarius: Constellation of the *Zodiac,* the "water carrier," south of the equator.

Ariel: Innermost of the set of four large moons of *Uranus.*

Asteroid: Synonym for *Minor Planet.* A type of small body on a planetary orbit about the *Sun,* usually found in the asteroid belt, which is a collection of these debris-like objects between *Mars* and *Jupiter* in a gap where one would expect to find a *Major Planet.*

Astronomical Unit: The average distance from the *Earth* to the *Sun,* 149,597,900 kilometers (about 93,000,000 miles). Used as a unit for measuring other distances in our solar system. Abbreviated "au."

Baryon: A class of fundamental atomic particles of matter which includes protons and neutrons.

Betulia: A *Minor Planet* with a peculiar light curve.

Big Bang: A theory of the origin of the universe, based on the apparent expansion of the universe. It is assumed that all matter was collected together in an infinitesimal point before there was space or time. It suddenly exploded to form space and start time, and to fill the universe with the matter we now observe. The theory is derived from the redshifts of galaxies, which are assumed to be proportional to their velocities of recession.

Black Axiom: The hypothesis that all atmosphereless bodies in the outer solar system that rotate more slowly than one month will be coated on one side with extremely dark carbonaceous material from a breakup event in the *Asteroid* belt. *Iapetus* is the most outstanding example.

Black Hole: A theoretical object, usually a former giant star that has collapsed. If the star is massive enough, after collapse it becomes so compact that escape velocity from its surface is greater than the speed of light. Since not even light can escape from it, it cannot be seen; hence, "black." When the giant star collapses, its own self-gravitation becomes stronger and stronger, until it exceeds the strength of any known substance to resist further collapse. The collapse continues until the object is infinitely small and has no dimensions; hence, "hole." Such objects are not definitely known to exist, but their existence is widely assumed. This book challenges that assumption.

Bubbles: A feature of the structure of the universe. Galaxies are organized into clusters, which are organized into superclusters. Superclusters of galaxies seem to appear only on the surfaces of "bubbles" in space, with voids in their centers. More recent data suggest this structure is more like waves than bubbles.

Callisto: Outermost of the set of four large moons of *Jupiter,* called the Galilean *Satellites* after their discoverer.

Catastrophe Theory: In general, the idea that evolution occurs primarily as the result of discrete, traumatic events rather then through continuous small changes. Here, the idea that important bodies of knowledge ("paradigms") evolve without constant re-examination of the hypotheses on which they are built, departing ever more from reality as time goes on until some "revolution" occurs in which entire models are replaced. The old, false models are often retained well beyond their useful time because the nominal authorities in fields interpret new data with *Ad Hoc* modifications to the existing paradigm, and tend to ignore or resist evidence for alternative models, whether it comes from sources inside or outside their own field. See the "Introduction" for a description of the five stages of evolution of a scientific paradigm — learning, disputation, reaffirmation, crisis, and resolution.

Ceres: Largest *Minor Planet,* 1000 kilometers in diameter. Contains somewhat more mass than the rest of the minor planets put together — about 0.001 of the *Earth's* mass.

Charon: Only known *Satellite* of *Pluto,* discovered by Jim Christy at the U.S. Naval Observatory in 1978.

Chiron: Comet-like *Asteroidal* object orbiting primarily between *Saturn* and *Uranus* in a solar orbit that crosses the orbits of both these planets. Because of frequent close planetary encounters, its orbit is unstable and could not have been like this for more than about a million years.

Coma: Atmosphere-like glow around the nucleus of a *Comet,* consisting of gas and dust particles. Visible by reflected sunlight. May also contain *Satellites.*

Comet: Small solar system body distinguished by presence of a Coma, usually with a tail of particles pointing away from the *Sun* and escaping the coma because of radiation pressure. Orbits are usually highly eccentric, with many comets (called "new") coming from distances of about 40,000 astronomical units from the *Sun.* Do not confuse with *Meteor.*

Comet Encke: Comet of shortest known period, 3.3 years. Observed on more returns than any other comet.

Comet Halley: Most famous of all *Comets* because of its brightness and regular 75-year visits near the *Earth's* orbit. Crosses *Neptune's* orbit at *Aphelion,* and *Mercury's* orbit at *Perihelion.*

Constellation: A grouping of stars. Eighty-eight are officially recognized. Grouped by the Greeks and Romans and named after figures they appear to resemble.

Cosmic Microwave Radiation: In the *Big Bang* theory, the remnant of the fireball from the original explosion that formed our universe; hence, the most distant radiation detectable from the universe. Actually a continuous unresolved radiation from all directions on the sky, distance unknown. Its intensity at different *Wavelengths* varies like that from a Black Body, i.e., a perfect radiator of energy.

Cosmic Rays: Extremely high-energy *Photons* or atomic nuclei or sub-atomic particles of matter or *Antimatter.* See also *Electromagnetic Spectrum.*

Cydonia: A desert region in the northern hemisphere of *Mars* (near latitude 40 degrees) which contains some unusual terrain features with a somewhat "artificial" appearance. Includes a "face" and "pyramid." Some persons have suggested that these features are what they appear to be and were built by extraterrestrials.

Cygnus: A *Constellation* in the northern hemisphere, "the swan," with brightest star named *Deneb.*

D'Arrest: A *Comet* with a well-observed and highly unusual light curve (variations in brightness as it rotates).

Dark Matter: Invisible matter inside and outside *Galaxies,* hypothesized to exist because galaxies appear to have stronger gravity fields than can be accounted for by their visible matter. Dark matter neither emits not absorbs *Photons* at any *Wavelength.* It is required to be the dominant ingredient of the universe, yet cannot be made of ordinary *Baryons.* In the *Meta Model,* the required finite range for the force of gravity explains the behavior of galaxies and eliminates the need to hypothesize dark matter.

Deimos: Outermost of a pair of tiny *Martian* moons that appear to be captured *Asteroids.*

Deneb: Brightest star in the *Constellation* of *Cygnus,* "the swan." One of the 20 brightest stars in the sky.

Dione: Middle *Satellite* of *Saturn* with orbit between satellites *Tethys* and *Rhea.*

Dwarf Star: Member of the smallest and most common class of stars by mass. Our *Sun* is a dwarf star.

Earth: Third *Major Planet* out from the *Sun,* having one large *Satellite,* the *Moon.*

Eccentricity: Ellipticity, or egg-shaped quality, of an orbit. Zero eccentricity indicates a circle; $0 - 1$ indicates an ellipse;

eccentricity = 1 indicates an "infinite ellipse," or parabola. Eccentricities above 1 refer to hyperbolic orbits.

Eclipse: The passage of one dark celestial body in front of a brighter one with smaller angular diameter, or the passage of one body into the shadow of another. In a "total eclipse," the light from the body is totally cut off. Eclipses of the *Moon* (when it goes into the *Earth's* shadow) and of the Sun (blocked by the Moon) are the most familiar.

Ecliptic: The plane of the *Earth's* orbit. Hence the path through the sky followed by the apparent motion of the *Sun,* and approximately also by the *Moon* and *Major Planets.*

Electromagnetic Spectrum: The full range of possible energies or *Wavelengths* of *Photons.* The borders between different parts of the spectrum are loosely defined and slightly overlapping. Visible light refers to wavelengths between 3,000 and 10,000 *Angstroms.* Moving down in energy, *Infrared* light refers to wavelengths between 10,000 Angstroms (= 1 micron) and 1000 microns (= 1 millimeter). Microwave photons lie between 1 mm and 10 cm. Radio waves lie between 10 cm and 10 meters. Infraradio refers to everything beyond radio wavelengths, which generally has too little energy to be observable. Moving upward in energy from visible light, the ultraviolet lies between 3000 Angstroms and 100 Angstroms, with the extreme ultraviolet being the portion from 1000 to 100 Angstroms. Soft X-rays cover the energy range from 80 electron volts (corresponding to 155 Angstroms) to 3000 eV. Hard X-rays lie between 3 keV and 100 keV. Gamma rays lie between wavelengths of 0.1 and 200 MeV. Anything more energetic is classified under the broad heading of *Cosmic Rays.* Only energies up to the laboratory limit of about 10^7 MeV can be usefully studied.

Electron Volt: A unit of energy equal to 1.60×10^{-12} *Erg.* For *Photons, Wavelength* in *Angstroms* equals 12,400 divided by energy in electron volts. Abbreviations: eV = electron volt; keV = 1000 eV; MeV = 10^6 eV.

Enceladus: Inner *Satellite* of *Saturn* with orbit between satellites *Mimas* and *Tethys.*

Entropy: A measure of the degree of disorder in the motions of a large number of particles. Usually applied to gases. In classical physics, the entropy or disorder of the universe must progressively increase. In the Meta Model, gravitational entropy tends to decrease, and the entropy of the universe over all scales is conserved.

Erg: A unit of energy. A mass of one gram moving 1 cm/s has an energy from its motion of 0.5 erg.

Escape Velocity: Minimum velocity required to leave the *Sphere of Influence* of a gravitating mass.

Europa: Second large Galilean moon of *Jupiter,* with orbit between moons *Io* and *Ganymede.*

Explosion Signature: A characteristic of the distribution of the orbits of fragments from an explosion, which exists because all fragment orbits originated at one point at one time.

Fireball: An unusually bright *Meteor* in the *Earth's* atmosphere, usually leaving a trail. Must be brighter than a full *Moon* to receive this classification.

Fission: The breaking apart of a body into two or more fragments. The opposite of "fusion."

Foucault Pendulum: A long, nearly frictionless pendulum, often seen in museums, demonstrating the *Earth's* rotation. The pendulum tries to swing in the same plane in space while the Earth rotates beneath it. The result is that the pendulum swings in a plane which appears to an Earth observer to rotate slowly as the Earth turns beneath it.

Galaxy: A huge, flattened collection of gravitationally bound stars and clusters of stars. Our *Sun* is in the "Milky Way" galaxy.

Gamma Rays: Very high-energy *Photons.* See *Electromagnetic Spectrum.*

Ganymede: Third large Galilean moon of *Jupiter,* with orbit between moons *Europa* and *Callisto.*

Gemini: Constellation of the *Zodiac* in the northern sky, "the twins," with bright stars Castor and Pollux.

General Relativity: Einstein's theory of gravitation that calls for small corrections to Newton's Universal Law of Gravitation, of importance near large masses or for rapidly moving masses. Its largest effect in the solar system is to cause the *Perihelion* of the orbit of *Mercury* to slowly change its direction.

Globular Cluster: A compact cluster consisting of 10,000 to more than 1,000,000 stars. Often found in a spherical "halo" surrounding the central regions of a *Galaxy.*

Gravitational Mass: A measure of the mass of a body through the strength of its external gravity field. Contrasted with *Inertial Mass.*

Gravitational Screen Capture: A process whereby a planet captures moons from the breakup of a more distant mass. It first captures smaller fragments which graze the planet's atmosphere into temporary orbits. Larger fragments arriving later collide with these smaller fragments and are captured permanently.

Graviton: A hypothetical ultra-small particle representing a unit of gravitation. In standard quantum physics, the carrier of the gravitational force having a spin of measure two. In the *Meta Model,* gravitation is caused by the pressure of impact from a universe filled with classical particles called "C-gravitons" (CGs) to distinguish them.

Great Dark Spot: A large, darkish spot in *Neptune's* southern hemisphere, similar to *Jupiter's Great Red Spot* but with "lenticular" (stationary) clouds over its edges at times.

Great Red Spot: A large, reddish spot in *Jupiter's* southern hemisphere, usually described as a "giant hurricane" which has lasted at least since telescopes were invented three centuries ago. Here proposed to be the impact residue from a planet-sized mass.

Hubble Age: The supposed "age of the universe," representing the time since the hypothetical *Big Bang* for the universe to reach its present state, given the observed rate of apparent expansion.

Hubble Expansion: The apparent expansion of the universe, as inferred from the *Redshifts* of *Galaxies* — generally, the more distant the galaxy, the greater the redshift (and therefore the inferred velocity of recession).

Hyperion: Outer, irregularly shaped *Satellite* of *Saturn,* orbiting between satellites *Titan* and *Iapetus.*

Iapetus: Outer *Satellite* of *Saturn,* orbiting between *Hyperion* and *Phoebe,* having a relatively long orbital period and slow rotation (both 79 days long). Outstanding characteristic is one icy-bright and one coal-dark hemisphere.

Inclination: The angle of tilt of the plane of an orbit to a reference plane such as the plane of the *Earth's* orbit (the *Ecliptic*).

Inertia: The property of all bodies to remain at rest or in uniform motion until an external force is applied.

Inertial Mass: A measure of the mass of a body from its resistance to acceleration when a given force is applied. Contrasted with Gravitational Mass.

Infrared: A part of the spectrum where *Photons* have less energy (longer *Wavelength*) than visible light, yet more energy than microwaves. Often equated with heat, since objects warmed by stars usually re-radiate that heat into space at infrared wavelengths. See also Electromagnetic Spectrum.

Io: Innermost large Galilean moon of *Jupiter,* orbiting inside moon Europa, with active volcanism on its surface.

Jupiter: Largest *Major Planet,* fifth out from the *Sun,* with four large Galilean moons: *Io, Europa, Ganymede, Callisto;* plus numerous smaller *Asteroidal* moons, and some faint, dark rings.

Kinetic Energy: The energy of a mass by virtue of its motion. Proportional to mass times velocity squared. See also *Potential Energy.*

Kirkwood Gaps: Gaps in the distribution of the mean distances of *Asteroids.* The largest of these occurs at an asteroid period of half of *Jupiter's* period of revolution around the *Sun.*

Kreutz: The name of a family of related *Comets* on similar orbits, members of which show up from time to time, all of which are *Sun-Grazing;* i.e., they pass very close to the Sun's surface and are sometimes consumed in the process.

Lagrangian Point: One of five so-called "equilibrium points" near the orbit of a planet or *Satellite.* A particle placed at one of these points, which all move with the planet or satellite, would stay there indefinitely. Only two of them, the ones in the planet's or satellite's orbit that lead and trail by 60 degrees, are stable. The other three are on the line joining the planet or satellite to its parent (e.g. the *Sun*) and are unstable. The "inner" *Lagrangian Point* provides the easiest pathway to capture or escape from the *Sphere of Influence* of the planet or satellite.

Leonid Meteors: A famous *Meteor* shower, visible annually in November. Associated with the breakup of a *Comet* on an orbit with a period of 33 years. Has been known to provide the most spectacular meteor showers (called "meteor storms") in recorded history. Meteor storms occurred in 1833 and 1866, and again in 1966; so the 1999 shower is eagerly awaited.

Light-Carrying Medium: The hypothetical medium pervading space through which light propagates, as required by the *Meta Model.* It must be continuous (like an ocean), and its density must be altered by the presence of nearby mass.

Lightspeed: The speed of light, about 300,000 km/s, or from the *Sun* to the next nearest star in about four years. According to *Special Relativity* theory, no material body can travel faster than light.

Lightyear: The distance light travels in one year. This is about 10^{13} km, or slightly more than the distance to the hypothetical *Oort Cloud* of *Comets.* The nearest star other than our own *Sun* is about four lightyears away.

Libration: The to-and-fro swing of one body in the gravitational field of another. Can be applied to rotation or revolution. If the *Moon's* rotational lock with the *Earth* (keeping the same side toward us) were disturbed, the Moon's rotation would librate freely, just as it now undergoes a small "forced" libration due to the *Eccentricity* and *Inclination* of the Moon's orbit. Trojan *Asteroids* in *Jupiter's* orbit librate orbitally, keeping their same average distance from Jupiter (either ahead of or behind it).

Major Planet: One of the nine "large" planets of the *Sun. Pluto* was given this designation before it was found to be so small. *Mars:* Fourth *Major Planet* out from the *Sun,* with two small *Asteroidal* moons, *Phobos* and *Deimos.*

Mascons: Short for "mass concentrations." Coined for regions of extra mass found in association with the "mare" (dark "seas" of solidified lava) on the *Moon.*

Matter Ingredient: A hypothetical particle of the *Meta Model.* The smallest constituent of matter which is impervious to penetration by C-*Gravitons.*

Mercury: Innermost *Major Planet* of the *Sun,* no known moons.

Meta Model: A new cosmological model of the universe, arrived at deductively, in which the universe is infinite in five dimensions and filled with substance at all scales. In it, gravitation produces the *Redshift* of *Galaxies,* is limited in range, and is produced by the pushing action of tiny agents on matter.

Meteor: Fragment of space debris entering the *Earth's* atmosphere and burning up. Seems to flash across the sky in seconds.

Meteorite: A *Meteor* which partially survives burning up in the Earth's atmosphere and reaches the ground.

Meteoroid: A small, potential *Meteor,* still in orbit around the *Sun.*

Micron: A unit of length equal to 10^{-6} meters $= 10^{-4}$ cm. Used primarily to measure the *Wavelengths* of *Photons* of *Infrared* light. One micron $= 10,000$ *Angstroms.*

Mimas: Inner *Satellite* of *Saturn,* orbiting inside *Enceladus. Voyager* has discovered other moons orbiting still closer to Saturn.

Minor Planet: Synonym for *Asteroid.* Small solar system body orbiting the *Sun* in a planetary orbit. Most are concentrated in the gap between *Mars* and *Jupiter.*

Minor Satellite: Satellite of a *Minor Planet,* or of any other small solar system body (e.g. *Comets, Meteoroids*).

Miranda: Small moon of *Uranus,* interior to *Ariel.*

Moon: The only natural *Satellite* of the *Earth.* Generically, a satellite of any other body.

Neptune: The eighth *Major Planet* out from the *Sun.* Best known moons are *Triton* and *Nereid,* but *Voyager* has found several other small inner moons and rings.

Nereid: Outermost *Satellite* of *Neptune,* in a highly eccentric orbit, near the threshold of escape. It has one dark and one bright hemisphere. *Neutrino:* Elementary particle with little or no mass which can readily pass through solid bodies such as the *Earth.* One source should be the *Sun's* deep interior, but the observed flux coming from the Sun is only about one third of the predicted amount.

Nova: The explosion of an ordinary star.

Nucleus: The hypothetical center of a *Comet* and source of the *Coma* and *Tail* particles.

Oberon: Outermost large moon of *Uranus,* exterior to the orbit of *Titania.*

Oblate: Flattened at the poles and bulging all around the equator from spin. See also *Prolate.*

Occam's Razor: A tenet of ordinary *Scientific Method,* "Invent no unnecessary hypotheses"; often mistaken to mean "Invent no extraordinary hypotheses."

Occultation: Passage of one body in front of another; e.g. the *Moon* in front of a star, or *Jupiter* in front of one of its own moons.

Olbers' Paradox: The assertion that the night sky should be bright if the universe is infinite, because every line of sight sooner or later encounters the surface of a star.

Oort Cloud: Hypothetical cloud of *Comets* located at an average distance of 40,000 astronomical units from the *Sun.* The alleged source of all "new" comets (those which have not been close to the Sun before). By calculation, contains 100,000,000,000 comets with an average separation of 2,000,000,000 km between each.

Orion: Bright *Constellation* near the celestial equator, containing the bright stars Betelgeuse and Rigel.

Pallas: Second-largest *Minor Planet.*

Pericenter: Point in an orbit closest to the primary body.

Perihelion: Point in a planetary orbit closest to the *Sun.*

Period: Time to complete one revolution in an orbit.

Phobos: Innermost moon of *Mars.* Probably a captured *Asteroid.*

Phoebe: Outermost *Satellite* of *Saturn,* beyond the orbit of *Iapetus.* Probably a captured *Asteroid.*

Photon: A unit of light. Always travels at the speed of light and has properties of both particles and waves. Usually associated with visible light, but can be applied equally well to all parts of the *Electromagnetic Spectrum;* e.g. radio photons.

Planet K: Hypothetical planet formerly in *Asteroid* belt region which exploded, leaving the *Minor Planets* as residue. "K" comes from "Krypton," the mythical home planet of the fantasy character "Superman," which also exploded.

Planet V: Hypothetical "fifth" planet slightly exterior to present orbit of *Mars,* possible former parent of Mars, possible source of "S-type" *Asteroids.*

Planet X: Hypothetical "tenth" planet beyond *Pluto;* conjectured to be the disrupter of the *Neptune Satellite* system, as well as the source of unexplained perturbations on the outer planets and certain *Comets.*

Pluto: Ninth *Major Planet* out from the *Sun.* Now known to have only the mass of a medium-sized moon, probably escaped from *Neptune.* One *Satellite, Charon,* is also probably a Neptune refugee.

Potential Energy: Energy of a body by virtue of its height above another gravitating body. Proportional to mass over distance. Conventionally taken as zero at infinity, and negative at lesser distances. See also *Kinetic Energy.*

Poynting-Robertson Effect: The deceleration experienced by a body in orbit by virtue of the extra pressure of sunlight on its leading hemisphere over that on its trailing hemisphere. *Aberration* causes the leading hemisphere to receive slightly more sunlight than the trailing.

Precession: The progressive motion of the axis of a spinning body under the influence of applied torques. The *Earth's* poles, with their 23.5-degree tilt, precess with a period of 26,000 years.

Prograde: Orbital motion that is in the same direction as the spin of the primary. Contrasted with *Retrograde.*

Prolate: Bulging along one axis, usually from tidal distortion by another body. See also *Oblate.*

Pulsar: A radio source with pulsed emission, repeating at extremely regular intervals ranging from milliseconds to seconds for different sources. Theory explains these objects as rapidly rotating neutron stars, the collapsed remnants of past *Supernova* explosions.

Quasar: A "quasi-stellar radio source" in the sky; i.e., a source of strong radio noise which is either so small or so far away that its image appears no bigger than a star's. Usually thought to be a *Galaxy* at a great distance because of its large *Redshift.*

Radiation Pressure: The pressure of light; in the solar system, usually sunlight.

Radio Galaxy: A *Galaxy* of stars detectable from its radio emissions.

Redshift: A shift of spectral lines in light toward the red. Usually indicative of the object moving away (approach causes "blueshift"). A characteristic of *Galaxies* — the greater the distance, the greater the observed redshift.

Refraction: The bending of light rays by passage through an atmosphere. In general, the bending of any wave while passing through a medium.

Relativity: Theory of Albert Einstein, which starts from the premise that there is no absolute frame of reference (all motion is relative). Divided into *General Relativity* and *Special Relativity.*

Retrograde: Orbital motion that is opposite to the direction of spin of the primary. Contrasted with *Prograde.*

Revolution: Motion in an orbit about a primary. Contrasted with *Rotation.*

Rhea: Middle *Satellite* of *Saturn,* orbiting between *Dione* and *Titan.*

Roche Limit: The limiting distance at which one body can orbit another before it will break up under tidal strain. Usually calculated for liquid bodies with no cohesive strength beyond self-gravitation.

Rotation: The spin of a body about its own axis. Contrasted with *Revolution.*

Satellite: A body in orbit around a larger ("primary") body.

Saturn: The sixth *Major Planet* out from the *Sun.* Well-known moons — *Mimas, Enceladus, Tethys, Dione, Rhea, Titan, Hyperion, Iapetus, Phoebe* — plus new inner moons discovered by *Voyager,* and spectacular rings.

Scientific Method: The procedures whereby experiments and observations are conducted to test hypotheses. Goals are to free the conclusions from experimenter bias, the influence of systematic errors, and other factors that may lead to false conclusions.

Semi-Major Axis: Half the major axis of an ellipse. Synonym for the mean distance of an object from its primary.

Sirius: The brightest star in the sky (other than the *Sun*) as seen from the *Earth.* Located in the *Constellation* "Canis Minor."

Solar Nebula: Hypothetical cloud of gas and dust from which the *Sun, Major Planets,* their moons, and *Comets* are all thought to have condensed at the beginning of the solar system.

Solar System: The *Sun,* its nine *Major Planets,* their moons, the *Minor Planets,* the *Comets,* and *Meteoroids.* Its boundaries are considered to extend about half the distance to the nearest star.

Solar Wind: High-velocity particles streaming out from the *Sun* in all directions.

Space-Time: The extension of the three dimensions of space (length, width, height) to the fourth dimension of time. Treats motion through time like a distance by multiplying time intervals by the speed of light.

Special Relativity: That part of Einstein's Relativity Theory dealing with the contraction of space and time for masses that approach the speed of light, and the absence of absolute frames of reference for measuring velocities.

Spectrum: The colors of light. In general, a mapping of the energies of the *Photons* in a light source. Usually contains emission or absorption lines. Emission lines are extra photons at a particular energy; absorption lines are deficiencies in photons at particular energies. The lines indicate what chemicals are present in the light source or in space between us and the source. Hot chemical elements emit light, and cool ones absorb it. The *Redshift* or blueshift of the lines usually indicates the velocity of the source: redshift for receding, blueshift for approaching.

Speed of Light: 299,792 km/sec, or about 500 seconds to travel one *Astronomical Unit.*

Sphere of Influence: The distance within which a body can hold stable *Satellites* of its own indefinitely against the disrupting effect of some competing source of gravitation.

Sun: The dwarf star residing at the center of our solar system, about which all nine *Major Planets* (including the *Earth*) revolve.

Sun-Grazing: An orbit that passes so close to the *Sun* that the objects in it may be vaporized. Usually a reference to the *Kreutz* family of Sun-grazing comets.

Sunspot: A dark spot on the surface of the *Sun,* thought to be a magnetic storm. These come and go in 11-year cycles.

Supermassive Star: A single contiguous object exceeding the theoretical upper limit for the mass of a single star in the standard model, about 100 solar masses. Predicted to exist in the Meta Model as an intermediate stage in stellar evolution between giant stars and quasars. These come in two varieties — red and blue supermassive stars — each with properties that match those of known objects not understood in the standard model.

Supernova: The explosion of a supergiant star, often reaching greater brightness than an entire *Galaxy,* and quite destructive to everything near it in the galaxy.

Swidget: An idea contrived to save a theory, rather than to explain some observational evidence or data. The term was coined by the author as short for "scientific widget." "Widget" refers to a useless commercial product.

Synchronous: The revolution of a *Satellite* with the same period as the rotation of its primary, hence maintaining the same position relative to the surface of the primary. In general, motion with the same period or a simple multiple of the period of another body, so that the same configurations repeat from time to time.

Tail: Gas and dust particles streaming away from the coma of a *Comet* due to solar *Radiation Pressure;* always points away from the *Sun.*

Tektites: A class of glassy *meteorites* on the *Earth,* believed by some to have come from Earth volcanism, and by others to have come from the *Moon.* Average measured age on Earth is estimated at 700,000 years.

Tethys: Inner *Satellite* of *Saturn,* orbiting between *Enceladus* and *Dione.*

Tidal Friction: Slowing of the flow, spin, or orbital motion of one body due to its distortion by another, or due to the distortion of the shape of the other body.

Tidal Lock: The condition that one body keeps the same face toward another because tides have adjusted its spin period to equal its orbital period. The *Moon* keeping the same face toward the *Earth* is one example.

Titan: Middle *Satellite* of *Saturn,* orbiting between *Rhea* and *Hyperion.* Saturn's largest satellite, and the only one with a detectable atmosphere.

Titania: Third large moon of *Uranus,* orbiting between *Umbriel* and *Oberon.*

Triton: Largest moon of *Neptune.* Has thin atmosphere and orbits *Retrograde* (the only large moon to do so).

Trojan Asteroids: Asteroids in the same orbit as *Jupiter,* stable because they *Librate* and avoid close approaches to Jupiter.

Umbriel: Second large moon of *Uranus,* orbiting between *Ariel* and *Titania.*

Uranus: Seventh *Major Planet* out from the *Sun.* Moons — *Miranda, Ariel, Umbriel, Titania, Oberon* — plus some *Voyager*-discovered moons and rings.

Venus: Second *Major Planet* out from the *Sun.* Most similar to *Earth* in size and distance from the Sun. No natural *Satellites* at the present time.

Volatile: A gaseous substance, easily vaporized and lost by its host.

Vulcan: Hypothetical planet closer to the *Sun* than *Mercury,* sought by LeVerrier and others to explain the shift in Mercury's perihelion (later explained by *General Relativity*).

Wavelength: The distance between two consecutive crests of a wave. As applied to *Photons,* a measure of the color or energy of light. See also *Electromagnetic Spectrum.*

Zodiac: The band of twelve *Constellations* through which the *Sun, Moon,* and planets appear to move: Aires, Taurus, *Gemini,* Cancer, Leo, Virgo, Libra, Scorpius, Sagittarius, Capricornus, *Aquarius,* Pisces.

Notes

•••••••••••••••••••••••••••

1. Van Flandern, T. "A determination of the rate of change of G." *Mon.Not.Roy.Astr.Soc.* 170, 333–342 (1975).

2. Van Flandern, T. "Is gravity getting weaker?" *Scient.Amer.* 234, 44–52 (1976).

3. Gamow, G. *One, Two, Three ... Infinity,* Viking Press, New York, 14–23 (1947).

4. Boscovich, R.J. See, for example, *Roger Joseph Boscovitch, S.J., F.R.S., 1711–1787,* L.L. Whyte, ed., George Allen & Unwin Ltd, London (1961).

5. I wish to thank Hal Finney, address 74076,1041 on the CompuServe computer network, for this example. On the INTERNET, that address translates to: <74076.1041@compuserve.com>.

6. This and some of the other discussion points were raised by R.H. Dicke of Princeton University in private correspondence.

7. Suggested by Emory Kimbrough, address 72777,1553 on the CompuServe computer network.

8. I wish to credit on-line discussions with a number of people, but especially Paul Kramarchyk, address 72137,1150 on the CompuServe computer network, and Thomas R. Jones, address 71570,460, for helping me straighten out and clarify the concepts in this section.

9. Eddington, S.A. *Space, Time & Gravitation,* Cambridge University Press, Cambridge & New York (1920; reprinted 1987). See p. 94.

10. *Ibid.,* p. 109.

11. Damour, T. "General relativity and experiment: a brief overview." *Class.Quantum Grav.* 9, 55–59 (1992).

12. I would like to thank Eric M. Bram, address 70045,1171 on the CompuServe network, for extensive discussion which ultimately inspired the form of the twin paradox presented here.

13. Rubin, V.C. "What's the matter in spiral galaxies?" In *Highlights of Modern Astrophysics,* S.L. Shapiro and S.A. Teukolsky, eds., John Wiley & Sons, New York, 269–297 (1986).

14. Liboff, R.L. "Generalized Newtonian force law and hidden mass." *Astrophys.J.* 397, L71–L73 (1992).

15. Rubin, V.C. "Large-scale motions from a new sample of spiral galaxies: field and cluster." In *Large-Scale Motions in the Universe,* V.C. Rubin and G.V. Coyne, eds., Princeton University Press, 187–195 (1988).

16. Wright, A.E., Disney, M.J., and Thompson, R.C. "Universal gravity: was Newton right?" *Proc.Astron.Soc.Australia* 8, 334–338 (1990).

17. Bahcall, J.N. "K giants and the total amount of matter near the Sun." *Astrophys.J.* 287, 926–944 (1984).

18. Hartwick, F.D.A. and Sargent, W.L.W. "Radial velocities for outlying satellites and their implications for the mass of the galaxy." *Astrophys.J.* 221, 512–520 (1978).

19. Information in the rest of this section is from: Townes, C.H. and Genzel, R. "What is happening at the center of our galaxy?" *Sci.Amer.* 262, 46–55 (1990).

20. Standish, E.M. "Pitfalls in predicting a tenth planet." In *Planets Beyond,* M. Littmann, John Wiley and Sons, New York, 218–219 (1988).

21. Geller, M.J. and Huchra, J.P. "Cosmic cartographers find 'Great Wall.'" *Sci.News* 136, 340 (1989).

22. Kurki-Suonio, H. "Galactic beads on a cosmic string." *Sci.News* 137, 287 (1990).

23. Tifft, W.G. "A fundamental test for time variations in redshifts of galaxies." *Bull.Amer.Astr.Soc.* 22, 841 (1990).

24. Tifft, W.G. "Properties of the redshift. III. Temporal variation." *Astrophys.J.* 382, 396–415 (1991).

25. Lynden-Bell, D. and Lahav, O. "Whence arises the local flow of galaxies?" In *Large-Scale Motions in the Universe,* V.C. Rubin and G.V. Coyne, eds., Princeton Univ. Press, Princeton, NJ, 199–217 (1988).

26. Yahil, A. "The structure of the universe to 10,000 km/s as determined by IRAS galaxies." In *Large-Scale Motions in the Universe,* V.C. Rubin and G.V. Coyne, eds., Princeton Univ. Press, Princeton, NJ, 219–253 (1988).

27. Arp, H. *Quasars, Redshifts, and Controversies,* Interstellar Media, Berkeley, CA (1987).

28. Arp, H. and Sulentic, J.W. "Analysis of groups of galaxies with accurate redshifts." *Astrophys.J.* 291, 88–111 (1985).

29. Burbidge, E.M., Burbidge, G.R., Solomon, P.M., and Strittmatter, P.A. "Apparent associations between bright galaxies and quasi-stellar objects." *Astrophys.J.* 170, 233–240 (1971).

30. Burbidge, G.R., O'Dell, S.L., and Strittmatter, P.A. "Physical associations between quasi-stellar objects and galaxies." *Astrophys.J.* 175, 601–611 (1972).

31. Broadhurst, T.J., Ellis, R.S., and Glazebrook, K. "Faint galaxies: evolution and cosmological curvature." *Nature* 355, 55–58 (1992).

32. Arp, H. C., Burbidge, G., Hoyle, F., Narlikar, J. V., and Wickramasinghe, N. C. "The extragalactic universe: an alternative view." *Nature* 346, 807–812 (1990).

33. Gilmore, G., *et al.* "First detection of beryllium in a very metal-poor star: a test of the standard Big Bang model." *Astrophys.J.* 378, 17–21 (1991).

34. Maddox, J. "Down with the Big Bang." *Nature* 340, 425 (1989).

35. Lerner, E. J. *The Big Bang Never Happened,* Times Books, (1991), p. 151.

36. Arp, H. C. and Van Flandern, T. "The case against the Big Bang," *Phys.Lett. A* 164, 263–273 (1992).

37. *Sci.News* 137, 184 (1990) is source for all quotes in paragraph.

38. Lerner, E.J. "Radio absorption in the intergalactic medium." *Astrophys.J.* 361, 63–68 (1990).

39. Allen, C.W. *Astrophysical Quantities,* Athlone Press, Dover, NH, 3rd edition, 268–269 (1973).

40. Van Flandern, T. "New COBE results and the big bang 'fireball.'" *MetaRes.Bull.* 1, 17–21 (1992).

41. Most observational data in this section are from H. Arp's book *Quasars, Redshifts, and Controversies,* Interstellar Media, Berkeley, CA (1987), unless otherwise credited.

42. Heckman, T.M., Lehnert, M.D., Breugel, W. van, and Miley, G.K. "Spatially resolved optical images of high-redshift quasi-stellar objects." *Astrophys.J.* 370, 78–101 (1991).

43. Remillard, R.A., *et al.* "A rapid energetic X-ray flare in the quasar PKS0558–504." *Nature* 350, 589–592 (1991).

44. Webster, R.L., Hewett, P.C., Harding, M.E., and Wegner, G.A. "Detection of statistical gravitational lensing by foreground mass distributions." *Nature* 336, 358 (1988).

45. Hintzen, P., Romanishin, W., and Valdes, F. "Galaxies clustering around QSOs with $z = 0.9$–1.5 and the origin of blue field galaxies." *Astrophys.J.* 366, 7–15 (1991).

46. Burbidge, G., Hewitt, A., Narlikar, J. V., and Gupta, P.Das. "Associations between quasi-stellar objects and galaxies." *Astrophys.J.Supp.* 74, 675–730 (1990).

47. Heckman, T.M., *et al.* "Spatially resolved optical images of high-redshift quasi-stellar objects." *Astrophys.J.* 370, 78–101 (1991). (See Table 2.)

48. Smith, L. "Hydrogen clouds colder than expected." *Sci.News* 138, 253 (1990).

49. Boroson, T.A., Meyers, K.A., Morris, S.L., and Persson, S.E. "The appearance of a new redshift system in Markarian 231." *Astrophys.J.* 370, L19–L21 (1991).

50. Lipari, S. *et al.* "Iron quasars." *Sky&Tel.* 81, 246 (1991).

51. Morris, S. L., *et al.* "First results from the GHRS: the galactic halo and the Lyα forest at low redshift in 3C 273." *Astrophys.J.* 377, L21–L24 (1991).

52. Osmer, P. S. and Hewett, P. C. "A new survey for quasar clustering." *Astrophys.J.Supp.* 75, 273–295 (1991).

53. Perley, R. A. "Recent progress in observations of extragalactic radio sources." *Bull.Amer.Astr.Soc.* 22, 822 (1990).

54. Tyler, D. and Fan, X. M. "Systematic QSO emission-line velocity shifts and new unbiased redshifts." *Astrophys.J.Supp.* 79, 1–36 (1992).

55. Djorgovski, S., Spinrad, H., McCarthy, P., and Strauss, M. A. "Discovery of a probable galaxy with a redshift of 3.218." *Astrophys.J.Lett.* 299, L1–L5 (1985).

56. Kron, R. G. and Chiu, L.-T.G. "Stars with zero proper motion and the number of faint QSOs." *Publ.Astr.Soc.Pac.* 93, 397 (1981).

57. Ma, C. & Shaffer, D. B. "Stability of the extragalactic reference frame realized by VLBI." *Proc. IAU Colloq.* 127, 135–144 (1991).

58. Pagels, H. R. *The Cosmic Code,* Bantam Books, New York, 113 (1982).

59. Herbert, N. *Quantum Reality,* Anchor Press/Doubleday, Garden City, NY (1985).

60. Bell, J. S. *Speakable and Unspeakable in Quantum Mechanics,* Cambridge University Press, New York, 27 (1987).

61. Tifft, W. G. "Discrete states of redshift and galaxy dynamics: II. Systems of galaxies." *Astrophys.J.* 211, 31–46 (1977).

62. Brown, H. and Patterson, C. "The composition of meteoritic matter: III. Phase equilibria, genetic relationships and planet structure." *J.Geol.* 56, 85–111 (1948).

63. Van Flandern, T. C. "A former asteroidal planet as the origin of comets." *Icarus* 36, 51–74 (1978).

64. Van Flandern, T. "A review of dynamical evidence concerning a former asteroidal planet." In *Dynamics of the Solar System,* R. L. Duncombe, ed., D. Reidel, Dordrecht, 257–262 (1979). (Includes technical discussion.)

65. Carter, N. L. and Kennedy, G. C. "Origin of diamonds in the Canyon Diablo and Novo Urei meteorites." *J. Geophys.Res.* 69, 2403–2421 (1964).

66. Heymann, D., Lipschutz, M. E., Nielsen, B., and Anders, E. "Canyon Diablo meteorite: metallographic and mass spectrometric study of 56 fragments." *J.Geophys.Res.* 71, 619–641 (1966).

67. Anders, E. and Lipschutz, M. E. "Critique of paper by N. L. Carter and G. C. Kennedy, 'Origin of diamonds in the Canyon Diablo and Novo Urei meteorites.'" *J.Geophys.Res.* 71, 643–661 (1966).

68. Carter, N. L. and Kennedy, G. C. "Origin of diamonds in the Canyon

Diablo and Novo Urei meteorites—a reply." *J.Geophys.Res.* 71, 663–672 (1966).

69. Anders, E. and Lipschutz, M. E. "Reply." *J.Geophys.Res.* 71, 673–674 (1966).

70. Van Flandern, T. C. "A former major planet of the solar system." In *Comets-Asteroids-Meteorites: Interrelations, Evolution and Origins,* A. H. Delsemme, ed., Univ. of Toledo, 475–481 (1977).

71. Eberhart, J. "Episodic oceans." *Sci.News* 137, 283–284 (1990).

72. Napier, W. M. and Dodd, R. J. "The Missing Planet." *Nature* 242, 250–251 (1973).

73. Ostro, S. J., Chandler, J. F., Hine, A. A., Rosema, K. D., Shapiro, I. I., and Yeomans, D. K. "Radar images of asteroid 1989 PB." *Science* 248, 1523–1528 (1990).

74. Wetherill, G. W. and ReVelle, D. O. "Which fireballs are meteorites? A study of the Prairie network photographic meteor data." *Icarus* 48, 308–328 (1981).

75. Hartmann, W. K. and Cruikshank, D. P. "The nature of Trojan asteroid 624 Hektor." *Icarus* 36, 353–366 (1978).

76. Van Flandern, T. "Minor satellites and the Gaspra encounter." In *Proceedings of the Workshop on Comets, Asteroids, and Meteorites,* E. Bowell and A. Harris, eds., Univ. of Arizona Press, Tucson (1992).

77. Weissman, P. R. "The Oort cloud." *Nature* 344, 825–830 (1990).

78. Yabushita, S. "A statistical study of the evolution of the orbits of long-period comets." *Mon.Not.R.Astr.Soc.* 187, 445–462 (1979).

79. Duncan, M., Quinn, T., and Tremaine, S. "The formation and extent of the solar system Oort cloud." *Astron.J.* 94, 1330–1338 (1987).

80. Duncan, M., Quinn, T., and Tremaine, S. "The origin of short-period comets." *Astrophys.J.* 328, L69–L73 (1988).

81. Van Flandern, T. "The Kuiper belt of comets does not exist." In *Periodic Comets,* J. A. Fernandez and H. Rickman, eds., Universidad de la Republic, Montevideo, 75–80 (1992).

82. Cowen, R. "Frozen relics of the early solar system." *Sci.News* 137, 248–250 (1990).

83. Van Flandern, T. C. "A former asteroidal planet as the origin of comets." *Icarus* 36, 51–74 (1978).

84. Gabbard, J. R. "Orbits of fragments from exploded satellites." *Technical Memorandum* 74–3, Headquarters NORAD/CONAD/ADC, Colorado Springs, Colo. (1974).

85. Marsden, B. G., Sekanina, Z., and Everhart, E. "New osculating orbits for 110 comets and analysis of original orbits for 200 comets." *Astron.J.* 83, 64–71 (1978).

86. Tomanov, V. P. "New statistical properties of the long-period comet system." *SolarSys.Res.* 7, 73–76 (1973).

87. Ovenden, M.W. "Bode's law and the missing planet." *Nature* 239, 508–509 (1972).

88. Whipple, F.L. "A comet model: I. The acceleration of Comet Encke." *Astrophys.J.* 111, 375–394 (1950).

89. Whipple, F.L. "A comet model: II. Physical relations for comets and meteors." *Astrophys.J.* 113, 464–474 (1952).

90. Whipple, F.L. "A comet model: III. The zodiacal light." *Astrophys.J.* 121, 750–770 (1955).

91. Huebner, W.F., Rahe, J., Wehinger, P.A., and Konno, I., eds. *Workshop on Observations of Recent Comets (1990),* Southwest Research Institute, San Antonio, TX (1990).

92. Millman, P.M. "The chemical composition of cometary meteoroids." In *Comets, Asteroids, Meteoroids,* A.H. Delsemme, ed., Univ. of Toledo, Toledo, OH, 127–132 (1977).

93. Wetherill, G.W and ReVelle, D.O. "Relationships between comets, large meteors, and meteorites." In *Comets,* L.L. Wilkening, ed., Univ. of Arizona Press, Tucson, 297–319 (1982).

94. Degewij, J., Hartmann, W.K., and Cruikshank, D.P. "P/Schwass-man-Wachmann 1 and Chiron: near-infrared photometry." Oral presentation to comets meeting in Flagstaff, AZ (1981).

95. Bobrovnikoff, N.T. "Halley's Comet in its apparition of 1909–1911." *Publ.Lick Obsy.* 17, 309–482 (1931).

96. Kamoun, P.G., Pettengill, G.H., and Shapiro, I.I. "Radar detectability of comets." In *Comets,* L.L. Wilkening, ed., Univ. of Arizona Press, Tucson, 288–296 (1982).

97. Van Flandern, T. "An alternative to the dirty snowball model of comets." In *Workshop on Observations of Recent Comets (1990),* W.F. Huebner, P.A. Wehinger, J. Rahe, I. Konno, eds., Southwest Research Inst., San Antonio, 144–149 (1990).

98. Binzel, R.P. and Van Flandern, T.C. "Minor planets: the existence of minor satellites." *Science* 203, 903–905 (1979).

99. Tedesco, E.T. "Binary asteroids: evidence for their existence from lightcurves." *Science* 203, 905–907 (1979).

100. Van Flandern, T.C., Tedesco, E.T., and Binzel, R.P. "Satellites of asteroids." In *Asteroids,* T. Gehrels, ed., Univ. of Arizona Press, Tucson, 443–465 (1979).

101. Van Flandern, T. "Minor planet satellites." *Science* 211, 297–298 (technical comment) (1981).

102. Sekanina, Z. "Relative motions of fragments of the split comets. III. A test of splitting and comets with suspected multiple nuclei." *Icarus* 38, 300–316 (1979).

103. Tedesco, E., Drummond, F., Canoy, M., Birch, P., Nikoloff, I., and Zellner, B. "1580 Betulia: an unusual asteroid with an extraordinary

lightcurve." *Icarus* 35, 344–359 (1978).

104. Opik, E. J. "The stray bodies in the solar system: Part I. Survival of cometary nuclei and the asteroids." *Adv.Astron.Astrophys.* 2, 219–262 (1963). See p. 242.

105. Lyttleton, R. A. "What is a cometary nucleus?" *Quart.J.Roy.Astr.Soc.* 18, 213–233 (1977).

106. Wurm, K. "On the interpretation of the spectra of comets and their forms." *Astrophys.J.* 89, 312–319 (1939).

107. Weissman, P. R. "Physical and dynamical evolution of long-period comets." In *Dynamics of the Solar System*, R. L. Duncombe, ed., Reidel, Dordrecht, 277–282 (1979).

108. Meisel, D. D. and Morris, C. S. "Comet head photometry: past, present, and future." In *Comets*, L. L. Wilkening, ed., Univ. of Arizona Press, Tucson, 413–432 (1982).

109. Sekanina, Z. "Relative motion of fragments of the split comets: I. A new approach." *Icarus* 30, 574–594 (1977).

110. Sekanina, Z. "The problem of split comets in review." In *Comets*, L. L. Wilkening, ed., Univ. of Arizona Press, Tucson, 251–287 (1982).

111. Donn, B. and Rahe, J. "Structure and origin of cometary nuclei." In *Comets*, L. L. Wilkening, ed., Univ. of Arizona Press, Tucson, 203–226 (1982).

112. A'Hearn, M. F. and Dwek, E. "Where is the ice in comets?" Oral presentation to comets meeting in Flagstaff, AZ (1981).

113. Whipple, F. L. and Sekanina, Z. "Comet Encke: precession of the spin axis, non-gravitational motion, and sublimation." *Astron.J.* 84, 1894–1909 (1979).

114. Yeomans, D. K. "Comet Temple-Tuttle and the Leonid meteors." *Icarus* 47, 492–499 (1981).

115. I would like to gratefully acknowledge the contributions of Fred Mrozek of German Valley, IL, to at least half-a-dozen significant entries in this outline.

116. Van Flandern, T. See especially: "A former asteroidal planet as the origin of comets." *Icarus* 36, 51–74 (1978). See also: "Do comets have satellites?" *Icarus* 47, 480–486 (1981). See also chapters in this book that elaborate on certain specific lines of evidence.

117. Wyckoff, S. "Ammonia and nitrogen abundances in comets." In *Workshop on Observations of Recent Comets (1990)*, W. F. Huebner, ed., Southwest Research Institute, San Antonio, TX, 28–33 (1990).

118. Palmer, P., Pater, I. de, and Snyder, L. E. "VLA observations of the OH emission from Comet Wilson (1986l): the value of high resolution in both spatial and velocity coordinates." *Astron.J.* 97, 1791–1797 + plates on p. 1842 (1989).

119. Huebner, W. F. "Results from the Comet Giacobini-Zinner and Hal-

ley campaigns." In *Workshop on Observations of Recent Comets (1990)*, W. F. Huebner, ed., Southwest Research Institute, San Antonio, TX, 1–7 (1990).

120. Donahue, T. M. and Hodges, R. R. "Past and present water budget of Venus." *JGR-Planets* 97, 6083–6091 (1992).

121. O'Keefe, J. A. *"Tektites and their origin,"* Elsevier, New York (1976).

122. Baker, V. R. "The Spokane flood controversy and the Martian outflow channels." *Science* 202, 1249–1256 (1978).

123. Melosh, H. J. and Stansberry, J. A. "Doublet craters and the tidal disruption of binary asteroids." *Icarus* 94, 171–179 (1991).

124. Shoemaker, E. M. and Wolfe, R. F. "Cratering time scales for the Galilean satellites." In *Satellites of Jupiter,* D. Morrison, ed., Univ. of Arizona Press, Tucson, 277–339 (1982). See p. 318.

125. Danes, Z. F. "Rebound processes in large craters." *Astrogeologic Studies,* Annual Progress Report, 7/1/64–7/1/65, Pt. A: Lunar & Planetary Investigations, Dept. of Interior, USGS, pp. 81–100 (1965).

126. Peale, S. "Dynamical puzzles from *Voyager.*" *Bull.Amer.Astr.Soc.* 22, 947 (1990). Invited talk, not yet published. Information is private communication from the author.

127. Johnson, T. V. and Cruikshank, D. P. Presented to AGU, 1989.

128 Banfield, D. J. and Murray, N. W. "Neptune's 'forbidden' moons." *Sky&Tel.* 84, 7 (1992).

129. Brown, H. and Patterson, C. "The composition of meteoritic matter, III. Phase equilibria, genetic relationships and planet structure." *J. Geology* 56, 85–111 (1948).

130. Walker, R. M. "Meteorites, isotopic analyses." *The Astronomy and Astrophysics Encyclopedia,* S.P. Maran, ed., 434–437 (1992).

131. Russell, S. S., *et al.* "A new type of meteoritic diamond in the enstatite chondrite Abee." Science 256, 206–209 (1992).

132. Carlisle, D. B. "Diamonds at the K/T boundary." *Nature* 357, 119–120 (1992).

133. "Interstellar graphite in meteorites." *Sci.News* 137, 335 (1990).

134. Frank, L. A. *The Big Splash,* Avon Books, New York (1990).

135. Verschuur, G. L. *Interstellar Matters,* Springer-Verlag, New York (1989).

136. Innes, D. E. and Hartquist, T. W. "Are we in an old superbubble?" *Mon.Not.R.Astr.Soc.* 209, 7–13 (1984).

137. Hajivasiliou, C. A. "Distribution of plasma turbulence in our galaxy derived from radio scintillation maps." *Nature* 355, 232–234 (1992).

138. Cowen, G. A. "A natural fission reactor." *Sci.Amer.* 235, 36–47 (1976).

139. Attela, J.L., *et al.* "Statistical evidence for a galactic origin of gamma-ray bursts." *Nature* 351, 296–298 (1991).

140. Bhat, P. N. *et al.* "Evidence for sub-millisecond structure in a gamma-ray burst," *Nature* 359, 217–218 (1992).

141. Shoemaker, E. M. and Izett, G. A. "Did the 'big one' pack a one-two punch?" *Sky&Tel.* 84, 8 (1992).

142. Wolbach, W. S., *et al.* "Global fire at the cretaceous-tertiary boundary." *Nature* 334, 665–669 (1988).

143. Gentry, R. V. "Radioactive halos in a radio chronological and cosmological perspective." *Proceedings of the 63rd Annual Meeting of the Pacific Division, AAAS* 1, 38 (1984).

144. Gribbin, J. R. and Plagemann, S. H. *The Jupiter Effect,* Walker, New York (1974).

145. Elliot, J.L., Dunham, E., and Church, C. "A unique airborne observation." *Sky&Tel.* 52, 23–25 (1976).

146. Van Flandern, T. C. and Harrington, R.S. "A dynamical investigation of the conjecture that Mercury is an escaped satellite of Venus." *Icarus* 28, 435–440 (1976).

147. Newsom, H. E. and Runcorn, S. K. "New constraints on the size of the lunar core and the origin of the Moon." *Lunar and Planetary Science Conference Abstracts* XXII, 973–974 (1991).

148. Ringwood, A. E., Kato, T., Hibberson, W., and Ware, N. "Partitioning of Cr, V, and Mn between mantles and cores of differentiated planetesimals: implications for giant impact hypothesis of lunar origin." *Icarus* 89, 122–128 (1991).

149. Sinclair, A. T. "The orbits of the satellites of Mars determined from Earth-based and spacecraft observations." *Astron.& Astrophys.* 220, 321–328 (1989).

150. O'Keefe, J. D. "The Cyrillid meteor shower: remnant of a circumstellar ring?" In *Lunar and Planetary Science Abstracts* XXII, NASA, 995–996 (1991).

151. Schultz, P. H. and Crawford, D. A. "Martian impacts and Phobos' grooves." *Sci.News* 136, 334 (1989).

152. Van Flandern, T. "New Saturnian satellites?" *Observatory* 99, 8–9 (1979).

153. Dones, L. "A recent cometary origin for Saturn's rings." *Icarus* 92, 194–203 (1991).

154. Bosh, A.S., Young, L. A., Elliot, J.L., and Hammel, H. B. "Photometric variability of Charon at 2.2 micrometers." *Icarus* 95, 319–324 (1992).

155. Cruickshank, D. P., *et al.* "Solid C-N bearing material on outer solar system bodies." *Icarus* 94, 345–353 (1991).

156. Byl, J. and Ovenden, M. W. "On the satellite capture problem." *Mon.Not.R.Astr.Soc.* 173, 579–584 (1975).

157. Pearl, J. C. and Sinton, W. M. "Hot spots of Io." In *Satellites of Jupiter,* D. Morrison, ed., Univ. of Arizona Press, Tucson, 724–755 (1982).

158. I would like to thank Roger Venable, address 73300,2642 on the CompuServe computer network, for his stimulating discussion of this point in the Astronomy Forum.

159. Van Flandern, T. "Rings of Uranus: invisible and impossible?" *Science* 204, 1076–1077 (1979). [Related artwork by S. Bensusen on cover.]

160. Harrington, R. S. and Van Flandern, T. C. "The satellites of Neptune and the origin of Pluto." *Icarus* 39, 131–136 (1979).

161. McKinnon, W. B. and Van Flandern, T. "Worlds apart." A Focal Point debate between the two authors over the origins of Pluto, Charon, and Neptune's moons. *Sky&Tel.* 82, 340–341 (1991).

162. McKinnon, W. B. "On the origin of Triton and Pluto." *Nature* 311, 355–358 (1984).

163. Lyttleton, R. A. "On the possible results on an encounter of Pluto with the Neptunian system." *Mon.Not.R.Astr.Soc.* 97, 108–115 (1936).

164. McKinnon, W. B. "On the origin of the Pluto-Charon binary." *Astrophys.J.Lett.* 344, L41–L44 (1989).

165. Peale, S. "Orbital resonances, unusual configurations and exotic rotation states among planetary satellites." In *Satellites,* J. A. Burns, ed., U. of Arizona Press, Tucson, 159–223 (1986).

166. Binzel, R. P. "Pluto." *Sci.American* June, 50–58 (1990).

167. McKinnon, W. B. and Mueller, S. "Pluto's structure and composition suggest origin in the solar, not a planetary, nebula." *Nature* 335, 240–243 (1988).

168. Littmann, M. *Planets Beyond: Discovering the Outer Solar System,* John Wiley & Sons, New York (1988).

169. Anderson, I. "Maverick mathematician's planetary prediction comes true." *New Scientist* 14 December 1991, p. 13.

170. "Still seeking a Martian magnetic field." *Sci.News* 137, 335 (1990).

171. Von Daniken, E. *Chariots of the Gods?* Bantam Books, New York (1970).

172. Sitchin, Z. Five books available from Avon Books, New York: *The Twelfth Planet* (1976); *The Stairway to Heaven* (1980); *The Wars of Gods and Men* (1985); *The Lost Realms* (1990); *Genesis Revisited* (1990).

173. Hoyle, F. and Wickramasinghe, N. C. *Diseases from space,* Harper and Row, New York (1980).

174. Tompkins, P. *Secrets of the Great Pyramid,* Harper & Row, NY, 217 (1971).

175. Brandenburg, J. E., DiPietro, V., and Molenaar, G. "The Cydonia hypothesis." *J.Scientific Exploration* 5, 1–25 (1991).

176. Hoagland, R. C. *The Monuments of Mars,* North Atlantic Books, Berkeley (1987).

177. Carlotto, M. *The Martian Enigmas,* North Atlantic Books, Berkeley, 1991.

178. Sitchin, Z. *The Stairway to Heaven,* Avon Books, New York (1980).

179. Schoch, R. M. "Redating the Great Sphinx of Giza." KMT, *Modern J.Anc.Egypt* 3, 52–59 & 66–70 (1992).

180. *Skeptical Inquirer,* the journal of the Committee for the Scientific Investigation of Claims of the Paranormal, K. Frazier, ed., published quarterly at Buffalo, NY.

181. Velikovsky, I. *Worlds in Collision,* Macmillan, New York, NY (1950).

182. Arp, H. *Quasars, Redshifts, and Controversies,* Interstellar Media, Berkeley, CA, 178 (1987).

Name Index

419

Subject Index

423

5